LIFE SCIENCE LIBRARY

THE CELL

**OTHER BOOKS
BY THE
EDITORS OF LIFE**

LIFE WORLD LIBRARY

LIFE NATURE LIBRARY

THE LIFE HISTORY OF THE UNITED STATES

LIFE PICTORIAL ATLAS OF THE WORLD

THE EPIC OF MAN

THE WONDERS OF LIFE ON EARTH

THE WORLD WE LIVE IN

THE WORLD'S GREAT RELIGIONS

THE LIFE BOOK OF CHRISTMAS

LIFE'S PICTURE HISTORY OF WESTERN MAN

THE LIFE TREASURY OF AMERICAN FOLKLORE

AMERICA'S ARTS AND SKILLS

THE SECOND WORLD WAR

LIFE'S PICTURE HISTORY OF WORLD WAR II

PICTURE COOK BOOK

LIFE GUIDE TO PARIS

LIFE SCIENCE LIBRARY

CONSULTING EDITORS

René Dubos
Henry Margenau
C. P. Snow

THE CELL

by John Pfeiffer
and the Editors of LIFE

TIME INCORPORATED, NEW YORK

A STONEHENGE BOOK

ABOUT THIS BOOK

RECENT DISCOVERIES about the cell, the focal point of modern biology, make up the central theme of this book. Since the 1940s, biologists have achieved incredibly precise observations of the interior of cells, making possible such remarkable diagrams as the cutaway close-up on page 17 and the picture essay on the DNA molecule *(pages 62 through 79)*.

This volume is made up of text chapters, with marginal illustrations on specific points, and picture essays. The picture essays complement the chapters they follow, sometimes by illustrating the subject in depth, sometimes by taking up supplementary subject matter. The two components of the book were designed to make up a unified whole, but each is self-contained and can be read separately.

A glossary in the appendix defines the most essential terms in the vocabulary of cellular biology.

THE AUTHOR

JOHN PFEIFFER is an author who has been exploring the frontiers of science as a writer for the lay reader. Born in New York City in 1915, he studied at Yale University. His books and articles chronicle a decade of advances in the life sciences. For "DNA," published in 1960 in *Natural History*, he won the Westinghouse Award from the American Association for the Advancement of Science. Among his books are *From Galaxies to Men, The Changing Universe, The Human Brain* and *The Thinking Machine*. He is a former science editor of *Newsweek*, a former science director of CBS and past president of the National Association of Science Writers.

THE CONSULTING EDITORS

RENE DUBOS, member and professor of The Rockefeller Institute, is a microbiologist and experimental pathologist world-famous for his pioneering in antibiotics, including the discovery of tyrothricin. He has written, among other books, *Mirage of Health* and *The Dreams of Reason.*

HENRY MARGENAU is Eugene Higgins professor of physics and natural philosophy at Yale and an editor of the *American Journal of Science*. His books include *Open Vistas* and *The Nature of Physical Reality*. He has made noteworthy . contributions in spectroscopy and nuclear physics.

C.P. SNOW has won an international audience for his novels, including *The New Men, The Search* and *The Affair*, which explore the scientist's role in contemporary society. Trained as a physicist, he directed recruitment of scientific personnel for Britain's Ministry of Labour in World War II. He was knighted in 1957.

ON THE COVER

Cartilage cells, from the leg of a newt, are magnified 3,500 times. They are one type among hundreds of specialized cells that together produce, form and power almost all that lives. The amoeba on the back cover leads an active life as a single, multipurpose cell.

CONTENTS

PAGE

INTRODUCTION   7

1   THE CELL: A BUSTLING METROPOLIS   8
Picture Essay: The Living Forces inside the Cell   16

2   VITAL ENERGY FROM A RAY OF LIGHT   32
Picture Essay: Twin Dynamos of Existence   42

3   THE ARCHITECT AND THE MASTER BUILDER   52
Picture Essay: The Basic Blueprint of Life   62

4   THE FIRST LIVING THING ON EARTH   80
Picture Essay: The Awesome Mystery of the Beginnings   90

5   CELL DIVISION AND THE MARVEL OF REPRODUCTION   100
Picture Essay: A Finer and Finer Division of Labor   108

6   THE MECHANICS OF MUSCLE POWER   122
Picture Essay: Probing the Innermost Secrets   132

7   THE MESSAGE CARRIERS   146
Picture Essay: The Body's Expert Signal Corps   156

8   THE CELL IN SICKNESS AND IN HEALTH   168
Picture Essay: Medicine's Journey from Faith to Fact   176

APPENDIX   193
Glossary: The Vocabulary of Cellular Biology

BIBLIOGRAPHY AND ACKNOWLEDGMENTS   196

INDEX   197

CREDITS   200

TIME / LIFE BOOKS

EDITOR
Norman P. Ross

TEXT DIRECTOR   ART DIRECTOR
William Jay Gold   Edward A. Hamilton

CHIEF OF RESEARCH
Beatrice T. Dobie

Assistant to the Editor: Carl Solberg
Assistant Text Director: Jerry Korn
Assistant Chief of Research: Monica O. Horne

EDITORIAL STAFF FOR "THE CELL"

EDITOR, LIFE SCIENCE LIBRARY
George McCue
TEXT EDITORS: Richard Thruelsen, Stanley Fillmore
ASSISTANT TO THE EDITOR: John MacDonald
DESIGNER: Arnold C. Holeywell
ASSOCIATE DESIGNER: Edwin Taylor
STAFF WRITERS: Stephen Espie, Harvey B. Loomis,
Peter Meyerson, Timothy Carr
CHIEF RESEARCHER: Sheila Osmundsen
RESEARCHERS: Norbert S. Baer, David Beckwith,
Sarah Bennett, Robert W. Bone, Joan C. Coates,
Beatrice M. Combs, Mollie Cooper,
Leah Dunaief, Owen Fang, Leonard Lipton,
Victor H. Waldrop, Dori Watson
PICTURE RESEARCHERS, Margaret K. Goldsmith,
Barbara Sullivan
ART ASSOCIATE: Robert L. Young
ART ASSISTANTS: James D. Smith, W. Lee Einhorn,
Charles Mikolaycak, Douglas B. Graham
COPY STAFF: Marian Gordon Goldman,
Suzanne Seixas, Dolores A. Littles

PUBLISHER: Jerome S. Hardy
GENERAL MANAGER: John A. Watters

LIFE MAGAZINE

EDITOR: Edward K. Thompson
MANAGING EDITOR: George P. Hunt
PUBLISHER: C. D. Jackson

The text for the chapters of this book was written by John Pfeiffer, for the
picture essays by the editorial staff. The following individuals and depart-
ments of Time Inc. were helpful in the production of the book: Larry Burrows, Alfred Eisenstaedt, Eliot Elisofon, Fritz Goro, Ralph Morse, Arthur
Rickerby, Paul Schutzer and George Silk, LIFE staff photographers; Margaret Sargent, LIFE film editor; Doris O'Neil, Chief of the LIFE Picture
Library; Richard M. Clurman, Chief, TIME-LIFE News Service; and Content Peckham, Chief of the Time Inc. Bureau of Editorial Reference.

INTRODUCTION

THROUGH A HAPPY COINCIDENCE, this book commemorates the 300th anniversary of the recognition and naming of the fundamental unit of living organisms. It was three centuries ago that Robert Hooke of London, while observing slices of cork under his primitive microscope, saw that they were made up of a vesicular structure which reminded him of a honeycomb pattern. He called these walled cavities "cells."

In the 150 years that followed Hooke's discovery, scientists came to regard cells simply as little boxes that contained the stuff of life. By contrast, it is realized today that even the most primitive cell is an immensely complex and highly integrated piece of biological machinery in which every part plays an indispensable role for the maintenance of life. The cell is, indeed, less the container than the very fabric of life.

In some ways, however, many modern laymen and even some scientists are still thinking about the cell from a primitive point of view. They are fascinated by the construction of the cellular machine, but pay little heed to what makes it behave as a living organism. I believe that this LIFE book will help correct that attitude by making vividly clear the fundamental truth that there is no life without action.

The reader will observe the machinery of the cell endlessly at work, generating energy and building new materials through processes of an incredible subtlety and efficiency which occur nowhere but in living organisms. In the first chapter, the astounding fact is revealed that the simple unicellular euglena continues for a few days to behave in the dark as if it knew when the sun was rising and setting. Euglena is not the only organism that exhibits this property. However primitive, all cells perceive cosmic forces and respond to them through mechanisms which are not yet understood. In the last chapter, the cell is shown to be capable of undergoing all sorts of transformations under the influence of various stimuli. Of particular interest in this regard are the processes of immunity, so resourceful and so exquisitely specific. No chemist can yet duplicate the production of specific antibodies, even though the cell does this every day as a matter of course. Fortunately, physicians are learning to make use of this cellular versatility in the treatment of disease.

During the past 300 years, microscopists and molecular biologists have gone far toward describing the most intimate details of cell structure. But life cannot be understood only from a knowledge of structure. To live is to function. This book is written in the mood of tomorrow's biology, which will be concerned with the responses of the organism to the environment, the phenomenon which makes living such a versatile and dynamic process.

—RENE DUBOS
The Rockefeller Institute

The Cell: A Bustling Metropolis

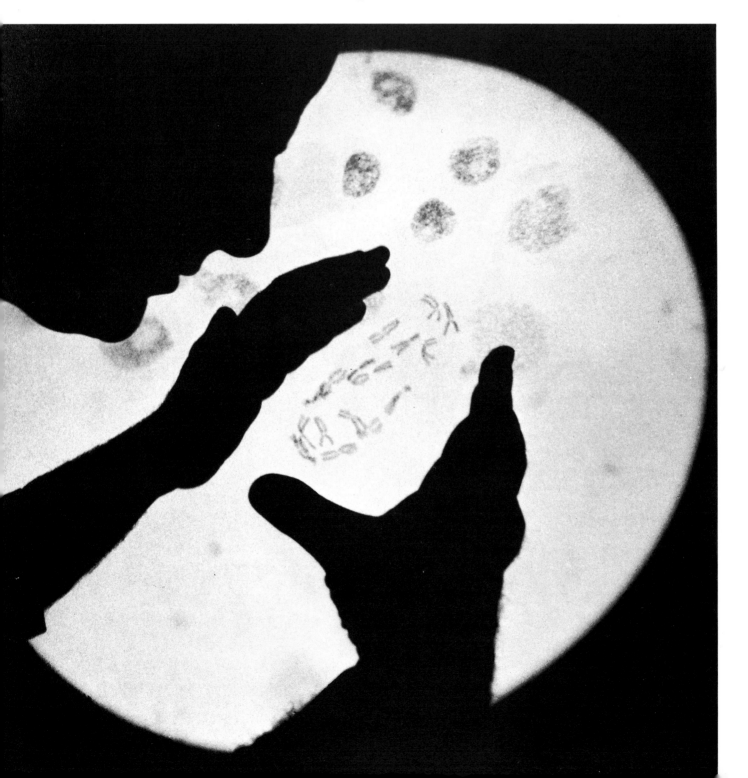

THERE IS NO LIFE WITHOUT CELLS. And just as life itself is diverse, so are the forms and functions of the cells that constitute life. Some cells live alone, as free-moving, independent creatures, some belong to loosely organized communities which move from place to place and some spend their lifetime in fixed immobility as part of the tissue of a larger organism. Whatever its form, however it behaves, the cell is the basic unit of all living matter. In the cell, nature has enclosed in a microscopic package all the parts and processes necessary to the survival of life in an ever-changing world.

Though the cellular divisions of organic matter were identified and given the name of cells as long ago as 1663 by the English scientist Robert Hooke, the groundwork of modern cell theory—that all animal and vegetable tissue is made up of collections of cells—was not established until the early part of the 19th Century. In 1838 Matthias Schleiden, a German botanist, announced that the cell was the basic structural unit of all vegetable matter. A year later one of his countrymen, Theodor Schwann, pointed out that "cells are organisms and entire animals and plants are aggregates of these organisms arranged according to definite laws." All subsequent investigations into the role of the cell were launched from this solid base line experimentally established by Schleiden and Schwann.

The modern microscope has revealed an astonishing diversity in both the structure and the functions of the cell. Cells are shaped like rods, spirals, shoe boxes, rectangles, circles, daisies on their stalks, snowflakes, string beans and blobs of jelly. In some cases the shape of a cell is dictated by its surrounding environment; this is apparently true of the neatly shaped rectangular cells packed in the stalk of a plant and of the spherical floating eggs of certain marine animals. The shape of other cells is often related to their function; human red-blood cells are saucer-shaped and fairly flat, permitting the ready transfer of the oxygen and carbon dioxide they carry throughout the body, while nerve cells have long, thin extensions to transmit messages.

Cells can be self-sufficient generalists capable of carrying on an independent existence; single-celled creatures such as the amoeba and the paramecium are examples of these free-living units. Cells can also be specialists with a particular job to do; these cells (including most of those which form the higher organisms) depend for their existence upon a highly integrated community life with other cells. Such cells group together to form creatures with luminous eyes on stalks, sponges that cling to rocks, praying mantises, peacocks, tigers and men—the whole visible, living world around us.

A cell can be a pleuropneumonia microbe one two-hundred-and-fifty-thousandth of an inch in diameter or it can be the yolk of an ostrich egg,

HEREDITY IN THE HANDS OF MAN
Scientists probing the cell are particularly interested in chromosomes, the tiny ribbons of proteins and nucleic acids that dictate growth and heredity. By subjecting a cell to a powerful electric field, they can disperse the chromosomes (opposite) and thereby prevent the cell from reproducing. Such techniques may play a major role in the future control of cancer.

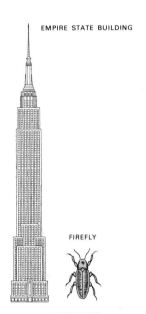

EMPIRE STATE BUILDING

FIREFLY

THE FIREFLY AS A MICRON

The drawings on these pages compare familiar objects and units of measurement with the infinitesimal units scientists use when they study the microscopic universe of the cell. The picture above illustrates the comparative sizes of the micron (from the Greek, "small") and the inch. The Empire State Building, 1,472 feet high, bears the same size-relationship to a firefly as an inch does to a micron: both are 25,000 times larger.

which is the size of an orange. An organization of cells can be a buttercup, a mayfly, a 125-ton blue whale or a 1,000-year-old redwood tree.

This is variety with a vengeance. And yet, for all this diversity, all cells are built according to a fundamental design which provides them with certain common features apparently necessary to life. Every cell has an outer wall which makes it a room (the Latin meaning of "cell"). Within the surrounding membrane is a semifluid material called cytoplasm in which the life activities of the cell are carried on. At the heart of the cell is the nucleus, a control center that bears within it the cell's hereditary material, ensuring the survival of its line.

To understand both the nature of a cell as an independent unit and its role in the life processes of larger organisms, it is necessary to examine it on various levels; it should be studied as a whole organism, as an organization of structural parts and, finally, in terms of the molecular units which form the basic building blocks of the cell and its parts.

The case of the animal plant

The *Euglena gracilis*, one of the most versatile of all single-celled organisms, is an excellent subject through which to examine the structure and behavior of the cell as a unit. Euglenas are often found in the green scum that covers stagnant ponds. Though they are unique in a number of ways, euglenas share certain basic features with other single-celled organisms and with all the higher organisms, including man. One of the euglena's most unusual attributes is its ability to change its very nature—from plant to animal and back again to plant—as its environment changes. This microscopic half-plant, half-animal thus provides a showcase of cell operations in both worlds.

The stage upon which the euglena is seen as a whole cell is a relatively spacious one in which the unit of measurement is the micron, which equals one twenty-five-thousandth of an inch. At this level, enlarged 100 times under the light microscope, euglenas appear as bright green, mistily transparent creatures about the size of the head of a thumbtack and shaped something like long narrow boats: rounded at one end, tapering at the other and broadest amidships. They glide along with a sort of tadpole movement, with a bit of a wiggle, as they touch and veer away and slip over and past one another.

When the magnification is increased from 100 to 1,000 times, the euglena organism takes on the appearance of a kind of animated corkscrew. It literally "bores" its way through its watery world, revolving about its long axis with a screw-type motion with the aid of a single flagellum, a whiplike extension which slashes around in the water. Sometimes the euglena stops boring and shifts to another type of locomotion. It pulls its rear end toward its front end, forming a ball, then extends its front end, then pulls its rear forward again and so on. Moving this way within its cellular wall, the euglena suggests the antics of a person trying to crawl while secured in a burlap bag.

The sheath of transparent membrane which forms the cell wall of the euglena is permeable, allowing molecules of certain food substances to enter the cell. There is also a mouth opening and a primitive gullet which ingest food particles. The cell wall encloses the cytoplasmic fluid, a jellylike substance carrying the structures within which most of the life processes of the cell take place. Floating in the cytoplasm are a number of green bodies resembling bits of colored glass in a kaleidoscope; they are the chloroplasts, minute manufacturing centers which contain the plant pigment, chlorophyll. Deep within the cytoplasm lies the nucleus containing the cell's hereditary material—the blueprint for all succeeding generations of each particular euglena.

Since the euglena uses its chloroplasts to synthesize plant food from sunlight, air and water, it is generally listed as a simple plant. The euglena, however, is not this easily categorized, for it often slips over into the other great division of living matter—the animal world. In the absence of light, the plant transforms itself into an animal—that is, the euglena temporarily loses its green color and its ability to use light in producing food and, like amoebae and other microorganisms classified as members of the animal kingdom, lives on ready-made foods available in the environment. When exposed to sunlight again, the euglena can revert to its green form and its plantlike existence.

A cell that sees

Though it is a relatively simple organism, the euglena can "see." Up front, not far from the gullet, is a single reddish eye or eyespot—one of the most primitive light-sensing structures known. As the euglena revolves and bores its way through the water, its eyespot scans the world outside. Apparently there is a link between the eyespot and the euglena's propulsion mechanisms, for the organism bends its body to swim toward the light. The creature also seems to be able to distinguish between red and blue light.

Communities of euglenas also exhibit a sense of time. Though individual euglenas live less than a day before passing through their reproductive cycle and dividing into two creatures, it has been proved by experiment that the movements of a colony of euglenas will follow a 24-hour rhythm. This experiment involves a euglena colony, a tank of water with a beam of light shining through it and a photocell, or electric eye, placed outside the tank to measure the intensity of the beam of light. When the euglena colony migrates toward the light beam in order to absorb energy to fuel the creatures' life processes, some of the light

THE FIREFLY AS AN ANGSTROM
The angstrom is a tiny unit of scientific measurement whose size is indicated by this drawing of a firefly and the United States. It would take 250 million three-quarter-inch fireflies, end to end, to span the nearly-3,000-mile distance from coast to coast. It would take the same number of angstroms to span one inch. Even an electron microscope cannot reach below five angstroms.

FIREFLY

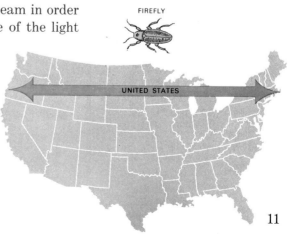

UNITED STATES

is dissipated or blocked off from the sensitive photocell. A recording device attached to the photocell keeps track of the colony's movements.

Repeated tests with this equipment reveal an approximate 24-hour rhythm in the euglena colony's movements. For 12 hours the euglenas respond to the light and gather in the beam; for the next 12 hours they ignore the light and scatter. The rhythm persists under unchanging laboratory conditions, where there is no night or day.

The rhythmic movements of the euglena colony, unrelated to any changes in the creatures' environment, will persist for a number of days. This suggests not only that the individual euglena possesses a biological clock, but also that the time-measuring facility is an inherited characteristic, being passed along from one euglena generation to the next. This sense of time is but one of the basic features which euglenas have in common with many other cells and with all the higher organisms.

These shared characteristics—such as the ability to reproduce, to react to stimuli and to produce the chemical compounds necessary to the cell's life processes—point to the familial relationship which joins all manner of cells. These shared features also underscore the fact that all species of living things, including the complex organizations of cells which form the larger organisms, have evolved from the single cell.

Into the submicroscopic world

Cells also disclose subtler signs of the unity of all life. To observe these less obvious relationships it is necessary to shift the level of observation—to turn from the cell as a unit to a study of its individual parts and their coordinated activities. The shift in scale demands the use of modern developments in electronics and biochemistry.

Until a relatively few years ago, man's conception of the cell was limited to what could be seen through a microscope employing light-waves. Magnifications of 1,000 to 2,000 times, the practical limit for the so-called light microscope, revealed the cell's outline, the cytoplasm and the nucleus at the center. Smaller structures either appeared as tiny dots or strands, or remained invisible. For many years the ability to observe these smaller entities of the submicroscopic world was restricted by the limitations of the light microscope, which resulted from the relatively long length of the waves of the visible light employed in the instrument. Something smaller than a light-wave was needed to "see" the minute working parts of a cell.

The most important step in the process of opening the interior of the cell to further visual exploration occurred about 30 years ago with the development of the first practical electron microscope. This relatively massive instrument employs high electrical voltages to drive a beam of electrons through a vacuum to magnify the image of the object being

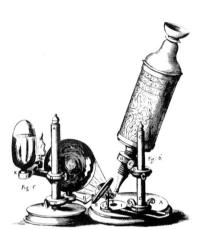

MICROSCOPE FROM HOOKE'S BOOK, 1665

THE FIRST FINDER OF THE CELL
In 1665 English scientist Robert Hooke published a description of an ornate new microscope he had perfected. Hooke did not invent the microscope (the invention is attributed to Dutch spectaclemaker Hans Janssen or his son Zacharias, about 1590), but his instrument was powerful enough for him to see and identify the entity which he named the "cell." Today's light microscopes work on the same basic principle.

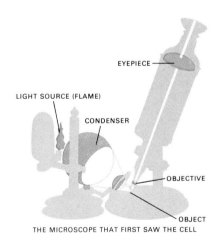

EYEPIECE

LIGHT SOURCE (FLAME)

CONDENSER

OBJECTIVE

OBJECT

THE MICROSCOPE THAT FIRST SAW THE CELL

observed. As the wavelength of these electrons is about one one-hundred-thousandth that of normal white light, the electron microscope can discriminate between far smaller objects than the light microscope. Actually, present-day electron microscopes can detect objects about 100 times smaller than those the best light microscopes detect.

A second modern aid to the study of the cell has been the development of biochemistry during the last two decades. Chiefly through the use of radioactive agents, scientists can now "tag" the atoms and molecules that form the building blocks of cells and follow them through the various life processes constantly at work within the cell.

The thinnest slices ever made

The electron microscope reduces the observational area of cell study to a stage on which the unit of measurement is the angstrom (a unit named for a Swedish physicist, who used it in his study of light-waves), which is equal to about one two-hundred-fifty-millionth part of an inch, or one ten-thousandth of a micron, the dimension used in light microscopy. Working at this level, investigators embed cells in transparent plastic, slice them into sections a few millionths of an inch thick by means of glass or diamond knives, and examine the specimens at magnifications which range up to 200,000 times.

From the electron microscope and biochemical research has come a precise picture of the cell's outer membrane. The single-celled euglena, the cells of men and the cells of all the intermediate species have the same basic type of outer coating, consisting of a layer of a compound called protein on either side of a thin layer of fat. The total thickness of the sandwich is about one three-millionths of an inch.

The electron microscope not only shows more details of previously known parts of the cell, it also reveals new parts. The light microscope and meticulous staining techniques disclose what appear to be stringy structures in the fluid portion of the cell. These barely visible structures spring into focus when seen at the high magnifications available in the electron microscope.

These structures, submerged in the fluids of the cell, form networks of hollow ducts, a maze of segmented microtunnels. These networks are known as the endoplasmic reticulum, or ER for short, and its branching channels extend throughout the cell's interior like a system of roots or blood vessels. Generally, the ER is believed to be a transport system designed to carry materials from one part of the cell to another.

The "factory district" of every cell also lies in the cytoplasm, in the form of numerous ribosomes, spheroids a little less than a millionth of an inch in diameter. Ribosomes are the site of the manufacture of the protein compounds which form a major part of every organism. Proteins,

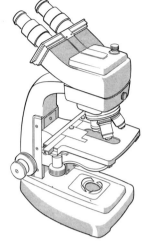

LIGHT MICROSCOPE WITH BINOCULAR VIEWING

A POWERFUL TOOL OF SCIENCE

Fundamentally the same as Hooke's instrument, the modern light microscope still preserves the sequence of light source, condenser, object, objective and eyepiece. But two centuries of improvements have made it a vastly superior tool. In this model, the object is seen by transmitted light; mirrors and prisms permit two-eye viewing; its effective magnification is about 2,000 diameters, contrasted with the 100 diameters for Hooke's instrument.

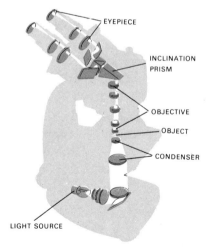

CUTAWAY PICTURE OF MODERN MICROSCOPE

various combinations of carbon, hydrogen, nitrogen, oxygen and usually sulphur, exist everywhere—in cells which make up tissues and organs, in membranes and muscle fibers and skin and bone and cartilage. (Among the most important proteins are substances called enzymes, which keep the wheels of life spinning by speeding vital biochemical processes.) To manufacture the many forms of protein it needs, a cell may utilize thousands of ribosomes, some floating in the cytoplasm and others attached to the ER like berries on a vine.

Two other parts of the cell are currently the subjects of intense study: Golgi complexes and mitochondria. The Golgi complex is named after Camillo Golgi, the Italian physician who discovered it nearly 70 years ago in the brain cells of barn owls. It consists of four or five flat hollow disks which may have swollen or bulbous edges and are piled one above the other like saucers. Biologists now know the Golgi complex is involved in the "packaging" of the proteins manufactured in the cell, turning them into units that can be distributed outside the cell.

Power plants of the cell

Mitochondria are so elaborately designed that they have been referred to as cells within the cell. Their interiors look something like cutaway models of ocean liners, with many chambers and compartments and dividing walls. They are miniature power plants and provide the cell with the energy it needs for growth, reproduction and other functions.

Most of the cellular structures revealed by modern microscopes—the ER, the ribosomes, the mitochondria, the Golgi apparatus and the nucleus, as well as many others—are common to all cells. Microphotographs disclose them in many specialized cells such as those of the human heart, brain and liver as well as in the free-living euglena. But a catalogue of parts does not explain how the assembled machine works. This emphasizes the chief limitation of the electron microscope; it provides pictures of dead material, pictures of cell sections in which all activity has been "frozen." The problem facing biologists is, therefore, to reconstruct the dynamic operation of a cell from static photographs which show how the cell looked during a brief instant of its life-span. This is like trying to deduce the plot of a feature-length motion picture from a few frames clipped from the entire roll.

One way to visualize a cell in action is to construct a hypothetical working model of an average cell and then to "feed" into the model information which has been gathered through microscopic and biochemical studies. Though such a procedure (sometimes called a "thought experiment") poses the danger of oversimplification and the risk of having conjectural material taken for fact, it has the great virtue of showing the cell as the restless and dynamic heart of life.

Let us assume, therefore, that someone has invented an instrument which would show a live, single-celled organism in three dimensions, magnified 100,000 times. The living model which resulted would be a globular mass about six feet in diameter enclosed in a thin, flexible membrane. This hypothetical giant is a viable body, continually changing in shape, heaving and pulsing, oozing out here and snapping back there, like a rubber sheet. Even the outer membrane operates as a highly active system. It extends tentaclelike arms in an incessant search for food and footholds. It folds around outside materials and engulfs them. It contains many gateways where only selected molecules may pass. The two-way traffic shuttling through these gates is swift and steady.

Swimming in the fluid interior of this giant model are the mitochondria, sausage-shaped bodies almost a foot long and several inches in diameter. Like fish among coral reefs, the mitochondria dart in and out of spaces near the lattice structures of the ER. Partly hidden at the center of the cell is the nucleus, a dense body which looks something like a medicine ball. The fluid between the nucleus and the cell's outer membrane is marked here and there by cloudy patches, indicating the presence of ribosomes. Even at this magnification the ribosomes are no larger than the head of a match.

Turmoil in the cytoplasm

The interior of the giant cell is in a continual state of upheaval. The ER network not only shifts and sways like seaweed in the surf along a rocky coast, but actually breaks up into pieces and re-forms and breaks up again. The mitochondria have been described as cylindrical bodies and that is true if one thinks in terms of photographs which catch them in a fraction of a second. But in the living cell they twist and slither along like eels—very peculiar eels since they are constantly splitting into equally active bits and fusing end to end to form elongated swimming systems. Moving with them, drifting about in the cytoplasmic currents, are fatty globules and fragments of the ER.

A few minutes in the presence of such a huge animated blob would hardly bolster one's faith in the harmony of nature. The initial impression would certainly be one of utter chaos. Yet there is an order in this strange commotion. It is the invisible and elusive kind of order called life, a phenomenon which in some ways seems increasingly difficult to comprehend as we learn more and more about it.

What delicate equilibrium of forces preserves the integrity of higher organisms? They are, after all, systems made up of these same ever-changing and hectically active cells. The adult human body is estimated to contain 60,000 billion cells, every one of them subject to the rules and regulations of the group. Yet every one of them also remains a rugged in-

A MOLECULAR MATCHMAKER

The drawings below illustrate the function of an enzyme. The boy and girl represent molecules that are capable of getting together, but are chemically shy. An enzyme —the matronly matchmaker—breaks the ice and then leaves, chemically unchanged. Such a substance, which causes a reaction but is not changed by it, is called a catalyst. There are some 700 kinds of enzymes—catalysts in the body —such as ptyalin in saliva, which breaks down starch, and pepsin from stomach cells, which aids digestion by splitting proteins.

ABLE BUT UNWILLING MOLECULES

THE ENZYME PERFORMS ITS DUTY

WILLING AND ABLE MOLECULES

dividualist and may go on rampages and break laws. An example of this antisocial behavior is cancer, which foists a sort of mob rule of errant cells upon the body.

It speaks well for the body's control mechanisms that things run smoothly more often than not. We are more or less the persons we were yesterday because a kind of cellular discipline has been maintained, although it is by no means a rigid discipline. Every organism must keep its biological books balanced throughout its lifetime. Every second some 50 million of your body cells die. During the same period 50 million infant cells are born to take the place of the dying cells.

All organisms endure in a "soft" way—by shifting and riding with punches, by avoiding impacts, by yielding to forces and slipping around obstacles. Life may be compared to a candle flame, a cool blue flame. Something enormously complex is going on inside the flame. It is a burning process that involves the continual play of atomic particles, a constant replenishment of fuel and a constant transformation of energy.

The flame is never the same yet always the same. The matter that makes up the flame at any given instant has vanished by the next instant and has been replaced by fresh matter. What persists in this luminous heart of chemical activity is not the substance but the form. And life itself persists in an analogous, although far more complex, fashion.

The Living Forces inside the Cell

The microscopic blob of jelly called the cell is a remarkable entity. The most remarkable thing about it is the very fact that it is alive—not with a murky primordial glow, but as fully and vibrantly alive as a tiger or an oak tree. In a remarkable miniaturization of life's functions, the cell moves, grows, reacts, protects itself and even reproduces. To sustain this varied existence, it utilizes a tightly organized system of parts that is much like a tiny industrial complex. It has a central control point, power plants, internal communications, construction and manufacturing elements. These basic cell components, common to cells which otherwise vary enormously in size and function, are illustrated in the painting opposite, which shows how a cell might look more than 10,000 times magnified. The following pages explore further these individual subcellular bits and pieces and take a look at some of the ways the cell goes about its business.

WORKING PLAN OF A CELL

The cutaway painting opposite shows a typical cell from a rat's liver. Though cells vary widely in shape, almost all have three basic components: the round ball of the nucleus; surrounding it, the cytoplasm containing various internal organelles vital to the cell's operation; enclosing everything, the cell membrane. The entire jelly-like mass of living matter is called protoplasm.

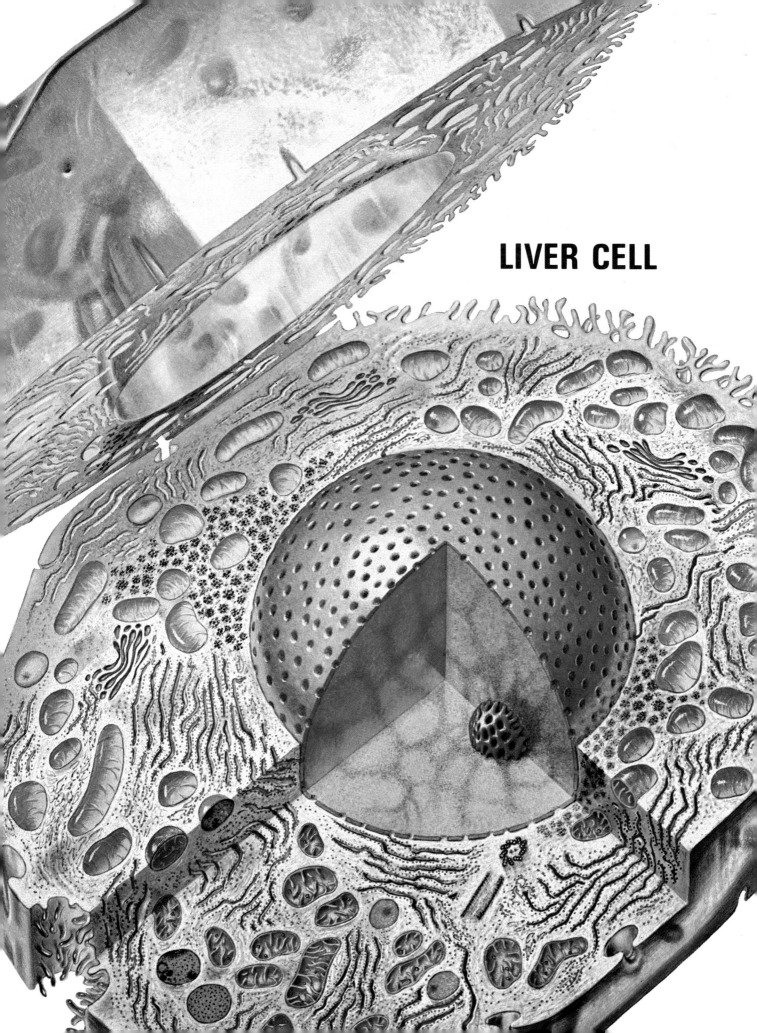

LIVER CELL

A SMALL WORLD

Seeking Answers to the Riddle of Existence

What makes a turtle tick? Will it grow up? Does it like its shell? What is inside? Few people—and certainly few small boys—can resist the miniature perfection of a small, moving creature. It is with this same curiosity and sense of excitement that biologists explore the minute complexity of the cell. And their search is enlivened by the bright hope that at their fingertips is the key to what makes the turtle—and all living things—tick.

Though that secret still eludes them, biologists have turned up an enormous amount of information. When English scientist Robert Hooke first called the cell a cell, just 300 years ago, he pictured a rigid, boxlike structure—a honeycomb—which was filled with some mysterious slime of life. Hooke's word stuck, but his single concept long ago gave way to the realization that the world of the cell is vastly complicated. Microscopes have picked out cells—bacteria—that are one hundred thousandth of an inch across.

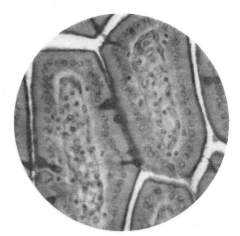

MOUSE'S INTESTINAL TISSUE

A SAMPLING OF CELLS
The four pictures at right illustrate the four basic categories of cells: animal cells living in communities or in association with others; associated plant cells; free-living animal cells; and free-living plant cells. The diatoms, a kind of algae, are demonstrating the tendency of some single cells to cluster together in casual, nondependent associations of primitive colonies.

MULTIPLIED TO FORM A FROG
The frog, though a humble inhabitant of pond and lily pad, is nevertheless a highly complex organism. Hundreds of millions of associated cells comprise the animal and they all work in harmony, each doing a special job in a special place. At the frog's level of organization, the cells have associated to form tissue and tissues have in turn associated to form organs.

Another cell—an ostrich egg—is 500,000 times longer. Between these extremes of size there are cells of every imaginable shape, texture and appearance.

These pages show four categories into which cells can be placed as a start toward putting them in order. To begin with, cells may be classified as either plant or animal. Plants, like the iris below, make their own food, but animals, like the frog, must catch theirs. So, generally, animals move around, while plants stand still. Furthermore, most plant cells have rigid shapes while most animal cells are flexible. Flesh, when pinched, gives and then returns to shape —a tree does not.

Finally, there are cells that live alone and cells that live in communities. The latter can be formed into structures of amazing complexity, like the turtle, frog, flower or a human being. The cells that go their own way remain mostly unseen, blowing around in the air or slopping about for a few silent hours in the sea.

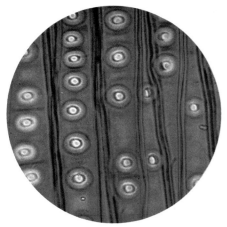

PINE TREE'S BARK

ACANTHARIA, ONE-CELLED ANIMAL

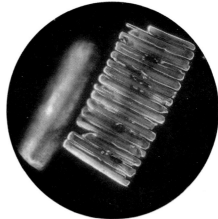

DIATOMS, ONE-CELLED PLANTS

SPECIALIZED TO REPRODUCE

As in animals, the cells of a complex plant combine to form tissues and then organs—the roots, stems and the leaves. This morning-iris blossom represents the plant's reproductive system.

THE SEA AND THE SINGLE CELL

The sea is home for many single-celled organisms, like the algae that carpet the coastline above. Others inhabit the vast expanse of the oceans, far from any land. Most stay near the surface: the plants to get sunlight, the animals, called protozoa, to feed on the plants. Together they form a living harvest of plankton, which ultimately feeds all the larger animals of the seas.

CONTROL

Keeping the Cell in Operation

Anything that works, works best under control. For a door, the knob provides the control point. For the cell, control is located in the nucleus (below)—a computer, design department, construction boss and board of directors all rolled into one. Almost all the cell does is supervised by the nucleus. Cut an amoeba (a one-celled animal) in half and that part with the nucleus grows back and thrives; the other half falters and dies. Graft an extra nucleus into an amoeba and the animal will grow in size as the dual command posts order double of everything.

But the nucleus's most dramatic performance comes during the cell's division. An urgent message brings about a mystifying change; cell activity appears to stop dead, as if in response to a factory's five-o'clock whistle. Gradually the nucleus dissolves; soon two nuclei form and the cell divides in two. Suddenly there are two cells, at full production, each under the competent command of a brand-new boss.

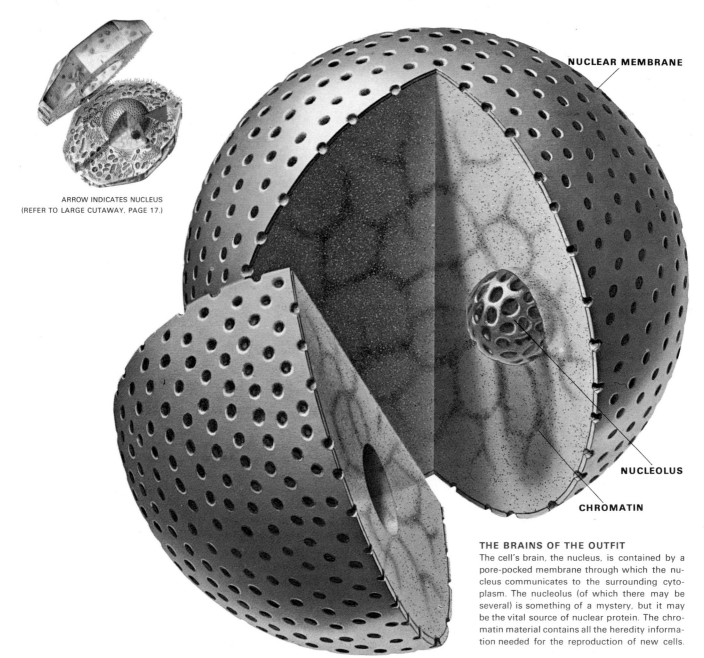

ARROW INDICATES NUCLEUS
(REFER TO LARGE CUTAWAY, PAGE 17.)

NUCLEAR MEMBRANE

NUCLEOLUS

CHROMATIN

THE BRAINS OF THE OUTFIT
The cell's brain, the nucleus, is contained by a pore-pocked membrane through which the nucleus communicates to the surrounding cytoplasm. The nucleolus (of which there may be several) is something of a mystery, but it may be the vital source of nuclear protein. The chromatin material contains all the heredity information needed for the reproduction of new cells.

Producing Energy
to Make Things Hum

Where does the energy come from that keeps a small boy going at full blast all day long? For little boys, as for all living things, plant and animal, it comes from a tiny, sausage-shaped pod *(below)* with a Greek name, mitochondrion. The mitochondrion—along with as many as 1,000 more per cell just like it—is the powerhouse of the cell.

Its job is just like that of a generating plant in which a raw material—coal—is burned to produce power—electricity—which is then sent out to light lamps, heat stoves and run machines. The mitochondrion's raw material is the food absorbed by the cell and broken down in the cytoplasm. In a chemical operation, the cellular powerhouse "burns" the food to release its energy and then loads this energy onto a chemical molecule with a jawbreaker for a name: adenosine triphosphate, or ATP for short. This precious stuff—essentially raw power—is to cells what electricity is to the machines in a factory: it runs them.

POWER

ARROW INDICATES MITOCHONDRION
(REFER TO LARGE CUTAWAY, PAGE 17.)

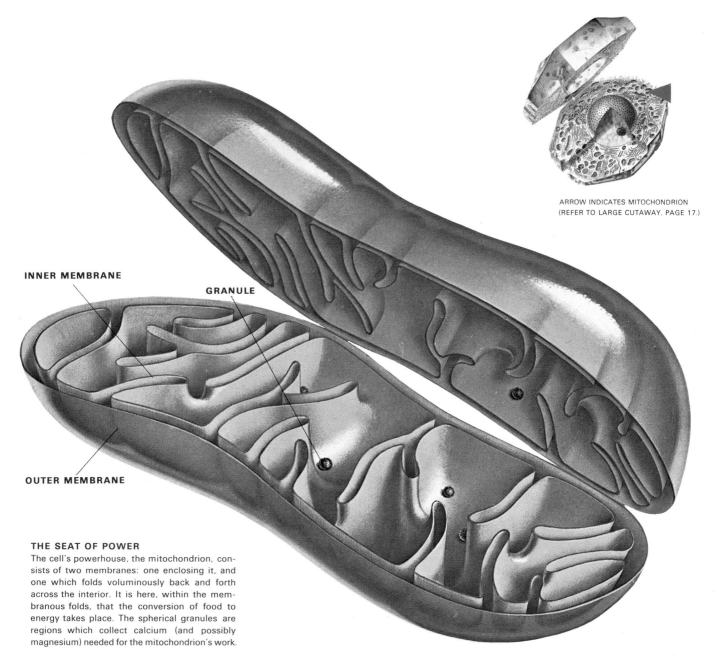

INNER MEMBRANE

GRANULE

OUTER MEMBRANE

THE SEAT OF POWER
The cell's powerhouse, the mitochondrion, consists of two membranes: one enclosing it, and one which folds voluminously back and forth across the interior. It is here, within the membranous folds, that the conversion of food to energy takes place. The spherical granules are regions which collect calcium (and possibly magnesium) needed for the mitochondrion's work.

PRODUCTION

Manufacturing for Growth

Just as any manufacturer does, the cell takes simple materials and transforms them into complex substances. And just as a manufacturer must be prepared to deliver his product to customers, so some cells deliver their materials where needed. Part of this manufacturing and trucking firm is shown below. What look like scattered buckshot are manufacturing units which put chemicals together—just as a child stacks blocks—to make protein, the prime building material of the cell.

These units are called ribosomes and they do their work under supervision of the nucleus. Sometimes they operate in isolation, but often they are linked in a transfer and delivery setup known as the endoplasmic reticulum, or ER for short. A fine mesh of hollow sheets like those below, the ER spreads in networks through the cytoplasmic material. It is connected to the nucleus, and scientists speculate that it transports the proteins made by the ribosomes around the cell.

ARROW INDICATES ER
(REFER TO LARGE CUTAWAY, PAGE 17.)

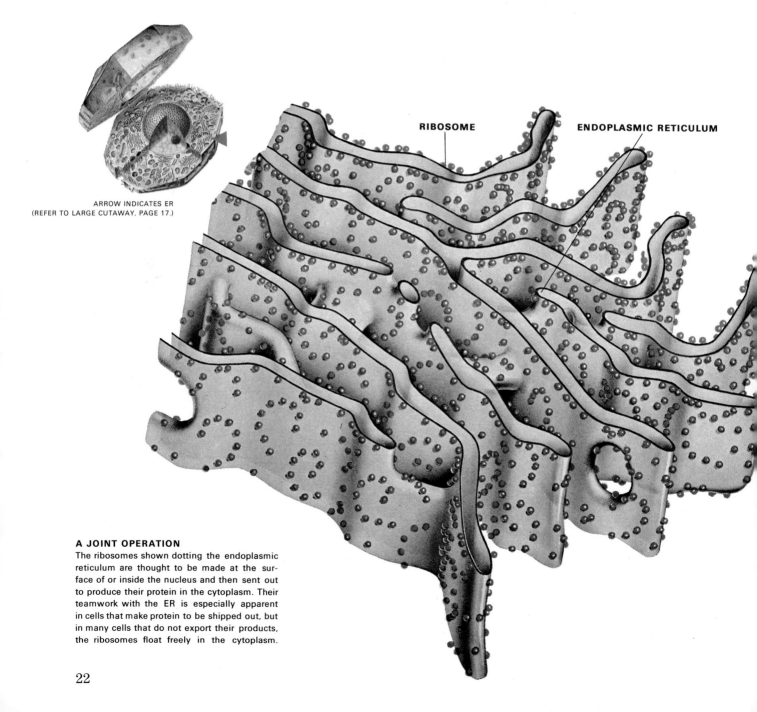

RIBOSOME

ENDOPLASMIC RETICULUM

A JOINT OPERATION
The ribosomes shown dotting the endoplasmic reticulum are thought to be made at the surface of or inside the nucleus and then sent out to produce their protein in the cytoplasm. Their teamwork with the ER is especially apparent in cells that make protein to be shipped out, but in many cells that do not export their products, the ribosomes float freely in the cytoplasm.

Wrapped for Shipment

Though it was discovered back in 1898, the odd-looking apparatus below is still one of the cell's most baffling mysteries. It was first seen by (and is named for) Italian physician Camillo Golgi in the brain cells of a barn owl, and later in the nerve cells of a cat, but its existence was emphatically disputed for many decades until the modern electron microscope proved its presence in almost all cells. All together, more than 2,000 learned papers have been written about it—and yet even now there are very few facts that can be stated with certainty.

Scientific consensus is that the Golgi bodies store and package proteins which the cell exports. Protein, produced and delivered by the assembly-line operation on the opposite page, comes to the Golgi body and collects in its hollow sacs. When protein is to be shipped out—or perhaps even when needed inside the cell—bits of the Golgi body break off and the protein, neatly packaged, goes off to market.

PACKAGING

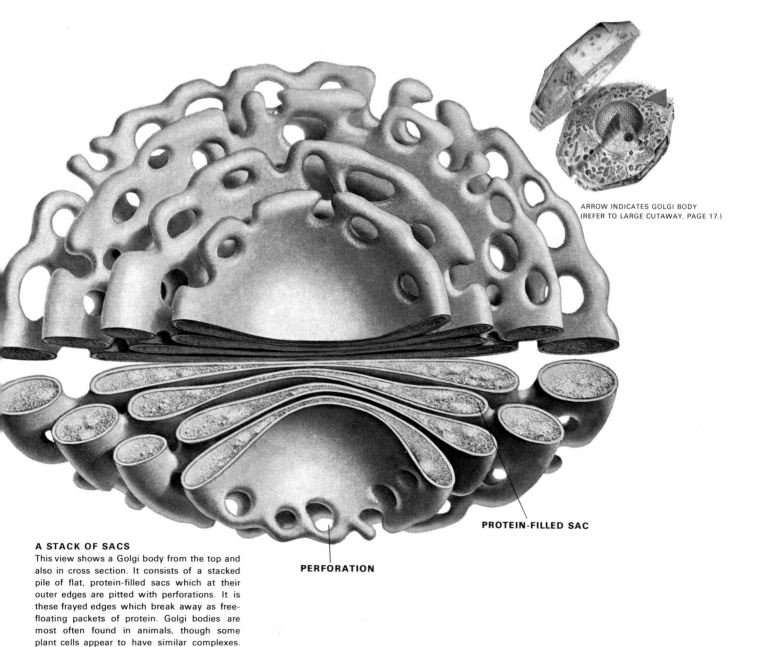

ARROW INDICATES GOLGI BODY
(REFER TO LARGE CUTAWAY, PAGE 17.)

PROTEIN-FILLED SAC

PERFORATION

A STACK OF SACS
This view shows a Golgi body from the top and also in cross section. It consists of a stacked pile of flat, protein-filled sacs which at their outer edges are pitted with perforations. It is these frayed edges which break away as free-floating packets of protein. Golgi bodies are most often found in animals, though some plant cells appear to have similar complexes.

23

FEEDING

Eating a Meal by Surrounding It

Every living thing must eat—and cells are no exception. A small boy can be a trencherman, but his performance seems tame compared to that of an amoeba, which literally spends its whole life eating. The moment it is "born," an amoeba starts after its prey (other animals, algae, almost anything smaller) with such a voracious appetite that within 24 hours—or less if food is plentiful—it has doubled its size and is too big to support itself any longer. So it divides into two new cells which immediately resume the orgy.

Boys, along with most other animals, have mouths to eat with, and plants have roots, but the cell's food must come in through the membrane which surrounds it. This envelope has a marvelous capacity for letting in only what the cell wants and rejecting what it does not. It also has a remarkable flexibility, which plays a vital part in many one-celled animals' hunting habits. The hungry amoeba shown here demonstrates how it ingests a meal.

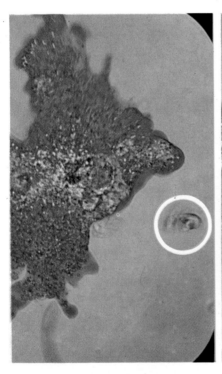

THE EVER-CHANGING AMOEBA
The amoeba above is closing in on a microscopic meal. Its name comes from a Greek word meaning change, since the amoeba constantly alters its shape as it moves. (It is so formless that one species is named *Chaos chaos*.)

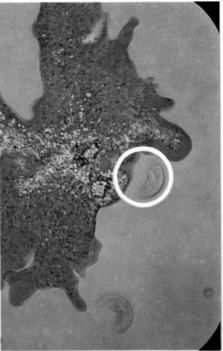

FALSE, BUT EFFECTIVE, FEET
The amoeba has no senses, but does react when close to food. Bulging extensions of cytoplasm flow out, extending the cell membrane one way as it retracts elsewhere. These extensions are called pseudopods (false feet).

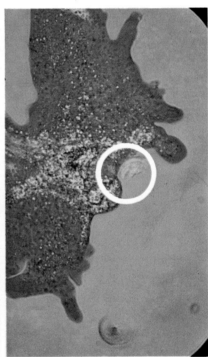

ENCIRCLING THE ENEMY
The pseudopods, which with their bulging and retracting move the animal slowly along, also catch its food. Flowing smoothly, they ooze over, under and around the prey, completely surrounding it and folding it into the amoeba.

ALL WRAPPED UP
The doomed prey, suspended in a drop of water called a vacuole, is taken into the cell whole. Digestion occurs within the vacuole, which stays intact. The cell digests and takes what it can, then moves on and disgorges the waste.

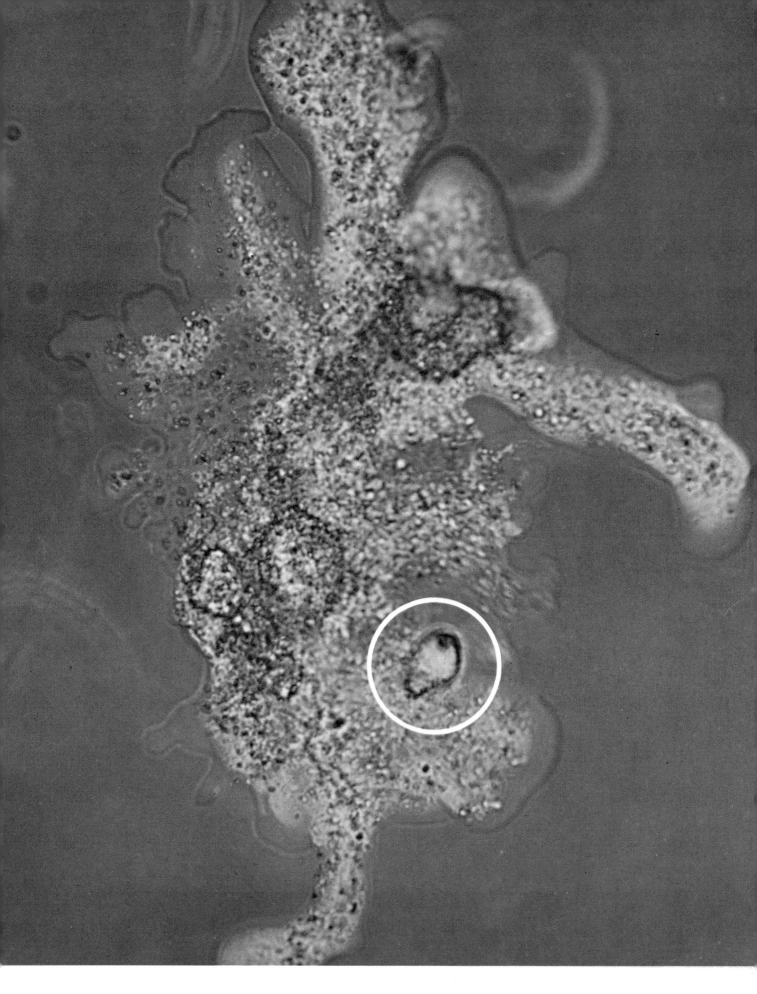

RESPONSE

Reacting to Remain Alive

A boy is touched by a burning match, jumps away and bursts into tears; a green brew of one-celled creatures is exposed to a ray of light and streams toward it; a one-celled animal "senses" danger and sends out a bushy barrage. These are all examples of behavior common to everything that lives: response to change, alternately known as irritability. To keep alive in a changing environment, organisms must be able to react to, protect themselves from and take advantage of, new situations. The boy's finger would have been badly burned, for example, if he had not jumped away from the flame.

The factor that elicits these responses is called a stimulus, and different kinds of cells behave differently when exposed to stimuli. For instance, a nerve cell in a frog's leg muscle responds readily to a minute electric current. But different kinds of cells in the same frog's stomach need an electric jolt 10 times stronger applied 10,000 times longer before they will respond.

A PATTERN OF RESPONSE
Euglenas are curious one-celled creatures that are both plant and animal. They have the green chlorophyll of plants, which uses light to make food, so when put into semidarkness *(above)* they go to the light. They avoid too bright a light, however, which accounts for the design at right. If there is no light at all, euglenas act like animal cells and catch their food.

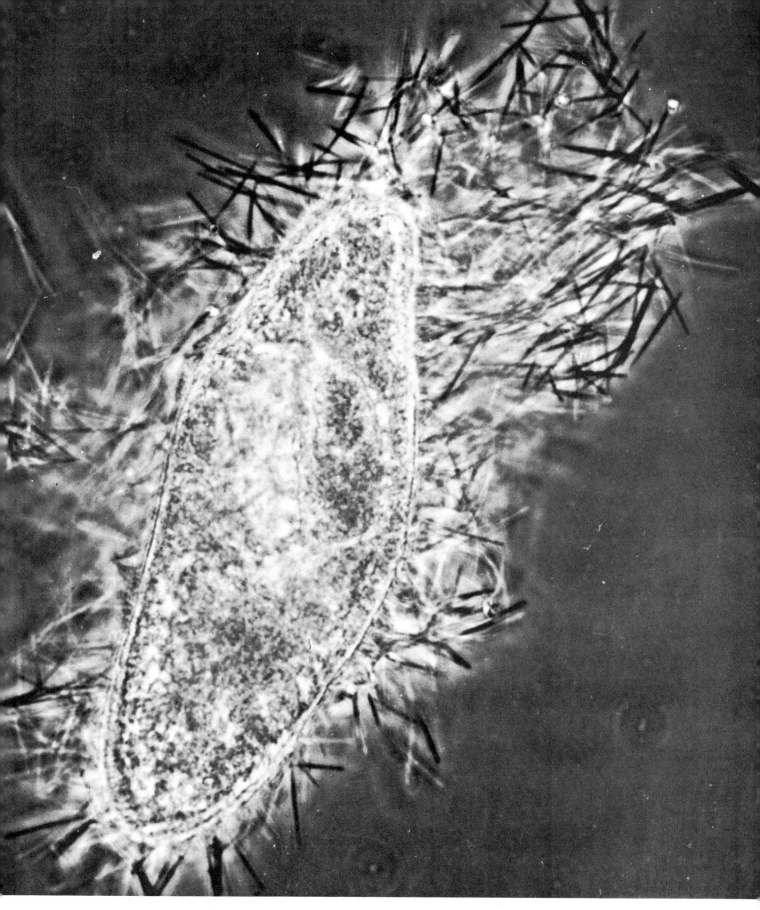

A REACTION OF ALARM

The one-celled animal above, called a paramecium, is seen in a dramatic but still mysterious
reaction to a change in its environment. The addition of iodine to its habitat acted as a stimulus which triggered the release of dozens of
spear-shaped filaments called trichocysts. Biologists are not sure what the trichocysts do, but
they probably serve as a defense mechanism.

A Number of Ways
of Getting Around

Not only do cells eat and react, they also move. At least, some do. Those living in complex communities are immobilized by the thousands of other cells which hem them in; and most plant cells do not have to move, since the sunlight, water and minerals they need come to them. But single-celled animals boast the same mobility enjoyed by larger creatures. Of course they do not move as fast or as far as a child playing hopscotch, but they are fast enough to be clocked. The amoeba going after its dinner on pages 24 and 25, for instance, is churning along at about one three-thousandth of an inch per second—it will cover an inch in just less than an hour. (Its smaller animal prey can usually move quite a bit faster, but makes the mistake of pausing in one spot long enough for the predator to catch up.) The amoeba's awkward flowing motion is called amoeboid movement, but some cells have other, increasingly efficient ways of getting from here to there.

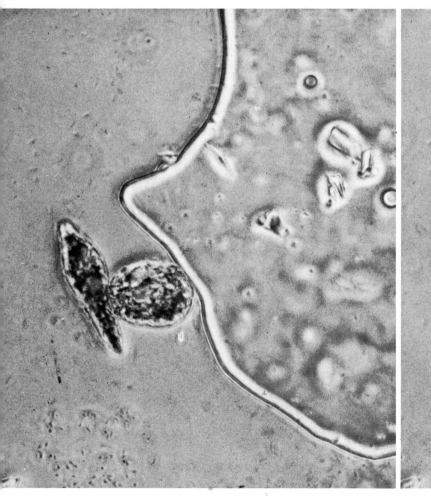
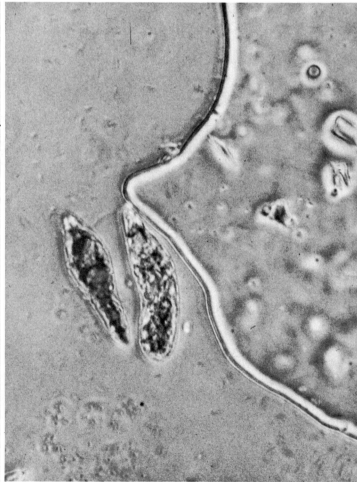

These photomicrographs show one of two euglenas "swimming" past an obstruction. Special fibers in the cell's cytoplasm bunch up, then

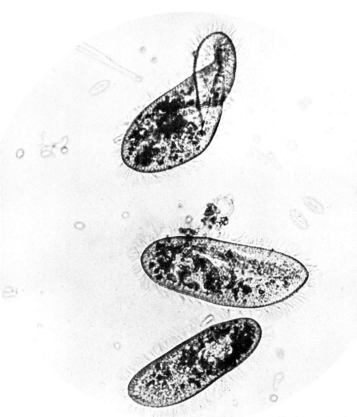

UPSIDE DOWN AND ALL AROUND

The paramecium moves by beating against the surrounding fluid with a hairlike fringe of short filaments called cilia. At the same time, it twists on its lengthwise axis so that it travels in a spiral path. It can also shift into reverse.

WAVING IN WAVES

Cilia, up to 2,500 of them on one cell, beat in rhythmic waves which move down the length of the animal. They go the other way to reverse the cell's direction. Some cells have fewer, longer, whiplike "propellers" called flagella.

Photographs clearly show how a paramecium twists as it moves.

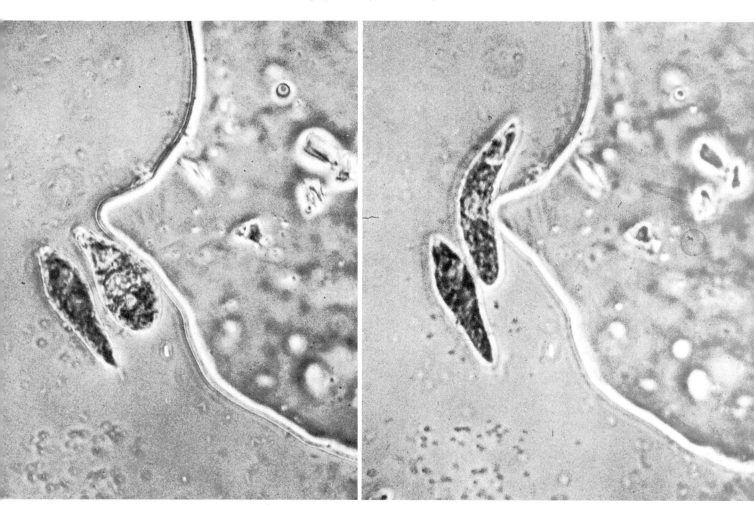

relax to ease the cell along in what is called euglenoid movement. Each euglena has a single flagellum, not visible here, to help it move.

PROTECTION

Bundling Up against the World Outside

The membrane which encloses all cells is an efficient device for absorbing nourishment, but it is a fragile defense against the buffeting from the outside world. So, like children bound for winter hills bundling up to keep warm, many cells build themselves an extra layer for protection.

Different cells use different building materials and methods. Plants manufacture cellulose and pile it up into rigid cell walls which, en masse, form the bark of trees and stalks of plants. Animals do not have such cell walls (one of the main differences between plants and animals) but they do have special cells (called epithelial cells) which make the armor, scales or skin that cover most creatures. Especially interesting are the one-celled animals which build their own protective shells. One amoeba species, for instance, gathers grains of sand, manufactures its own mortar and builds a house on its back. Other intriguing examples of cellular architecture are shown on these pages.

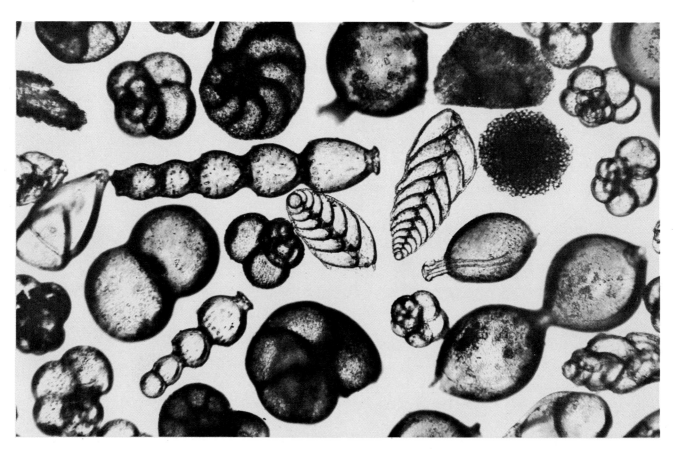

THE OCEANS' HARD CELL
The much-magnified photograph above shows dozens of foraminifers—pinhead-sized, one-celled animals that live in the sea by the billions. Foraminifers begin life soft and shapeless, then secrete chalky shells all around themselves, enlarging them with new chambers as they grow. Their remains form an ooze which covers 40 million square miles of ocean floor.

THE SEAS' SPINY SHELLBACKS
Pictured opposite is a glass model of a globigerina, a common foraminifer. Though it is one-celled, the globigerina secretes several round, interconnected shells. The shells, made of calcium carbonate, protect the cell, but have pores for the cell's long, fine pseudopods, which are actually extensions of the cell's living matter. The pseudopods help the cell catch its food.

2

Vital Energy from a Ray of Light

AN ENERGETIC USE FOR FOOD

Hurtling forward, these athletes drive toward the finish line in a college track meet. Their straining muscles are powered by energy released from food. In its turn, the food was initially produced by the sun, sparking sugar production in green plants. Similarly, every activity of life, from sprinting a 100-yard dash to exploring space, is powered by the sun.

LIFE, WHEREVER IT EXISTS, IS A PRODUCT OF STARLIGHT. All life on earth feeds on radiation coming from a yellow and middle-aged star which we call the sun. The energy of sunlight becomes life through the mediation of plant and animal cells. The essential operation involved consists of changing energy from one form to another—specifically, transforming radiant starlight from the sun into the chemical energy which enables the single cell to thrive and multiply, the tree to flourish, the tiger to stalk its prey and man to write his history in the stars.

Every cell needs energy to maintain its organized structure and to perform the varieties of mechanical, electrical and chemical work that constitute its life processes. This chapter traces the course of this energy, from its origin in sunshine through the electrical and chemical transformations that package it into food and fuel for the living cell.

Sunlight, the energy released from the fusion of matter by the thermonuclear furnace within our sun, radiates into space in all directions. A tiny fraction of the total, about one part in two billion, reaches the surface of the earth. Plants capture about a hundredth of this trickle of radiation and use it to drive the balanced processes of life.

The role the sun's energy plays in life processes on earth is illustrated by a simple experiment. A snail is placed in a glass test tube about two thirds full of pond water and a growing piece of any aquatic plant is added. Then the tube, its open end sealed, is exposed to the sun. Within the sealed glass tube, the life processes continue. Fueled by sunlight, the green plant takes in carbon dioxide and water from the surrounding atmosphere and gives off oxygen as it builds and replenishes its substance. The snail absorbs the plant's oxygen wastes, emits carbon dioxide and eats the plant tissues, which contain food for animal cells. If the cycle is properly adjusted and if the plant's life processes work just fast enough to replace the tissues which the snail is eating, the result is a system which may remain balanced for weeks or months.

The process by which cells use sunlight to transform carbon dioxide and water into life-sustaining chemical substances is called photosynthesis. Early naturalists believed that plants derive all their food from the soil—an assumption generally known as the Humus Theory. Johann van Helmont, a Flemish physician, disproved this hypothesis around 1630 when he planted a willow branch weighing five pounds in 200 pounds of soil—and found that after a five-year water diet the plant had gained about 164 pounds and the soil had lost only two ounces.

Van Helmont concluded that the water, rather than the soil, nourished the plant. It remained for scientists of a later day to prove that plant growth is a result of combining water and carbon dioxide, and that the energy for this manufacturing process comes from sunlight captured by the plant leaves.

We now know that the unique transformation process involved in photosynthesis is accomplished in two distinct steps. The first group of reactions is called the "sparking" sequence. This operation depends on the presence of light and is a characteristic feature of the life process of plant cells. Once this initial step, unique to the plant world, has been completed, the rest of the energy-transformation processes necessary to life can take place without light. These appropriately named "dark" reactions may be found throughout the living world, in animals as well as in plant cells.

The plant in the sealed test tube carries out the sparking sequence—a series of reactions that is still under intensive investigation. The best way to visualize the first link in the chain, the first reaction, is to imagine a single ray of sunlight as it enters the test tube and passes through the wall of one of the cells of the aquatic plant and then through a wall within a wall—the outer membrane of one of the many globular bodies floating in the cell's fluid interior. These bodies are called chloroplasts, and it is they that contain the apparatus for photosynthesis.

The light trap

Within the chloroplasts are light-trapping molecules of a substance called chlorophyll. The first reaction of the photosynthetic process takes place within these green-colored chlorophyll molecules. To understand how this reaction works, it is necessary to examine the arrangement of atoms which gives the chlorophyll its chemical character.

The chlorophyll molecule is a complex organization of carbon, hydrogen, nitrogen and oxygen atoms surrounding a magnesium atom. Associated with these atoms is a cloud of orbiting, negatively charged electrons which are normally in a low-energy state. When a ray of sunlight strikes the green plant, one of these low-energy electrons may absorb a particle (called a photon or quantum) of light energy and jump to a higher energy level.

For a rough idea of the nature of this reaction, think of a man at a test-your-strength circus sideshow. He swings a heavy mallet, slams it down on the padded end of a lever, and sends a weight shooting up a grooved shaft toward a bell at the top. The weight strikes the bell, making a loud clang.

The raised weight in this analogy represents the electron after it has absorbed a light photon and moved to a higher energy level. Now imagine that in another instant the electron, like the weight, will crash down to ground level and dissipate its energy. This, in fact, is exactly what takes place most of the time in the atomic world. Everywhere on the earth's surface, countless electrons are gaining and losing energy, absorbing and emitting light, jumping from one level to another.

LETTING THE SUN SHINE IN —AND THEN HOLDING IT

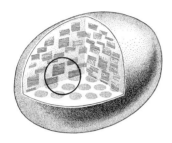

CHLOROPLAST WITH EXPOSED GRANA

GRANA: STACKS OF QUANTASOMES

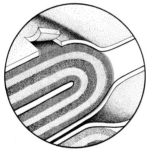

QUANTASOME CONTAINING CHLOROPHYLL

MICROSCOPIC MINT WAFERS

Before a plant cell can transform sunlight into chemical energy, it must first capture light. The snaring is done in the chloroplast *(top),* a highly organized structure about five thousandths of an inch long. The chloroplast is made up of columns called grana *(center).* A granum is a pile of quantasomes *(bottom)* arranged in a pattern resembling a stack of mint wafers and containing the light-snatching green molecules of chlorophyll.

It is at this point in photosynthesis that the life processes begin. Without an extraordinary intervention at this crucial moment, the earth might be as sterile today as it was in the beginning. To be of use in sparking life, an electron must be drawn into the photosynthetic process while it contains an extra charge of energy—while it is, as the scientists say, "excited." If the timing is not exact, the electron will lose its charge of energy spontaneously and return to its former low-energy state.

A bucket brigade for energy

As yet, the exact manner in which the excited electron enters the photosynthetic process is unknown. Current studies suggest that the electron excited by the light photon, having gained enough energy to leave the chlorophyll molecule, moves to a special site called a "trapping center." At this site the excited electron parts company with the chlorophyll molecule temporarily and hops to a neighboring body known as an "acceptor" molecule. This hop-and-catch of the electron must be a high-speed movement, for an electron usually remains in its excited state for less than a hundred millionth of a second.

Having trapped the energetic electron outside the chlorophyll, the first acceptor molecule now passes the charged-up runaway along a chain of four other acceptor molecules. Each one of these electron-carriers, or transfer agents, drains some of the energy from the excited electron before passing it on to a neighbor. The action of this transport chain could be compared to the tossing of a hot potato around a circle, from person to person, until it cools off. The last step for the electron involves a return to the chlorophyll molecule. In essence, the prodigal electron, having left by the front door and distributed its riches, now returns home through the back door.

According to current theory, this electronic bucket brigade works constantly in the photosynthetic process. As long as light is available, electrons move along definite pathways, out of chlorophyll molecules and along chains of acceptor substances and then back to the chlorophyll molecules again. In the course of this step-by-step movement, the electrons distribute their excess energy to provide fuel for the life processes. This movement of electrons is actually a kind of electricity. Life is powered by this energy and the generators which produce it are located in the chloroplast light-traps, the chlorophyll molecules.

The existence of electrical energy-producing processes within the cell carries certain implications. Sustained electric currents cannot be obtained simply by throwing some parts together. Organization, plans and circuit diagrams are needed, just as they are in the production of man-made electricity. Nature makes use of precise plans and specialized equipment in its energy-producing processes in the cell; furthermore,

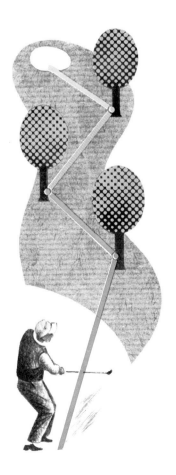

CAROMING A MOLECULAR GOLF BALL
In this drawing the golfer's club represents a photon and the ball is an electron. When a photon hits a chlorophyll molecule, an electron is slammed into an excited state. It then travels on an erratic course of "acceptor" molecules—trees, in this analogy. The electron loses energy at every bounce until it returns to its original level—at rest on the green. Energy at each step is used to produce ATP.

powerful microscopes reveal details suggesting the existence of an even more sophisticated circuitry at the molecular level—the present frontier of cell research.

Within the chloroplasts the higher magnifications of the electron microscope reveal certain drum-shaped cylindrical bodies, called grana, which are linked together in chain formations. Magnified 90,000 times, each one of the grana is seen to consist of about a dozen disk-shaped envelopes, stacked one on top of another like a pile of pennies. The flat chlorophyll molecules are too small to be seen, even at this high magnification, but it is believed they are contained within the envelopes of the grana.

It is at this level, where biology and electronics meet, that problems of cellular organization are encountered in their full complexity. The same basic phenomena seem to be taking place in the grana, the close-packed cylindrical bodies within the chloroplast, as in the crystal lattices of the transistors that are now used in many television, radio and radar sets, electronic wristwatches and the guiding systems of long-range missiles. The operation of transistors involves the controlled flow of electrons through fixed atomic structures; the plant bodies designed to capture solar energy appear to function in the same way. The substance of cells is a fluid, gelatinous material; but within it, beyond the present range of the most powerful microscopes, are rigid, semisolid structures. Something crystalline, something electronic, is at work within every plant cell.

Man's solar batteries

What has happened so far in the plant cell within the test tube? A controlled flow of electrons has been produced by the chlorophyll molecule in the chloroplast. Light energy has been converted into electrical energy, as it is in the solar batteries designed to provide power for artificial satellites.

The essential point of photosynthesis, however, is not to create currents but to make energy-rich food substances out of the carbon dioxide and the water which the plant extracts from its environment. The next step of the photosynthetic process employs another conversion, the conversion of electrical into chemical energy. The energy released by the chloroplasts' electrons must now become a part of a chemical compound.

This change in the form of the energy carried by the chloroplasts' electrons takes place while they are losing their excess energy along the electron-carrier chain of the acceptor molecules. The mechanics of the process can be explained through an analogy. The process resembles a waterfall dropping down a series of cascades. At each level the water spins a rotor which absorbs the energy of the falling water and uses it

A MATTER OF LIFE OR DEATH
In one of his famous experiments, Joseph Priestley used a mouse to demonstrate that plants "exhale" oxygen. He filled two jars with "thoroughly noxious" air; into one he put a mouse and a sprig of mint. The mint-and-mouse combination flourished, but the same mouse died almost immediately when put into the plantless jar. This gave Priestley some insight into photosynthesis, but he did not pursue the study.

to turn wheels and operate the machinery of a chemical plant. A somewhat comparable situation holds for electrons cascading along the chain of the acceptor molecules in the chloroplast; like the rotor, each acceptor molecule receives some of the passing electron's dissipated energy.

The sum of this energy-sharing process is the formation of a vital chemical compound, the adenosine triphosphate, or ATP, molecule. As the word "triphosphate" indicates, this molecule contains three phosphate (phosphorus-plus-oxygen) groups of atoms. They are hitched like a kite tail to the central group of atoms forming the molecule. The chemical energy that has resulted from the electronic activity within the chloroplast is now tied up in the force that ties, or "bonds," the last of these three phosphate groups to the ATP molecule.

Fuel for the flame of life

This synthesis of the charged ATP molecule is an all-important cell function because it provides essential fuel for the whole range of life processes. Energy originally released by the sun and converted successively into light and electricity has come to roost in an organic chemical. The energy required to attach that third phosphate group is now locked within the ATP molecule and will be released when the bond breaks and the third phosphate group is released. The molecule is like a tightly coiled spring ready to uncoil the instant a trigger is pressed.

While the charged ATP molecules (sometimes called the "energy currency" of the cell) are being produced, an associated reaction in the chloroplast uses energetic electrons to "split" the water the plant absorbs from the atmosphere. The result of this reaction is the formation of carrier molecules called $TPNH_2$ which appropriate some of the hydrogen from the split water molecule. This reaction also discharges oxygen into the atmosphere, where it is used by animal organisms.

ATP and $TPNH_2$ are the major products of the first stage of photosynthesis. The second stage consists of a set of interrelated reactions (the so-called "dark" reactions) which use carbon dioxide and hydrogen as raw materials to turn out the variety of substances required to build and maintain plant tissues. The carbon dioxide for this manufacturing process is absorbed from the atmosphere. The hydrogen is contributed by the $TPNH_2$ molecules. The energy for the process, supplied by ATP, is made available when the "trigger" is pressed, the coiled "spring" released and the third phosphate group is split apart from the ATP molecule.

The major end product of this ATP-fueled second stage of photosynthesis is the food-compound glucose, a form of sugar. The glucose molecule contains a definite pattern of six atoms of carbon, 12 of hydrogen and six of oxygen—all of these constituents coming from the flow of raw materials absorbed by the cell from the atmosphere and the soil. This

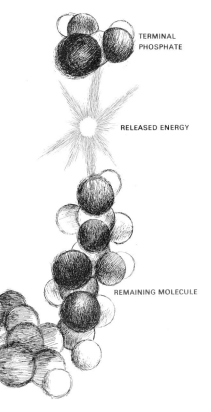

TERMINAL PHOSPHATE

RELEASED ENERGY

REMAINING MOLECULE

POWER-PACKED PHOSPHATE

Within every living cell are myriad molecules, performing chemical tricks which allow the cell to move, grow and reproduce. These reactions require energy supplied by ATP, a compound found in all cells. At one end, ATP holds a phosphate in an energy-rich chemical bond. Triggered by the proper enzyme, the molecule ejects its terminal phosphate and releases energy for such functions as building protein and contracting muscle.

MITOCHONDRION: THE POWERHOUSE OF THE CELL

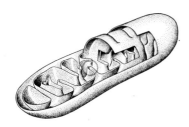

EXPOSED MEMBRANES

RESPIRATORY ASSEMBLY

CELLULAR LABYRINTHS OF ENERGY
The sausage-shaped cutaway above is a mitochondrion, the part of the cell that converts nourishment into energy. Its outer membrane dictates a fairly regular size and shape. But the inner membrane is a convoluted labyrinth containing the enzymes that are needed to produce ATP. The enlarged circled area shows the globules believed to be respiratory assemblies where the ATP-producing reactions take place.

production job—a recombination of chemical elements, using energy provided by the sun—is a kind of biological Tinkertoy game in which structures are built up step by step, bit by bit, with each change being made according to strict specifications. The final result of this assembly-line process is a chemical product, glucose, which has captured the energy of sunlight, and a waste product, oxygen, which is necessary to all animal life. Glucose will now keep the energy until it is needed.

Though the energy of sunlight is the essential fuel for photosynthesis, it needs help. The primary chemicals involved in each step of this process react sluggishly with each other, far too slowly to support the continuous and critical demands of living cells. In fact, if the basic chemicals involved in the photosynthesis process are mixed in a laboratory solution, nothing much happens.

Nature speeds up cellular chemical reactions with protein compounds called enzymes, which act as catalysts. The enzyme, like a bellows which fans a sluggish fire, can accelerate a chemical reaction immeasurably, enabling a cell to do in one minute what would otherwise require several thousand years. There would be no life without enzymes.

Though it is an involved process combining both electronic and chemical reactions, photosynthesis is an amazingly efficient operation. Laboratory analysis has indicated that it converts as much as 75 per cent of the light energy received by the plant into chemical energy packaged in the form of glucose. Man-made mechanisms for transforming energy—steam engines, for example—are generally around 30 per cent efficient.

It should be emphasized that many of the steps in the photosynthesis process are still under investigation. Scientists know that light, water and carbon dioxide go into one end of the photosynthesis assembly line and that glucose and oxygen are produced at the other end—the glucose being stored in the plant tissue and the oxygen being distributed in the atmosphere. But information on the intermediate steps of the process is so speculative that researchers often allude to the photosynthesis reactions as "the black box"—indicating that they know what goes in and what comes out but are not sure about everything that goes on inside.

Opening the energy package

The second part of the great natural system which, with photosynthesis, makes the life processes a regenerative cycle, takes place in animal cells; its function is to extract the energy packaged in the glucose in a form that can be used by animal organisms.

This second major system is also in operation in the sealed test tube containing the snail and the water plant. The process begins as the snail nibbles the green plant leaves and takes in the plant's oxygen wastes. The energy-providing glucose which the plant has synthesized is consumed by the snail, is carried to the individual cells by the bloodstream and is absorbed through the cells' outer membranes.

Animals, like plants, require the high-grade universal fuel, ATP, to run their life processes. But they do not make it from sunlight; instead, they synthesize it with energy obtained from glucose. The first step of this process, which takes place in the fluid part, or cytoplasm, of the cell, is known as glycolysis. In a series of reactions fueled by ATP and accelerated by appropriate enzymes, each glucose molecule yields two molecules of a substance called pyruvate. Glycolysis uses up two ATP molecules (which the cell has obtained from previous processing of glucose) but produces four new ATP molecules, for a net gain of two.

Glycolysis is a preparatory step to an involved process known as the Krebs cycle, after a German-born biologist who first suggested it in 1937. In this process, the animal cell, in the presence of oxygen, takes up the pyruvate and transforms it in a cycle of reactions that forms carbon dioxide. This activity also leads to the formation of water and an additional supply of ATP.

The cell's powerhouses

The Krebs cycle in animal cells uses bodies called mitochondria for what is, in effect, a reversal of the photosynthesis process. Mitochondria, often called the powerhouses of animal cells, are sausage-shaped capsules large enough to be seen with a powerful light microscope. They have a permeable outer wall which readily absorbs the materials necessary to the Krebs cycle.

The Krebs cycle within the mitochondria, like the photosynthesis process in plant chloroplasts, can be likened to a production line with an associated energy-producing system. Again, as in photosynthesis, the Krebs cycle uses specific enzymes to accelerate the chemical reactions which comprise each of the dozen or so steps of the process.

Starting with the pyruvate molecules delivered by the glycolysis operation, the Krebs cycle and its associated electron-transport system produce 36 ATP molecules for each original glucose molecule which entered the glycolysis operation. This immense energy gain is accompanied by the production of carbon dioxide and water as waste products.

Though there is still much to be learned about the many reactions involved in these processes, some of the steps are known to resemble those in the plant chloroplasts in which high-energy electrons are passed from one acceptor molecule to another as they give up the energy used to manufacture ATP. In the mitochondria, however, the electrons are originally excited by energy obtained from the Krebs cycle (which, in turn, gets the energy from pyruvate, the glucose product) rather than from the energy in sunlight.

The energy-deriving operation in the mitochondria (an operation

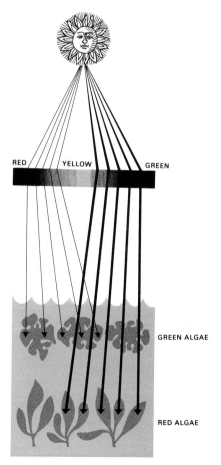

COLOR-CONSCIOUS SEA PLANTS
The sea absorbs the component colors of sunlight in varying degrees according to depth: red light is absorbed in the upper regions while green light penetrates much deeper. This phenomenon has forced algae, which derive energy from light, into some unique adaptations. Green algae near the surface utilize red light; deep-dwelling algae have a red pigment which helps turn green light to energy.

now being investigated by researchers such as Britton Chance and his associates at the University of Pennsylvania) apparently employs a process similar to that used in plant cells to produce ATP, but the end products are quite different. In plant photosynthesis, hydrogen atoms are removed from water to form oxygen. In the energy chain within the mitochondria, on the other hand, hydrogen atoms which are by-products of the Krebs cycle are split into positively charged protons and negatively charged electrons. The electrons are then passed from molecule to molecule (as in the photosynthesis process) until they have yielded most of their energy for the manufacture of ATP. Finally the protons combine with free electrons to form hydrogen atoms, which then combine with oxygen to form water. Thus the end products of two essentially similar reactions are in one case water and in the other oxygen.

Tracking down the invisible

Studies on *how* the cell transforms energy are only part of current investigations into photosynthesis, the Krebs cycle and their associated systems. On the principle that form and function are invariably related, scientists are also investigating the structure and organization of the working parts of these systems at the molecular level.

David Green and his colleagues at the University of Wisconsin are among those who have found that mitochondria, like chloroplasts, are built according to an elaborate blueprint. If mitochondria are exposed to ultrasonic vibrations or to the action of detergents, the semi-fluid material they contain escapes. When this happens the mitochondria can no longer carry on the main part of the Krebs cycle—indicating that the cycle takes place in the fluid-filled areas of the mitochondria. The electron-transport systems continue to work, indicating that they are firmly attached to the still-intact inner walls of the mitochondria.

Recent evidence from research centers suggests that the internal membranes of both mitochondria and chloroplasts are built in the form of mosaics of many thousands of pieces. Each basic unit of the mosaic is about two millionths of an inch in diameter and includes tadpole-shaped elements containing the individual acceptor molecules of the transport chain. These elements are clearly visible in remarkable enlargements of electron-microscope photographs giving effective magnifications of up to 800,000 times.

Studies show that, in all cells, the molecules of electron-transport chains are placed close to one another in definite patterns to form assembly lines that yield ATP. This suggests that the controlled flow of charged particles in animal and plant cells, in living as well as man-made electronic systems, apparently requires a fixed arrangement of components and a specifically designed circuitry. One of the most sig-

UNBEATABLE ENERGY PRODUCERS

Compared with more familiar energy producers, the cell operates with dazzling economy. A single submicroscopic mitochondrion—the merrily fleeting blob below, right—is proportionately six times more efficient than a steam locomotive. About half the food the mitochondrion assimilates is turned into useful energy; the locomotive converts a mere 8 per cent. Engineers have rarely equaled this feat of nature with their steam engines.

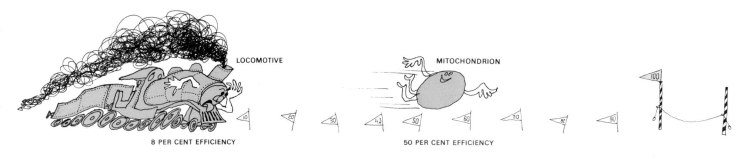

LOCOMOTIVE

MITOCHONDRION

8 PER CENT EFFICIENCY

50 PER CENT EFFICIENCY

nificant advances in the rapidly advancing life sciences is the discovery that nature has built its own carefully constructed electronic devices into all organisms.

Flowing electrons, the tiny electronic currents which move along the electron-transport chains, are the essence of life in both plant and animal cells. As might be expected, the currents increase as an organism becomes livelier. In a resting man, three electrons may flow along a single electron chain every second. During the height of a day's activity, this same chain may carry 30 electrons per second. When it is considered that there are about 15,000 chains in a single mitochondrion, between 50 and 5,000 mitochondria in a cell and billions of cells in the human body, it is obvious that the total flow of electrons taking place within us is enormous.

The processes occurring within the mitochondria play a central role in maintaining the energy balance of all organisms. If plenty of food and energy are available, for example, some of the compounds synthesized in the oxidizing process are shunted off the Krebs cycle and switched to another assembly line, where they are turned into fats and stored within the cell.

How we starve

These cellular reserves of fat are called upon during severe emergencies. When a man goes without food for a day or two, the deficiency is made up through use of sugars and starches stored in various organs such as the liver. If the emergency persists, however, the cellular fat reserves are drawn upon. The mitochondria of the fat-containing storage cells increase in number and extract the stored energy from the fats cached in the cell. During complete starvation the body may get along for nine or 10 weeks by running its fat reserves back through the Krebs cycle.

The use of stored reserves saved a pilot and his passenger whose plane crashed in the Canadian wilderness in 1963, an event widely reported at the time. The two were lost for seven weeks in sub-zero temperatures. With only enough food to provide restricted rations for the first week, they lived for six weeks without eating. By the time they were rescued, the couple had probably used up all their reserve fats. Their bodies were already taking last-resort measures—beginning to break down the proteins of the muscles and other tissues into materials for processing in the Krebs cycle. One result of this attrition is the gauntness characteristic of the last stages of starvation.

Current research in biology and in electronics are meeting and joining forces in these recent investigations of photosynthesis, the Krebs cycle and related biochemical processes. Future work promises to involve phenomena many times more complex than those of the past—and

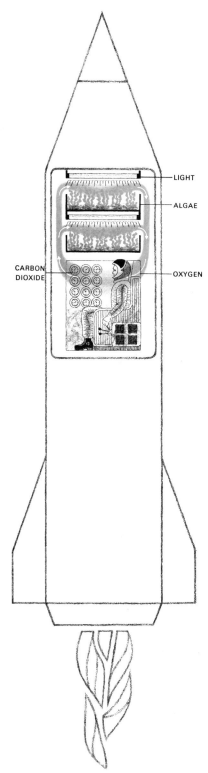

ASTRONAUTS AND ASTROPLANTS

To provide spacemen with an abundance of food and oxygen—vital commodities on a cosmic journey—scientists are perfecting a "closed ecological system": a two-way, life-giving alliance between astronaut and algae. The man will eat the plants and breathe the oxygen they produce; the algae, in turn, will thrive on the man's body wastes and exhaled carbon dioxide. Theoretically, this balanced situation will last as long as needed.

41

it has taken half a century of intensive efforts to learn what we know today. The problem is no longer limited to figuring out individual steps in the biochemical sequence from glucose through the Krebs cycle. Most of the steps have been identified and each represents a relatively simple reaction. The present challenge is to comprehend the relation of the parts to the whole system. There are around 22 different reactions in glycolysis and the Krebs oxidizing operation, all of them interlocking. A change of conditions at any place in the network influences the operation of the whole.

To understand the extent of this challenge it is important to realize the vast multitude of reactions involved in the cell processes. David Garfinkel of Chance's group at the University of Pennsylvania is using electronic computers to help in his studies; in one problem, nine hours of Univac II time was needed to calculate what would happen during 50 seconds of activity in a model of a cancer cell containing 65 substances involved in 89 reactions when glucose was introduced into the cell.

Some idea of the complexity of modern biology may be gained from the fact that an actual cell may be the site of more than 2,000 such reactions, instead of the 89 which were used as a basis for the model. Yet the biological cell, millions of times smaller than the modern computer, runs and regulates these reactions constantly.

Twin Dynamos of Existence

All life on earth—from the lowliest rock-bound lichen to the mightiest philosopher—exists because of a dual miracle of chemistry called photosynthesis and respiration. Through photosynthesis a plant cell traps a tiny amount of the sun's radiant energy and uses it to convert water (from the soil) and carbon dioxide (from the air) into sugar and oxygen. Through respiration, both plant and animal cells take in oxygen and use it to turn the sugar in food into energy; the by-products of respiration, water and carbon dioxide, are returned to the atmosphere—to be used once again in photosynthesis. This cycle of life is endlessly repeated. A cow eats the plants and by respiration uses the sugar's energy to produce milk and flesh; man uses the milk to slake his thirst and the flesh to assuage his hunger. And with the energy so provided, he plants more grain and scales mountains. Sunlight, photosynthesis and respiration sustain all life.

THE CYCLE OF LIFE
Sealed into its blue-wall home, a monkey proves that animals and plants can survive in a self-sustaining relationship. The glassware at the left contains millions of algae which throw off oxygen when exposed to a light source. The oxygen is piped to the monkey. The monkey's breathing, in turn, produces a waste product, carbon dioxide, which is essential to the algae's survival.

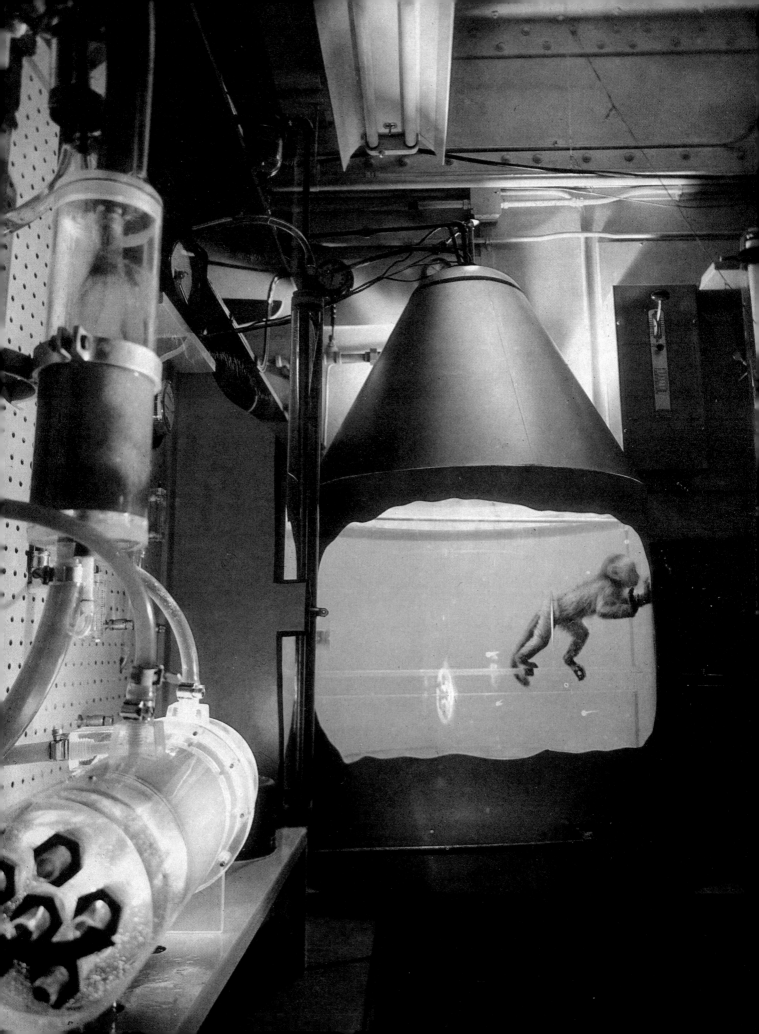

Making Sugar for Mankind's Survival

Some 300 years ago, Johann Baptista van Helmont, Flemish physician and chemist, planted a tree in a tub; in five years it gained 164 pounds—but its soil lost only two ounces. Van Helmont concluded that the tree's weight-gain must have come from the water it received, not—as had been thought—from the soil. Now, scientists know that it came also from the carbon dioxide in the air, and that the tree's growth could have happened only with light and the green pigment chlorophyll.

From Van Helmont's single tree to all the earth's green plants is a giant step. Yet the principle is the same. The earth's enveloping mantle of green plants annually manufactures more than a trillion tons of new organic matter from water, air and sunlight. The products—sugar and oxygen—of this massive effort are literally what keep man and all other animals alive.

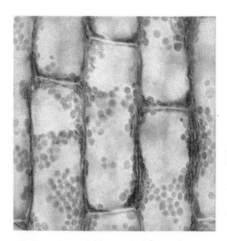

MINIATURE LABORATORIES
Under a microscope, the interior of a living plant cell appears almost placid. But this appearance of quietude is an illusion, for the cell churns with chemical activity, building up and tearing apart thousands of complex compounds. The numerous spherical bodies in the *Elodea* cell shown above are chloroplasts—the structures that hold the green, light-sensitive chlorophyll.

LIGHT AND PLANT GROWTH
Potted plants are positioned beneath lights of different colors in an investigation of the effects of different wavelengths of light on photosynthesis. The effect on photosynthesis can be gauged by the effect on green plant growth. Red and blue lights yield more usable energy for growth and photosynthesis than other colors, although yellow and orange are also useful.

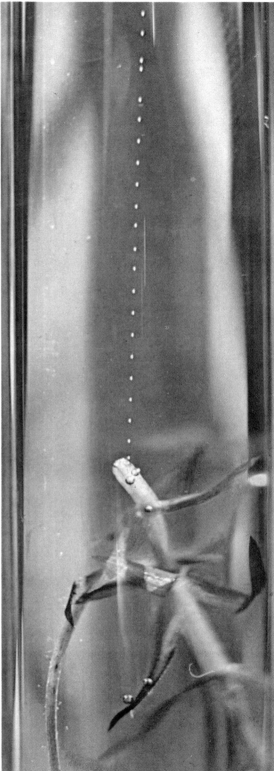

GREEN PLANT IN WATER
A sprig of *Elodea* demonstrates photosynthesis. Submerged in pond water which contains carbon dioxide, the plant is flooded in light. Immediately, it begins to extract carbon dioxide from the water, and uses it and the light to manufacture sugar and oxygen. The oxygen—a waste product so far as the plant is concerned—can be seen streaming up through the water.

ALL LIFE BEGINS with the sun. In this diagram, a plant's cell is represented as a factory, which is powered by the light-energy it receives from the sun (left).

THE ENERGY from excited electrons in the chlorophyll molecules is used to form ATP and to split molecules of water. Oxygen is thus freed into the air.

ENERGY FROM SUNLIGHT

ENERGY FROM ELECTRONS

WATER

OXYGEN

HYDROGEN

PHOSPHATE

ADP

A SOLAR-POWERED BUCKET BRIGADE

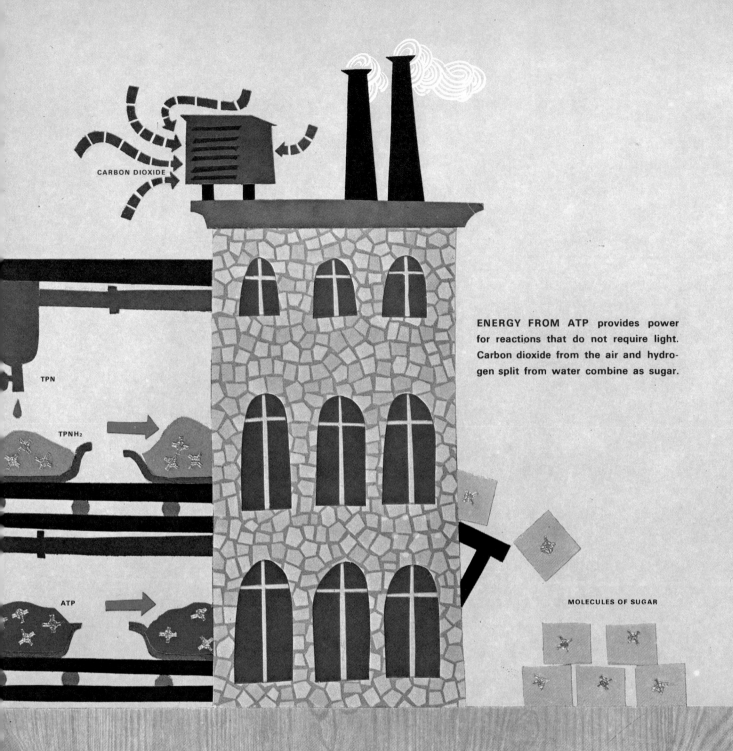

CARBON DIOXIDE

TPN

TPNH₂

ATP

ENERGY FROM ATP provides power for reactions that do not require light. Carbon dioxide from the air and hydrogen split from water combine as sugar.

MOLECULES OF SUGAR

ENERGY, like the Greek sea god Proteus, can change its form over and over again. At the flick of a switch, electrical energy is changed to light (in a lamp), heat (in a stove) or motion (in a blender); the chemical energy in gasoline eventually becomes motion when a car starts; as a match is struck, motion becomes heat and light. Energy changes occur continually. The energy is never lost, simply changed in form.

Photosynthesis, the intricate food-making process in green plants, is also a series of energy changes. Light-energy from the sun strikes the chlorophyll molecules in a green plant's cells. A small part of this solar energy becomes electrical energy—the energy of agitated electrons which are quickly passed along in bucket-brigade fashion from one molecule to the next. The electrical energy becomes chemical energy when it forms an energy-rich substance called ATP (adenosine triphosphate) from phosphate and the related compound, ADP.

At the same time, some of the remaining electrical energy splits water. Oxygen is released into the air, and the remaining hydrogen combines with another molecule, TPN, to form TPNH₂.

In a series of chemical reactions triggered by ATP, a simple sugar is formed from carbon dioxide, which the plant takes from the air, and hydrogen, which it takes from the TPNH₂ molecules.

FREEING SUGAR'S ENERGY

THE FIRST STEP taken by an animal cell in recovering the energy that plants have stored in sugar is to split each sugar molecule into two molecules of pyruvic acid, also called pyruvate. This procedure involves at least 11 separate steps, each step controlled by a specific enzyme. The result is the release of about 56,000 calories of energy bound up in each sugar molecule, and the formation of ATP molecules which catch some of the energy *(gold stars).*

PYRUVATE MOLECULES are taken up by the mitochondria, structures in the cytoplasm, where they are altered in an intricate series of enzyme-controlled steps known as the Krebs cycle. Discovery of this "mill," which alters not only pyruvate but also fats and amino acids, was a milestone in biochemistry.

THE PRODUCT of the Krebs cycle is carbon dioxide. Electrons extracted during the cycle are fed into a series of electron-carrier molecules of the respiratory chain, and finally combine with oxygen atoms, which can then attract hydrogen to form water. Some of the energy of the electrons is used to synthesize more ATP molecules. For every sugar molecule involved in respiration, 38 additional ATP molecules are produced. These supply the cell with energy.

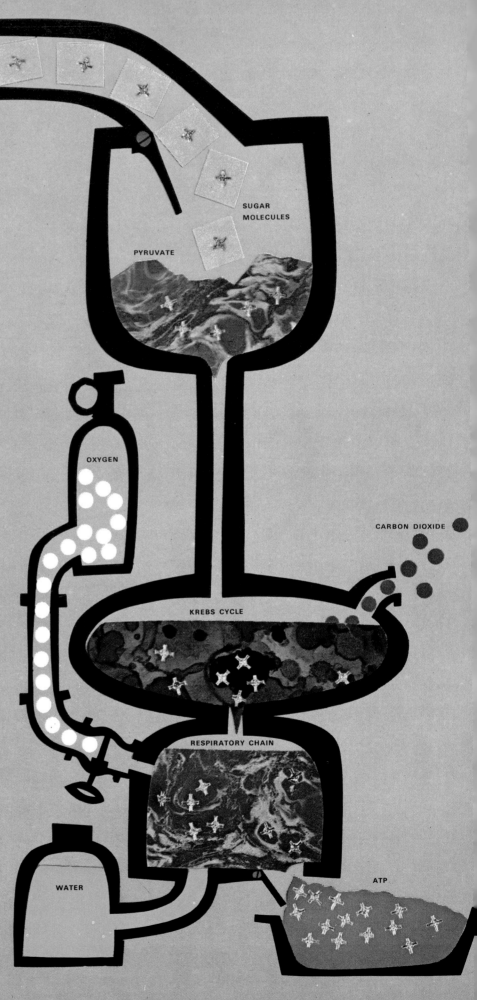

SUGAR MOLECULES

PYRUVATE

OXYGEN

CARBON DIOXIDE

KREBS CYCLE

RESPIRATORY CHAIN

WATER

ATP

Respiration: Unlocking Energy

Photosynthesis *(previous pages)* is the vital process which converts the sun's light-energy into food energy. The reverse side of the energy-conversion coin is another process, called respiration. Respiration uses the products of photosynthesis—sugar and oxygen—to release energy which powers all life. At the same time, respiration leaves behind carbon dioxide and water—precisely what photosynthesis began with. This cycle, a merry-go-round of life, is known to scientists as the carbon cycle. Its name refers to the continual turnover of the carbon (in carbon dioxide) through its various changes into sugar and back to carbon dioxide.

Photosynthesis is an exclusive function of plants. Respiration, on the other hand, is common to both plants and animals. It releases the energy needed to hold this book, to move the eyes across the lines and to turn the pages. It accounts for flowers blooming, goldfish swimming and a child spilling his milk.

During the day, when plenty of light is available, plants carry on photosynthesis and respiration at the same time. But they do considerably more photosynthesizing than they do respiring. That is why plants can produce food for themselves and still provide enough for the whole animal kingdom as well. It is also why plants can use oxygen for their own respiration and still have enough left over to distribute into the air for animals to breathe.

A step-by-step depiction of respiration is shown schematically opposite. Respiration is awesome in its complexity and efficiency. The essence of the process is the slow, controlled (by enzymes) burning of sugar—a series of complex reactions that releases chemical energy stored up in the chemical bonds of sugar molecules.

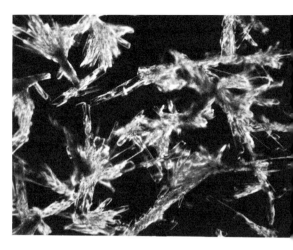

ENERGY LOCKED IN CRYSTALS
The energy-rich compound ATP (adenosine triphosphate) is pictured here in crystal form. ATP is essential to all living cells. It contains a strong chemical bond formed by the energy released during respiration. ATP molecules move this chemical energy throughout the cell.

Scuba divers illustrate the cycle of respiration—the intake of oxygen, the release of energy and the waste, bubbling toward the surface.

ATP: The Vital Link of Life

Fueled by radiant energy beams from the sun, the great carbon cycle of photosynthesis and respiration goes on endlessly. Out of the cycle spring ATP molecules with the energy which all living creatures require for growing, glowing *(right)*, fighting, fleeing and reproducing.

The ATP molecule stores the sun's energy in a chemical bond. The energy stays locked up until it is released when the bond breaks.

For every job requiring energy, a particular enzyme, specifically designed for that job, does the bond-splitting. Muscle cells, for example, store not only ATP but also the enzyme that splits ATP when the muscle contracts. The luminescent tissue of the railroad worm at right stores not only ATP but also the specific enzyme needed to release the ATP's energy for luminescence. Without ATP, living things would freeze in their tracks—deprived of the all-important link that holds together the chain of life. Similarly, the ATP, without its needed enzymes, would be unable to perform its important function.

LUMINESCENCE IN WORMS
Railroad worms are curled up undisturbed *(above)* and brightly lit with excitement *(right)*. These living flashlights are larval forms of the *Phrixothrix* beetle. The energy for their luminescence comes directly from ATP molecules located in certain specialized cells. Eleven pairs of greenish-yellow spots form two parallel rows along the body, and two luminous spots that glow bright red are in the head. At night, only the red spots glow—unless the larva is disturbed. Then the green lights flash on and the larva resembles a train with red head lamps.

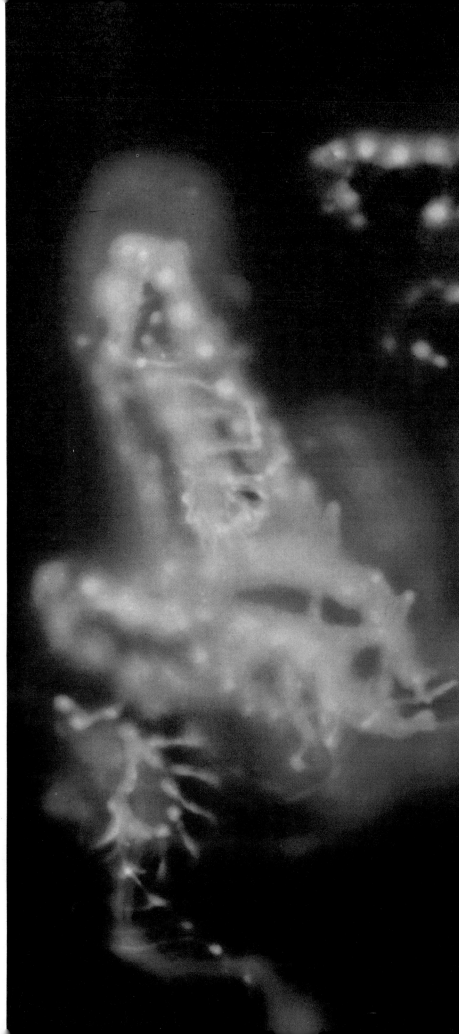

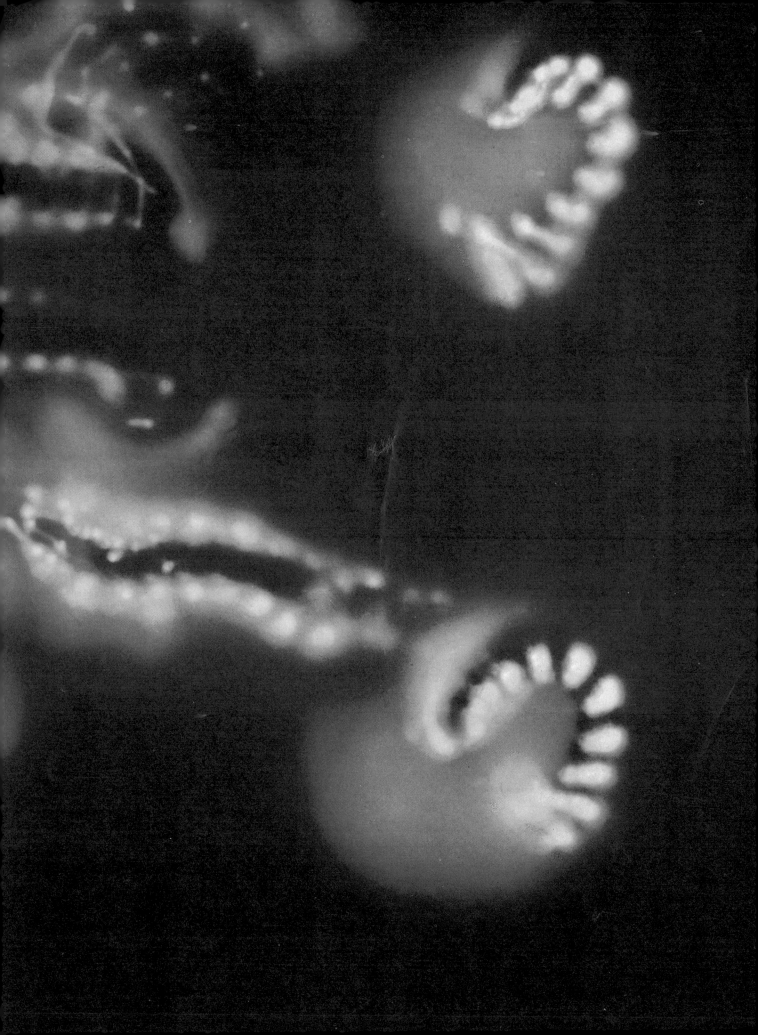

3

The Architect
and the
Master Builder

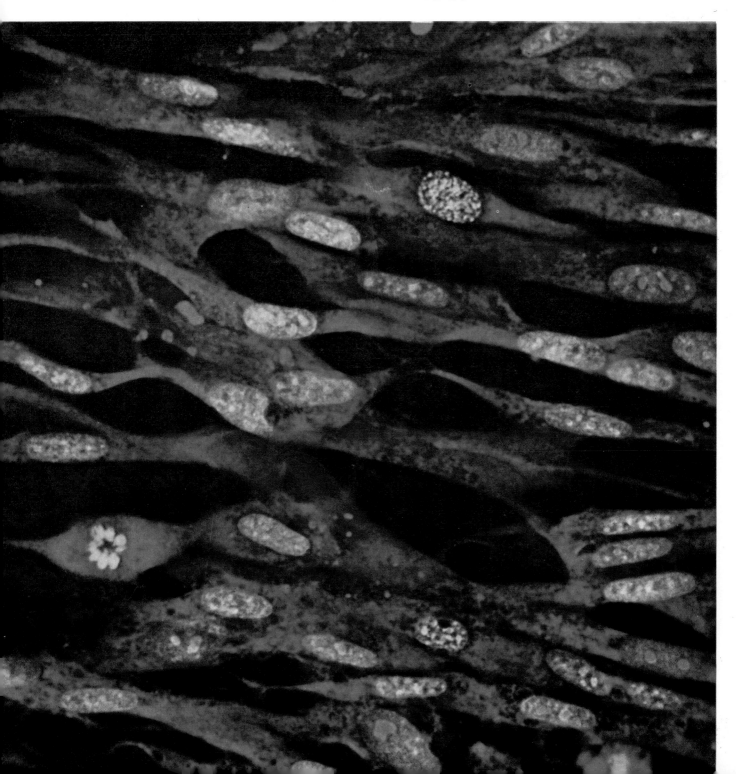

THE MOST VIVID VIEW of the activity within a cell is provided by time-lapse motion pictures taken at magnifications of a thousandfold or more. Such films speed up the natural pace of events, with every second of running time representing a minute in the cell's life, and exaggerate the normal state of commotion. They give the general impression of a bubbling, boiling and highly turbulent fluid, through which mitochondria dash like racing cars gone out of control.

In the midst of the turmoil lies the quiet heart of the cell—a "dead spot" where nothing much seems to be happening. This region, isolated by a double-membrane envelope from the surrounding fluids, is the cell's nucleus. Its apparent calm is illusory. It contains keys to life's greatest mysteries; new discoveries about how it operates are revolutionizing research in all branches of biology and medicine. Foremost among the discoveries are spectacular findings that are beginning to reveal for the first time the workings of heredity.

Heredity is the process by which the physical and mental traits of parents are transmitted to their offspring. As everyone knows, it is an uncertain process at best. A little boy may bear his father's facial features along with his mother's hair. Or he may show a totally unexpected talent for music in a family whose other members are too tone-deaf to appreciate even simple nursery songs. Or he may be born with a hereditary defect to a family that appears perfectly normal.

Man has been trying to solve the puzzle of heredity for centuries. During most of that time he has had a general understanding of its principles and has applied them to the problems of daily life, with results that have ranged from poor to excellent. Perhaps the worst results have come from a practice that probably began in prehistoric times, when some band of savages established hereditary leadership for its tribe, reasoning, perhaps, that if facial characteristics could be inherited, other qualities could be too. This assumption that strength and intelligence were passed on from father to son was rationalized in various ways over the succeeding centuries. One popular theory, which persisted into modern times, was that in the process of procreation a father implanted a tiny replica of himself in the mother's womb; the function of the mother was simply to protect and nourish this little fellow until he became big enough to be born. But possibly the widest misconception was that somehow characteristics were passed on to the child through the mixing of the blood of the mother and father. We perpetuate this idea when we talk about good and bad bloodlines, or describe someone as being a full-blooded Indian, or as being of royal blood.

Whatever the rationale, the evidence of history shows that the theory of inherited leadership is a faulty one. Human heredity is too uncertain. More than one royal family has petered out in quality, and tribes and nations have found themselves governed by oafs and madmen who were the sons of capable and respected sovereigns.

On the other hand, early man was much more successful when he applied the principles of heredity to the breeding of animals. Domestic animals were subjected to selective breeding which, as generations passed, consistently improved the stock.

Mendel's brilliant experiments

While farmers were applying rule-of-thumb principles of heredity, the scientific world remained in the dark about why these principles worked. It was not until the mid-19th Century that any real advance was made—and that was such a brilliant leap forward that decades passed before man could comprehend its significance. Its author was an Augustinian monk named Gregor Johann Mendel. Mendel was born in the village of Heinzendorf in what is now Czechoslovakia in 1822. His father was a poor peasant, but a man who was skilled in the growing of fruit. The boy, who had strong religious inclinations, was tutored in the tending of fruit and developed an abiding interest in experimenting with plants. Since there was little money in the family, he gave up hope for a university education and joined a monastery where, as he put it, he "would be spared perpetual anxiety about a means of livelihood." More to the point, as a monk he could satisfy his dual devotion, to religion and to his garden.

As a young monk, Mendel was assigned only a small strip of ground for his work (ironically, when he became the abbot of the monastery years later he had all the ground he wanted but was so absorbed in administrative duties that he had little time for his plants). However, he managed to grow great numbers of experimental vegetables and flowers, eventually focusing his investigations on the ordinary garden pea. In all, he grew 22 different varieties—some with tall stems, some with short, some with purple flowers, others with white; varieties with round seeds, varieties with wrinkled seeds. Then he started to hybridize them—to mix tall plants with short ones, purple blossoms with white ones and so forth. Each day during the brief spring blooming season he would patiently cross-pollinate the plants and cover each bloom with a tiny calico bag. As the pods ripened he would carefully collect the seeds. Then the next spring he would plant those hybrid seeds and see what happened.

The results of Mendel's work appeared in a short paper published in 1865, just about the time the American Civil War was drawing to a close. To the layman, the paper is a complex and apparently meaningless tabulation of figures. But behind the figures are some simple conclusions of vast importance. To begin with, Mendel determined that an inherited characteristic was inherited as a complete unit—that is, when a tall pea was crossed with a dwarf pea, the first-generation offspring from the

REPRODUCTION BY MITOSIS: A SIMPLE SPLITTING

Most cells reproduce by mitosis *(right)*, the process in which identical genetic information is transmitted to each daughter cell. In the first drawing, a cell is shown with two chromosome-balloons. When mitosis begins, the chromosomes replicate themselves *(second drawing)* and migrate to opposite sides of the cell *(third drawing)*. Then the cell itself splits *(fourth drawing)*, and finally there are two new cells, each identical to the parent.

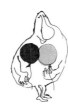  

CELL WITH TWO CHROMOSOMES   CHROMOSOME REPRODUCTION   PREPARATION FOR SPLITTING

cross were either tall or short; there was no haphazard mixing of "blood" that resulted in a plant of intermediate height. Furthermore, he found that the plants were far more likely to be tall than short, more likely to be purple than white and so on. Certain characteristics predominated.

Next, he observed that even though a purebred tall plant crossed with a dwarf plant usually produced tall progeny, these second-generation tall plants *could* have dwarf offspring. In other words, the hereditary characteristics of both parents are contained in each child, even when they are not visible. Further, these "concealed" characteristics can be transferred to the grandchildren without any change in their nature: the dwarf children of the tall parents were identical in size to the dwarf grandparents; the degree of "dwarfness" did not undergo any change while submerged for one generation.

Finally, Mendel concluded that although heredity, like gambling, contains an element of uncertainty, some things about it are predictable— just as they are in the roll of a pair of dice. Mendel could not predict whether any single pea plant would be tall or short—but he did show that in any given strain a certain mathematical proportion of pea plants would be tall and a lesser proportion would be short. He thus took heredity out of the realm of the unpredictable and put it under the jurisdiction of well-defined mathematical laws.

Mendel's work was revolutionary—but no one realized it at the time except Mendel. He died in 1884, still puttering in his garden at the age of 62, virtually unknown to the world of science.

Heredity and the cell

All during the years of Mendel's life, scientists using more powerful microscopes and new methods of preparing microscope slides had been examining the cell with increasing interest. Among other things, they had laid to rest, once and for all, some centuries-old misconceptions about heredity. They had discovered that this, too, was a cellular process—that children were conceived through the fusion of two cells, an egg contributed by the mother and a sperm by the father. All inherited characteristics, they now knew, were transmitted by these cells.

Even earlier, investigators had observed a fascinating phenomenon among cells viewed with the microscope. When the cell was resting (that is, when it was not in the process of dividing in half), its nucleus had a faintly netted appearance. The investigators were using a chemical to stain their slides for better visibility; whatever material made up the net seemed to soak up this coloring. The investigators therefore called the substance that made up the net chromatin, from *chroma*, Greek for color.

Then they observed an astonishing sequence. When the cell began to divide in half during mitosis, the chromatin pattern underwent an abrupt

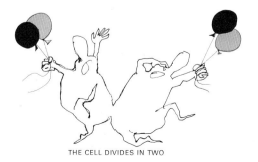

THE CELL DIVIDES IN TWO

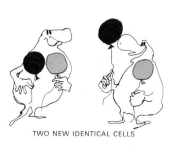

TWO NEW IDENTICAL CELLS

change. The netlike substance clotted into a batch of small threads; the scientists labeled them chromosomes, meaning colored bodies. As the researchers watched, each of the chromosomes split in half lengthwise and a half of each chromosome was pulled by some invisible force into each of the two new cells. The end result was two cells, each having the same number of chromosomes as the parent cell. When the new cells had entirely split apart, the chromosomes dissolved, and each new nucleus was clear again except for its faint chromatin pattern.

All of this had occurred during the familiar cell-splitting process of mitosis. But mitosis was not the end of the story. Scientists had observed that the number of chromosomes in a mature human reproductive cell was always the same. But if in the process of procreation a male cell bearing the proper complement of chromosomes fused with a female cell bearing the same number, the offspring of such a union would have *twice* that number—and if two humans thus endowed mated, their children would have four times the original number and so on. This was patently impossible—and the scientists soon discovered that nature had solved this problem in an ingenious fashion.

As the researchers watched certain cells through their microscopes following mitosis, they saw the chromatin thicken and the chromosomes form, almost as if the mitosis process were about to repeat itself. But then an important difference appeared. The cells did split—but the chromosomes did not. Instead, each of the chromosomes sought out a partner from among the other chromosomes, and as the cell broke in two, only one chromosome from each pair was pulled into the newly formed reproductive cell. Each cell then had only half as many chromosomes as the cell from which it was formed—so that when it later fused with another reproductive cell to make a child, the infant would contain the proper number of chromosomes. The investigators called this process meiosis.

Discovering Mendel's peas

In 1900, when the wrigglings and turnings of mitosis and meiosis had been completely worked out, scientists suddenly began to discover Mendel. That year three different investigators reported before learned societies that much of their current research in heredity had been anticipated more than 35 years before by the obscure monk. Once Mendel's laws had been unearthed, it was only a matter of time before the workings of meiosis were coupled with the phenomena the monk had observed in his pea patch. They matched perfectly. Mendel had observed that the characteristics of his pea vines were passed on as units; now scientists knew that it was because the cellular units of chromosomes were passed along intact from parent to child. Mendel

REPRODUCTION BY MEIOSIS: CUTTING DOWN THE NUMBERS

Nature faces a peculiar problem in sexual reproduction: parents must produce sex cells that have only half the usual number of chromosomes—so that their offspring, formed by the joining of two cells, will not wind up with double the number of chromosomes they need. The chromosome-reducing process in the sex cells is called meiosis. The first drawing below represents a cell like those found in mature sex organs (for simplicity, it is shown with four chromosomes; the actual number varies greatly in different creatures). Each chromosome reproduces and the cell splits *(bottom)*. But when the resulting cells divide, their chromosomes do *not* reproduce. At conception, a cell *(far right)* from each parent unites to form a fertilized egg with the correct number of chromosomes: four.

CELL WITH FOUR CHROMOSOMES

THE CHROMOSOMES REPRODUCE THEMSELVES

THE CELL BEGINS ITS DIVISION

TWO DAUGHTER CELLS

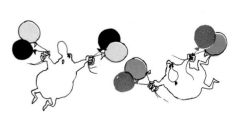

PREPARING FOR THE SECOND SPLITTING

had noted that a pea plant could look like one parent, yet hold latent in it the characteristics of the other; scientists were now aware that as a result of meiosis every child gets one set of chromosomes from its father and one from its mother, and then passes duplicates of half of these chromosomes on to its own progeny.

Gone were the days when heredity could be passed off as some sort of haphazard mixing of blood. At last it was clearly assigned to a well-defined structure in the cell. Biologists now know that every species of living thing has its own characteristic number of chromosomes. Man has 46, white rats 42, pea plants 14. Among the highest chromosome totals in any living thing is the more than 1,500 found in a lowly rhizopod, a one-celled creature.

Marvelous beads of heredity

Many problems remained, of course. For one thing, it is obvious that any animal or plant, no matter how simple, has thousands and thousands of inherited traits; the human face alone, for example, has hundreds of such characteristics, ranging from the depth of a dimple to the exact arc of an eyebrow. If only 46 chromosomes can carry from generation to generation all the hereditary material contained in the human body, then already each chromosome must be responsible for the transmission of many characteristics. Around 1915, scientists came to the conclusion that the chromosome did not resemble a solid threadlike structure at all, but rather should be likened to a necklace made up of many beads. These beads—as many as 1,250 on a single human chromosome—were the real sites of heredity. They were called genes, and the science of heredity became the science of genetics.

Mendel's observations on his pea plants can be restated in terms of genes. Every characteristic that he noted in each pea plant had been determined by one of the two genes which transmitted that characteristic from the parent plants. For example, one gene determining height had been inherited from the male parent, another from the female. These genes could both carry the characteristic of tallness, or one gene could be for tallness and the other for shortness, or both could carry the recipe for shortness. When either of the genes transmitted tallness, as Mendel had observed, that was certain to be the characteristic inherited—in any meeting of both kinds of gene, the "tall" gene somehow overwhelmed the "short" one. A gene with such overriding influence is said to be dominant; the weaker gene is described as recessive.

Mendel was extremely lucky in picking out such characteristics as height, blossom color and the like for his studies. Few characteristics of living things are transmitted by only one gene. Human skin color, for example, is affected by at least eight different genes, which is why

DAUGHTER CELLS SPLIT, WITH TWO CHROMOSOMES APIECE

FOUR NEW CELLS, UNLIKE ANY ANCESTOR

there is such a vast range of human skin color. Such complex human traits as intelligence, body build and facial appearance depend on hundreds of genes. So it is no wonder that the inheritance of these qualities is so erratic. And it is not surprising that primitive peoples who expected their strong, bright chieftains to produce strong, bright sons were sometimes disappointed.

As a matter of fact, the odds against two individuals being exactly alike are astronomical (except for identical twins, who both come from one fertilized egg and do indeed have the same assortment of genes). Mathematically, there are more than eight million ways the 23 chromosomes of a human mother and the 23 of a father can combine. The odds that any two children of the mother and father will have the same complement of chromosomes is about one out of 70 trillion. And since each chromosome may have 1,250 genes, the odds against two identical individuals being born form such a large number that it has no name; it could be written out as 1 followed by 9,031 zeros.

The mystery of mutation

Genes are subject to change, and the change is usually for the worse. A normal mother and father will occasionally produce an abnormal child. The abnormality may be relatively slight—perhaps the child has an extra finger or toe—or it may be severe: the child may be mentally defective or may have some gross physical defect such as a withered arm. Sometimes such congenital defects result from an accident to the pregnant mother, but too often the abnormality comes from an altered gene. Such changes in genes are called mutations.

In recent years scientists have pieced together some of the causes of mutations. These include X-rays, and the rays of natural and artificial radioactive materials. Anxiety aroused by atomic fallout is largely based on fear that radiation from the debris of nuclear explosions may cause mutations which will lead to malformed offspring in future generations.

Closely related to the problem of mutation is the nature of the gene itself—a subject that has intrigued researchers since the turn of this century. One of the earliest guesses regarding the nature of the gene was made in 1917 by the great American mathematician and geneticist Sewall Wright, then with the U.S. Department of Agriculture. In a suggestion which brought genetics and biochemistry into a union which has grown stronger over the years, Wright speculated that skin color in human beings was determined by a chain of enzyme reactions which was in turn controlled by genes. This was long before anyone had yet isolated any enzyme; it was not until 1926 that this was done. Once enzymes could be studied closely, it was discovered that an enormous assortment of them appeared necessary for the functioning of the cell.

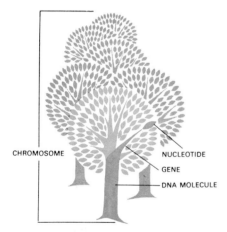

CHROMOSOME: A FOREST ANALOGY

This stylized forest is analogous to a chromosome, the part of a cell's nucleus that carries instructions for every phase of life. Each tree represents a DNA molecule, the material of heredity. The branches are the sections of the DNA that make up genes, each one occupying a specific location on the DNA strand, and the individual leaves are nucleotides, the subunits that make up the DNA molecule.

But it was not until 1940 that the first definite link was made between enzyme and gene. That year scientists Edward L. Tatum and George Beadle, working at Stanford University, concluded a series of brilliant experiments with a form of bread mold. They found that although mold, like other living things, needs all sorts of foods and vitamins for its growth, the bread mold prospered on nothing more than sugar, a few inorganic salts and a single vitamin called biotin. Obviously the bread mold came equipped with elaborate internal factories for making the vital missing substances out of a few basic materials.

Beadle and Tatum reasoned that enzymes—those magic substances that speed chemical transformations—must be involved in the mold growth. Furthermore, Beadle, following up Wright's association of enzymes and genes, speculated that each of the bread-mold enzymes might be controlled by the action of a single gene. There seemed a way to prove this: if they could cause mutations in the mold's genes, the result should be to knock out some of the enzymes. Using X-rays to cause the mutations, Beadle and Tatum succeeded on their 299th attempt in disrupting the enzyme that the mold needed to manufacture vitamin B_6; that particular strain proved unable to survive unless it was fed B_6 in addition to the standard diet of sugar, salts and biotin. The 1,090th spore they exposed mutated so that it needed doses of vitamin B_1 to survive. Dozens of other mutant strains followed. The linkage between genes and enzymes had been proved beyond any doubt.

The nature of the gene

Science was now prepared to ask a further question: what is the exact chemical nature of the gene? The answer seemed simple. It must be some sort of complex protein; analyses of chromosomes, the gene's parent body, had shown the presence of proteins. To be sure, a nonprotein substance called nucleic acid was also present, but it was dismissed as unimportant so far as the gene was concerned.

But then, in a series of experiments conducted between 1941 and 1944, three scientists at The Rockefeller Institute, Dr. Oswald T. Avery and his colleagues Colin MacLeod and Maclyn McCarthy, reversed this emphasis completely. They started with an experiment that had first been performed in 1928. At that time the English biologist Frederick Griffith had injected white mice with a mixture of two forms of pneumococcus bacteria called R and S. The R form was live but harmless. The S form was virulent but had been killed by heat. Neither bacteria, therefore, should have harmed the mice. Nevertheless, many of the animals died, and postmortem examinations revealed the presence of living form S. No one had ever been able to explain why this had happened—and it was this 13-year-old mystery that was reopened in the Rockefeller experiment.

The investigators acted on the assumption that, since the S form used in the Griffith experiment had been dead, the fatal dose must have come from the R injection—that is, part of the R form must have changed into S through genetic reproduction. Avery, MacLeod and McCarthy proceeded to grow vast quantities of bacteria in an effort to find out what it was that could transform harmless form R into virulent form S. The potent agent they finally isolated proved to be none other than nucleic acid—specifically, deoxyribonucleic acid, or DNA for short.

Final proof of DNA

The discovery that the gene was composed of nucleic acid did not exactly sweep the world of biology. The protein advocates died hard, and many scientists were unwilling to accept DNA as heredity's prime mover without further proof. Then came a telling piece of evidence. In 1952, two researchers from the Carnegie Institution at Cold Spring Harbor, Long Island, conducted a series of experiments with one of the simplest of all living things, the so-called bacteriophage, usually referred to merely as phage. Phages are certain viruses which infect bacteria the way other viruses affect man. The phage enters the bacterial cell, confiscates the cell's chemical apparatus and uses this machinery, together with its own genetic information, to construct hundreds of new phages—which are then poured out into the world to look for more bacterial victims.

The phage was known to be made up of two basic materials: protein and DNA. The protein had always been considered the active agent in the phage's duplication inside the bacteria. The Long Island scientists Dr. Alfred Hershey and Dr. Martha Chase proceeded on a contrary hypothesis which assumed that the DNA was the important factor. They postulated that the phage was merely a core of DNA surrounded by a coating of protein. To test this radical hypothesis they attached one kind of radioactive tracer to the protein and another kind to the DNA, then allowed the phage to attack bacteria. By analyzing the resulting mixture of phage and bacteria they found that only the DNA part of the phage had made its way through the bacteria's cell wall; therefore, it must be the DNA, and nothing else, that was affecting the bacteria's process of heredity so that the bacteria produced phages instead of more bacteria. Since this was genetic action it was now certain beyond any doubt that DNA composed the genes of the phage—DNA was the stuff of heredity.

Even before this clinching proof was in hand, chemists had begun to analyze the DNA molecule. It was relatively uncomplicated as large organic molecules go, being composed of just three types of ingredients: there were simple sugars of a kind known as deoxyribose, there were phosphate units and finally there were nitrogen compounds. There were four of these compounds, or bases: adenine, thymine, cytosine and guanine,

A LOOK INSIDE A DNA MOLECULE
This illustration shows how a section of DNA is put together. The bases are shown fitting together like building blocks, but in fact their bond is chemical. Only compatible bases can unite: adenine, for instance, joins only with thymine. The number of possible "messages" even in this tiny piece of DNA is staggering: with only the 15 pairs of positions shown below, there could be more than a billion combinations.

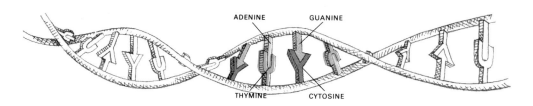

ADENINE   GUANINE

THYMINE   CYTOSINE

called A, T, C and G for short. Knowing the constituents of the molecule and knowing how these units fit together were two quite different things. And it was not until scientists understood how the molecule was constructed that they could hope to have any real idea about how it might transmit genetic information and reproduce itself. The task of figuring out the structure of DNA fell to a special group of scientists called X-ray crystallographers. By beaming X-rays through molecules the crystallographers were able to piece together vague shadow pictures which could be used to construct possible three-dimensional models of the molecule. Many interpretations of the X-ray pictures were possible and many unsatisfactory models of the DNA molecule were made. None of them really seemed to explain adequately how the molecule functioned.

Then in 1953, James D. Watson and Francis H. C. Crick, using data obtained by Maurice H. F. Wilkins, published an article describing *their* model of DNA. It may go down in scientific history as the most famous biological Tinkertoy ever put together.

The famous DNA model

According to Crick and Watson, the DNA molecule is built something like a spiral staircase *(pages 68 and 69)*. The phosphates and sugars form the twisted frame of the stairs, and the bases form the steps. Each step is made up of two bases joined in the middle. But it is not a random pairing. Adenine is always joined with thymine to form a step and guanine is always joined with cytosine. But the steps may follow each other endlessly and in any order, AT, GC, CG, AT, CG, GC, TA, TA, etc. A single gene might be a chunk of DNA stairway perhaps 2,000 steps long—and geneticists now think that it is the order of these steps, the arrangement of TA's, AT's, GC's and CG's, that gives every gene its special character.

The amount of DNA in a living organism and the complexity of the organism seem to be somewhat correlated. The coiled DNA stairway in the chromosomes of a simple virus, for example, might be 1/2,000 of an inch long and contain 170,000 steps; in a bacterium the DNA might total 1/400 of an inch and hold seven million steps. Human DNA in a single cell—when its pieces are joined they are a yard long and contain some six billion steps—is one of the most detailed of all the genetic recipes. These instructions are written in a fine hand; one molecule of DNA in a human cell contains as much information as several encyclopedia sets.

Naturally, in such immensely long chains of molecules there is always chance for error. Perhaps a single mistake among the six billion steps, a GC where an AT should be, is enough to cause an imperfect human being to develop. A mutation can be thought of as an accident affecting one or more of the base-pair steps in the DNA strand.

One primary requisite for any hereditary material is that it must be

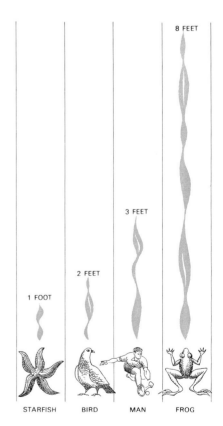

8 FEET

3 FEET

2 FEET

1 FOOT

STARFISH   BIRD   MAN   FROG

THE LONG AND SHORT OF DNA
Though no one has seen a DNA strip, scientists have experimentally measured it: if the strips in a human DNA cell were teased out to full length, they would make a thread about three feet long. The length of a DNA strip generally corresponds to the complexity of the creature whose life it regulates. There are notable inconsistencies, however: a frog's DNA strips from one cell are more than twice as long as those in a man.

able to reproduce itself. Information must be passed along exactly from generation to generation. The Crick-Watson model of DNA is admirably designed for replication. When cell division occurs, the whole DNA stairway comes apart in the middle in a kind of unzipping motion. All of the A's separate from the T's and the G's from the C's. Then each half of the stairway grows a new half, picking up raw materials from the cell contents around it. All of the old A's now link up with new T's and the old G's with new C's, etc., until two complete stairways of DNA exist.

The discovery of the biological significance of DNA, along with the explanation of how it may be responsible for heredity, has created an upheaval in biology. Certainly the DNA model has caused as much stir in scientific circles as did the model of the atom presented by Niels Bohr in 1913. No less than five scientists have been honored with Nobel Prizes in the last five years for their work with DNA.

But most exciting is the promise of the future. Even now at least one hereditary disease, sickle-cell anemia, has been pinned down to what appears to be a single fault in the DNA chain. There is great hope that chemical cures for such diseases will be worked out soon. Furthermore, there is hope that scientists will gain increasingly deep insights into the fundamental processes of heredity—and may even use this new knowledge to help shape man's future as a species.

The Basic Blueprint of Life

To "build" a living creature in the laboratory, to change one kind of life into another—these are age-old human dreams and the stuff of science fiction. In the last 10 years, one of the most awesome intellectual adventures in history has given the dreams some substance and the fiction some science. The new adventure is the science of molecular biology, and the questions it asks probe the meaning of life itself. What controls heredity? What is the inevitable thread common to all living organisms? What is it that gives a liver cell its "liverness," a heart cell its "heartness"? Molecular biologists give the same answer for all three questions: a molecule called deoxyribonucleic acid, or DNA (opposite), that issues the orders of life from the cell's nucleus. DNA is found in every living cell, from the leaf of a turnip to the brain of an Einstein. DNA, which molecular biologists have now made in their test tubes, is all things to all life.

A MODEL AT THE FAIR
A little girl at the Seattle World's Fair of 1962 stretches her neck for a better view of a gigantic model of life's blueprint, the DNA molecule. Resembling a modern sculpture, the model uses rods and spheres to represent the component parts of DNA. In total, these parts contain the formulas for all life processes and order the precise functioning of every living thing on earth.

Like a cluster of fruit in an invisible cornucopia, this model of a DNA molecule is demonstrated by its builder, British biophysicist Maurice Wilkins. This is only a partial model and there is little reason to complete it. The DNA molecule is highly complex but repetitive in its pattern; in effect, therefore, a study of one section of a DNA molecule becomes a study of the whole.

A Decade of DNA Exploration

In 1869 biochemist Friedrich Miescher isolated a substance from the nuclei of cells. He had no idea of its importance and he did not pursue his discovery to its conclusion. It hovered for decades in the limbo of unrecognized breakthroughs. More than a half century later, scientists began to suspect that Miescher's forgotten chemical, now called deoxyribonucleic acid, or DNA, was the missing link between inanimate and animate matter.

In the early 1950s a research group headed by British biophysicist Maurice Wilkins began an ambitious project: recognizing that the secret of life would involve some method of self-duplication, they used X-ray crystallography to expose the structure of the DNA molecule. Wilkins came to no conclusive answers. But in 1953 an American biologist, James Watson, and a British physicist, Francis Crick, used Wilkins' data to prove that DNA's structure was not a simple spiral, as Wilkins had guessed, but a double helix—like a twisted ladder—capable of zipping apart. The outstanding distinction of all living things—the ability to reproduce—was explained.

Using the same techniques as Wilkins, Watson and Crick, British scientists John Kendrew and Max Perutz pursued molecular biology further and analyzed the architecture of two kinds of protein. The Kendrew-Perutz study, while hailed as immensely significant, has had no practical application as yet.

In one decade these scientists and others like them found significant clues to an understanding of life's innermost secret.

A SKYLINE OF MYOGLOBIN

This complicated model of the protein myoglobin is being adjusted by Cambridge molecular biologist Dr. John Kendrew, who was discoverer of its structure. Myoglobin delivers oxygen to tissues in the muscles; its related protein, hemoglobin, carries it in the bloodstream. Kendrew's model represents a heightened understanding of all proteins, the cornerstones of life.

A BEVY OF NOBEL LAUREATES

Nobel Prize winners clutch their citations after the presentation in 1962. Five of the seven were for work in the field of molecular biology. From the left: Maurice Wilkins, Max Perutz, Francis Crick, John Steinbeck for his "realistic" novels, James Watson and John Kendrew. (The seventh winner, Russian physicist Lev Davidovich Landau, was hospitalized at the time.)

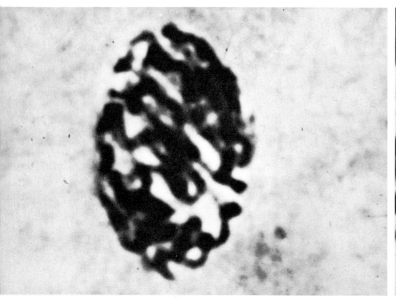

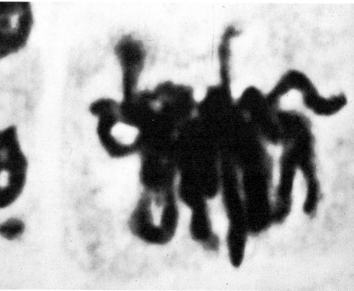

THE CHROMOSOMES REPRODUCE
The chromosomes in an onion-tip cell's nucleus have just completed the first step of reproduction: each strip of coded DNA has reproduced itself, and the conglomerate mass *(above)* now contains two identical sets of chromosomes.

CHROMOSOMES PREPARING TO DIVIDE
Here the chromosomes are beginning to align themselves at the center of the cell. Technically, they are known as chromatids until separation has actually been completed. At this point the cell's nucleus is completely dissolved.

A PAIR OF MERRY MACLAINES
Clowning happily, actress Shirley MacLaine and her daughter Stephanie exhibit a startling degree of "look-alikeness." Yet, similar as they may appear, any parent and child are significantly different and distinct beings: the child receives only half of its chromosomes—the coded instructions for growth—from its mother; it receives the other half from its father.

Copying with Life's Duplicator

The "dissection" of DNA *(previous pages)* made possible a greater understanding of conception and birth. With incredible versatility, DNA directs reproduction of an onion cell *(above)* into two identical cells, and also produces children *(left and opposite)* who are strikingly similar to their parents. In a sense, DNA is the master stencil of life's duplicating machine.

The two onion cells are identical because the duplicator used one stencil—the DNA of one chromosome set—to produce both cells. The actresses' daughters, however, are not carbon copies of their mothers: the duplicator used *two* DNA stencils —one set of chromosomes from each parent. Thus, in human reproduction, DNA produces varying degrees of similarity.

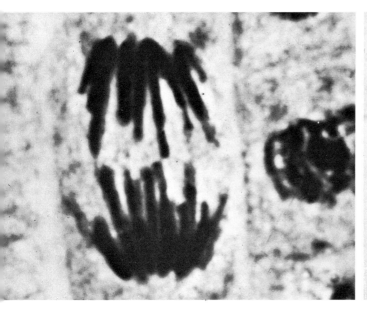

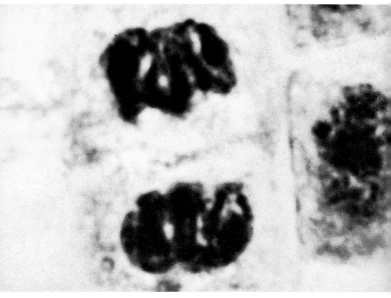

THE CELL PREPARES TO SPLIT
The chromosomes in this picture are separating and moving apart to form new nuclei. Each new cell will have both the same number and the same type of chromosomes the parent had, making it genetically identical to the parent.

MAKING GROWTH POSSIBLE
Two new cells have formed. This kind of cell multiplication is called mitosis, and it accounts for many of the common phenomena of growth —plants and bushes flowering, a child growing up, clipped fingernails growing out again.

A PAIR OF BLOOMING GARLANDS
Singing out lustily, Judy Garland and her daughter, Liza Minnelli, amaze listeners with their similar voices and mannerisms. In addition to her singing prowess, Liza, whose father is film director Vincente Minnelli, has shown an aptitude for acting. Geneticists are not certain to what degree special talents are passed along from generation to generation in the genes.

The Spiral Stairs and a Wider View

What is it about DNA that makes it the key to heredity and the basis of life? There is nothing unusual about its components—phosphates, sugars and bases containing nitrogen. Its secret, as Watson and Crick revealed, is its ingenious structure: two intertwined spirals connected to each other by thousands of rungs to form a long, thin, twisted ladder *(opposite).*

The spirals contain the sugars and phosphates. The rungs are made of the bases—each rung a combination of two bases. For any individual of any species, the sequence of base combinations on the ladder "spells out" an incredibly complex coded message that will transmit to the offspring all the instructions needed for every genetic trait. The particular message for each living creature is like a master die from which the pattern of his traits can be replicated again and again, just as the cloth-cutter's pattern *(left)* enables him to produce many identical replicas in cloth. It is the particular sequence and length of the nucleotide chain (the sugar-phosphate-base pattern) in the DNA molecules that make a horse give birth to a horse instead of a giraffe, an oyster or a fern—that determine color of eyes, texture of hair, shape of fingers. All the DNA instruction for a human being, if spelled out in English, would require several sets of a 24-volume encyclopedia.

1 A DNA MOLECULE

The twisted-ladder structure of a molecule of DNA is demonstrated by the model in the photograph opposite. Every human cell contains about three feet of DNA strands—a total of 10 billion miles of them in the trillions of cells of a grown man. Yet these threads are so thin that all the DNA of a fertilized human egg weighs no more than two ten-trillionths of an ounce.

Using a paper template, the cutter above duplicates by the hundreds his pattern in cloth.

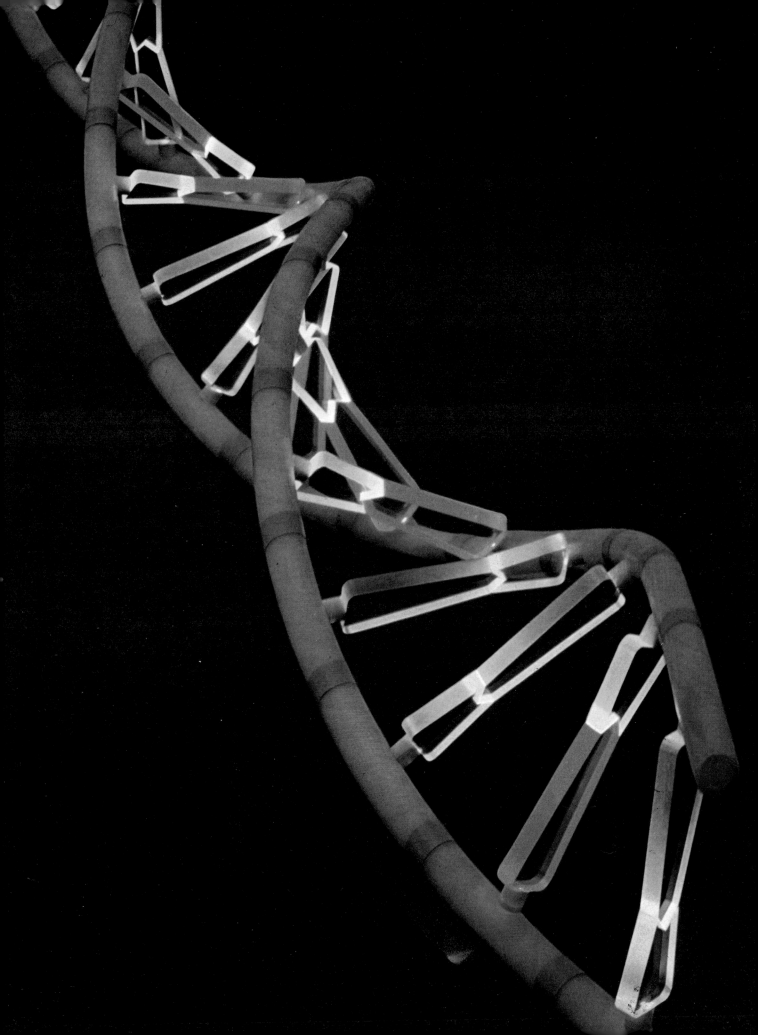

Reproduction: A Unique Solution

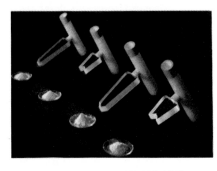

THE ALPHABET THAT SPELLS LIFE
The color-coded models above represent the DNA bases that transmit genetic data: red, adenine; green, thymine; blue, guanine; yellow, cytosine. Each points to the actual chemical.

However imaginative the architecture and however elaborate the message of DNA, there would still be no life on earth if this remarkable substance did not possess a power unique among chemical compounds: it can reproduce itself.

DNA's reproduction is centered about four of its component parts, called bases. These bases, the rungs of DNA's staircase, are adenine, thymine, guanine and cytosine (*left*), which geneticists abbreviate to A, T, G and C. Every rung of the DNA ladder is composed of two of these bases linked together; their structures are such that A will fit precisely only with T, and G only with C. Each base is attached to a small piece of sugar-phosphate backbone which forms the spirals of DNA.

The first step in DNA reproduction is the cleavage of the double spiral into two halves (*below, left*). Simultaneously, unattached nucleotide units floating in the cell's nucleus flock to join their cousins on the ladder (*below*). As the bases meet, the individual vertebrae also link. The result is two new DNA molecules (*opposite*), each carrying the same coded message as its parent because the bases have linked together in the same sequence.

The genes that determine heredity are thought to be "sentences" of different lengths making up the long coded message spelled out by DNA. This message can convey an immense amount of genetic data because a single human DNA molecule may have as many as 10,000 rungs in its ladder. Statistically, this means that the number of ways to spell the complete message of life is greater than the number of subatomic particles in the solar system.

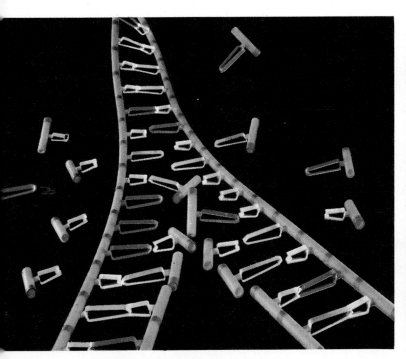

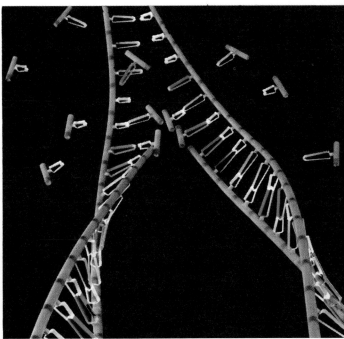

2 DNA UNZIPS ITSELF

The miracle of reproduction begins when a molecule of DNA starts to split, like a zipper coming undone (*above*). The two bases forming each rung snap apart. Free-floating nucleotides, always at large in the nucleus, start converging on both halves of the splitting ladder to repair them. Obeying the code, only a roaming nucleotide identical to that split off can attach itself.

3 DNA REPEATS ITSELF

Complete with their lengths of sugar-phosphate backbone (brown tubing), more and more bases-at-large fall in place (*above*). Red bases link with greens on the ladder; green loners team up with red. Footloose blues hunt fixed yellows; yellow wanderers seek out fixed blues. By repetition of this procedure, the original DNA molecule creates two exact replicas of itself.

4 TWO DNA'S FROM ONE

Each base on the two split strands has been linked with a base unit exactly like its former partner. And since the sequence of rungs in the two offspring is exactly the same as it was in the parent molecule, the process of replacement has been, in actuality, a process of duplication. Continuing the process, each offspring molecule can now split and produce two replicas.

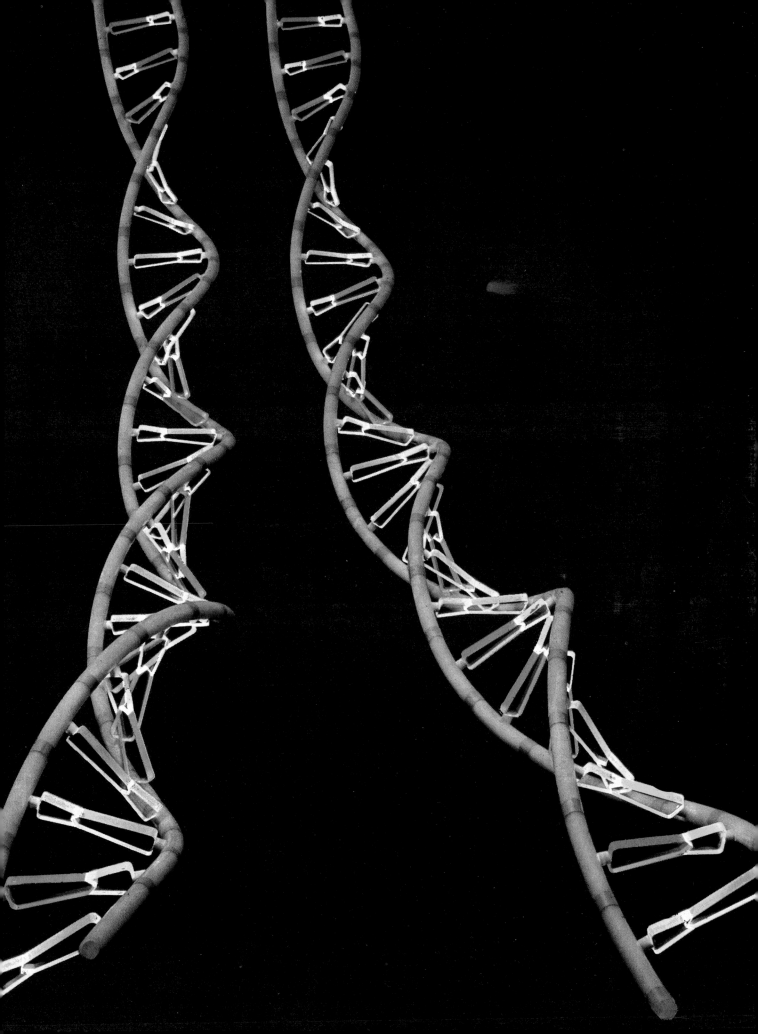

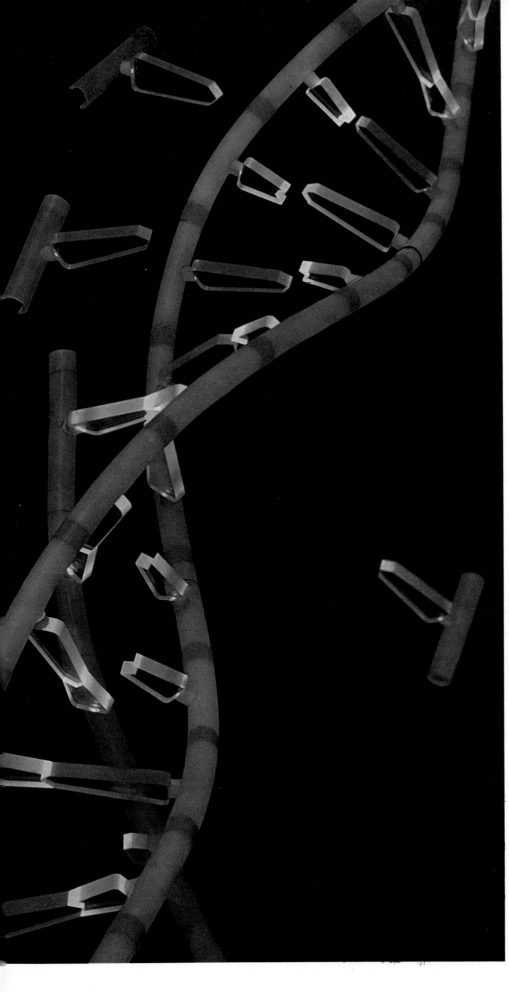

The Complexity of DNA-Computing

Life is more than creation. Once an organism is born, it must continue to live —a feat made possible by a formidable army of versatile compounds called proteins. Although there are thousands of different proteins, they have one thing in common: they are all manufactured according to precise instructions dispatched by the keeper of the code of life, DNA.

Too precious to leave the fortresslike protection of the nucleus, the DNA delegates its authority by producing a single-strand substance called "messenger-RNA" (shown forming from DNA, *left)* to carry the blueprints for protein construction to the ribosomes *(page 22).* DNA also makes smaller single-strand units called "transfer-RNA," conveyors to bring the raw materials called amino acids to the assembly line where they are locked together in the proper sequence for building the particular protein ordered by the messenger-RNA *(opposite).* DNA's prodigious feat of producing precise directions in correct proportions at the moment they are required has been compared to the operation of a staggeringly complex electronic computer.

5 DNA INTO RNA

The helix of a DNA molecule *(left)* unzips to produce RNA, an almost perfect copy of part of the DNA. Nucleotides, free-floating in the nucleus, lock into place along the unzipped molecule. In one respect the copy is different from its parent: the units of DNA represented by green in the model at left will be closely but not exactly duplicated by its opposite numbers in the RNA molecule. Produced in long strands, the RNA becomes the messenger variety; in shorter lengths it is transfer-RNA. As RNA is formed, the DNA helix zips itself back together.

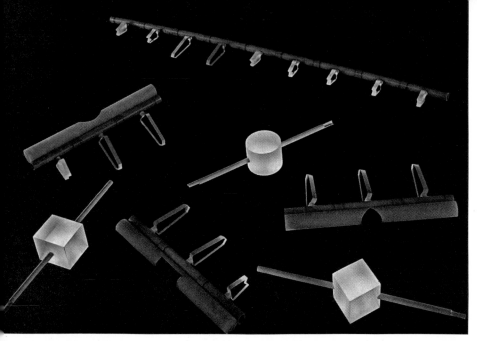

6 SEEKING AMINO ACIDS

Once produced by the DNA, the long strand of messenger-RNA and the shorter strands of transfer-RNA work as a team outside the nucleus to assemble the amino acids necessary to produce the protein called for in the messenger's coded signal. Each transfer-RNA is chemically attracted to a particular amino acid, represented at left by the clear plastic cubes and marshmallow. In addition, each unit of transfer-RNA carries a code which will help unite it eventually with the messenger-RNA after the amino acid it seeks has been found and captured.

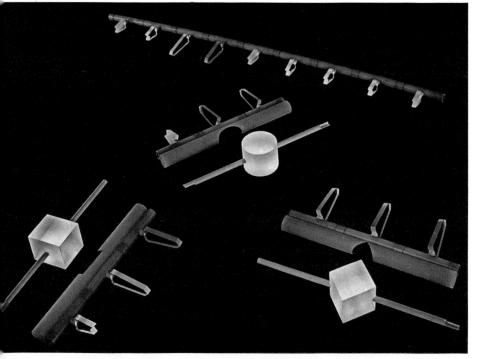

7 CAPTURING AMINO ACIDS

In the scene at left, the three transfer-RNAs are closing in on the three amino acids they have been designed to capture. The chemical attraction behind the kidnapping is symbolized by the different-shaped notches in the backbones of the transfer-RNA molecules. The cylindrical amino acid will fit only the RNA with the code message U, A, G (uracil, adenine, guanine). And this particular sequence will fit only one place on the strand of messenger-RNA: in the middle. The two other amino acids will be selected and categorized in exactly the same way.

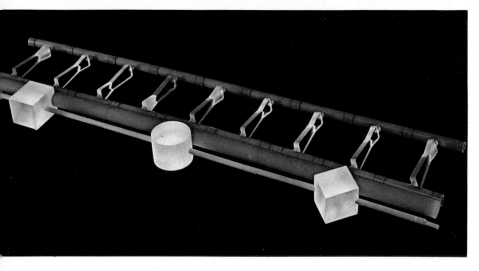

8 BUILDING A PROTEIN

The transfer-RNAs, having seized their prey, hitch themselves onto the assembly line of the messenger-RNA *(left)* in an order dictated by the coded sequence on the messenger. The amino acids are then linked in sequence to form the protein molecule, which promptly frees itself from the RNA to perform its specialized task in the body. Although there are only 20 different protein amino acids, there is an astronomical number of possible combinations in a complex protein built from a messenger-RNA holding hundreds or thousands of instructions.

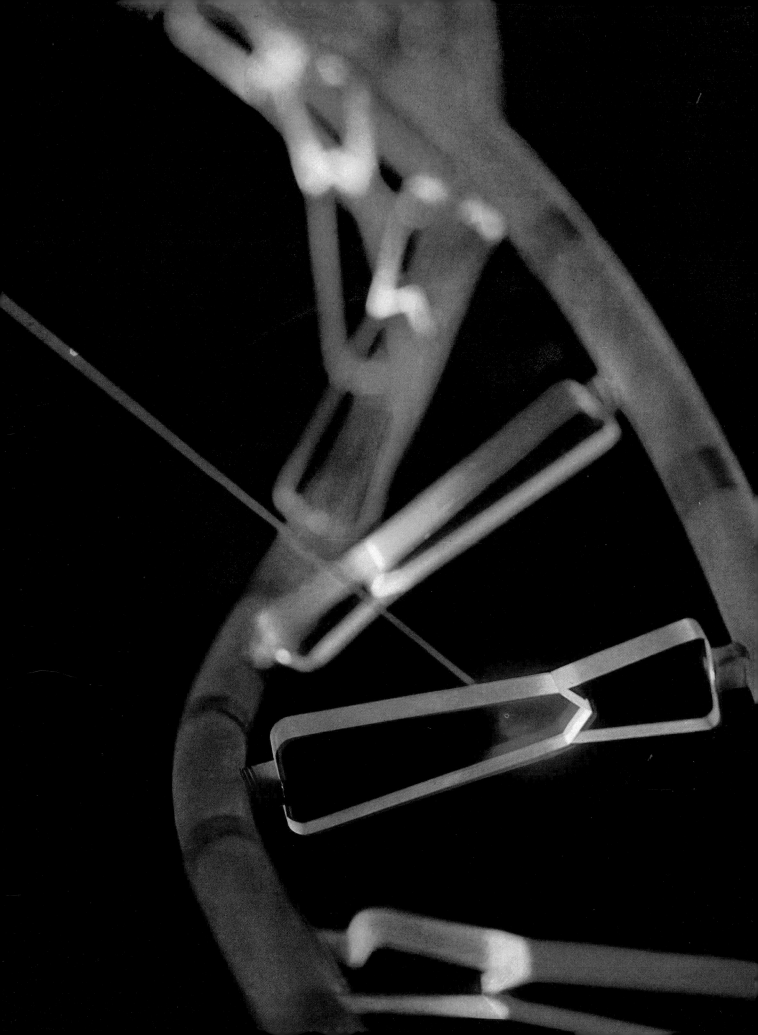

Garbled Messages in the Genetic Code

If DNA can produce so many million exact copies of itself without error, what accounts for genetic mishaps—the freaks and "sports" that occur in both animal and vegetable life? They are usually caused by attacks on the nucleus from chemicals, heat or radiation.

Since matter is mostly empty space, an X-ray, a gamma ray from fallout or a cosmic ray from space may penetrate billions of molecules without disturbing anything. But eventually it happens: a ray scores a bull's-eye in DNA *(opposite)*, garbling part of its coded message.

Mutation may mean a change in the appearance of the offspring, such as the naked-neck chicken at right. Another, more dangerous, result may be a misspelling in the part of the message that carries instructions for building proteins that sustain life, such as hemoglobin *(below, right)*. The normal hemoglobin molecule, a complex structure of 574 different amino acids, is designed to do a specific job: carry oxygen through the bloodstream. The deadly hereditary disease called sickle-cell anemia occurs when one of these amino acids is faultily placed in the molecule because of an altered DNA message.

Sickle-cell anemia is found in some 250,000 Americans and almost always kills its victims before age 40. But molecular biologists are planning a new assault on such genetic diseases. They hope that synthetic varieties of DNA and RNA, made to order in the laboratory and injected into the sick cells, will edit their DNA text so that its message will be once again a clear, unmistakable call for health.

9 A MESSAGE DEFORMED

From outer space, a cosmic ray strikes one of the rungs in the ladder of a DNA molecule *(model opposite)* and charges it with glowing energy. Since the rungs represent letters in the DNA message, the radiation may cause crippling deformities in succeeding generations. The scientist who discovers exactly what the ray does to the rung may win a Nobel Prize.

VICTIM OF A MIXED-UP MESSAGE
The naked-neck chicken above is a mutation that was probably caused by natural radiation striking the part of DNA that should have called for neck feathers. The species was once mistaken for a cross between a turkey and a chicken.

A KILLER LURKING IN THE GENES
The round shapes of normal, healthy human blood cells are shown in the photomicrograph below. They are interspersed with a sickle-shaped mutation, the cause of an almost always fatal hereditary disease called sickle-cell anemia.

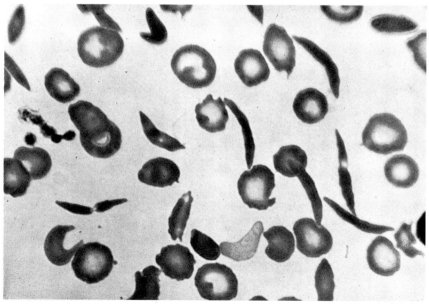

Mutations—Usually for the Worse

In the last three billion years, life on earth has evolved from primitive cells wallowing in the primeval ooze to that sophisticated labyrinth of nucleic acids and proteins that constitutes a human being. How did this miracle of evolution happen? A large part of the answer is mutations: no organism can go on producing exact replicas of itself for eternity. Mistakes are made; a mutant is born; environmental conditions determine whether or not the mutant survives.

Most mutations—like the albino kangaroo above—do not improve the species. But others, like the black peppered moth

(opposite), were born with certain traits that helped them live in an environment where the normal was dying out.

As molecular biologists become ever more knowledgeable about the ways of genes and DNA, the closer man will come to controlling the very evolution of life—a breathtaking possibility and a solemn responsibility. The adventure has already begun. DNA and RNA have been synthesized and analyzed. One species of bacteria has been changed into another. And a genetic tour de force—turning back the clock of evolution—is described in a story of Japanese goldfish on the next pages.

A MUTANT MOTH IN BRITISH SMOG

NORMALITY HIDDEN BY LICHENS

MUTATION HIDDEN BY GRIME

A BENEVOLENT CAPTIVITY

Fluttering white eyelashes over delicate pink eyes, albino kangaroos like the one above are about as rare as rain in the Australian outback. This mutation has deprived the kangaroo of its normal camouflage of tawny color, making it easy prey for predators. Fortunate mutants like this one are protected by one Australian breeder who keeps a herd of 40 purebred albinos.

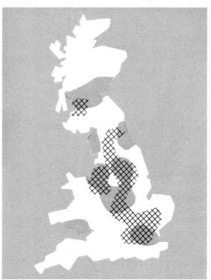

BRITAIN'S INDUSTRIAL AREAS

A SOOTY SURVIVAL

The English peppered moth, in its countryside surroundings, was perfectly camouflaged to match the lichens on tree trunks where it rested by day. But from time to time a mutation occurred—a peppered moth that was not only jet-black but also more hardy than the normal variety because its caterpillars needed less food and were more resistant to airborne chemicals. Although its hardiness should have made it survive, it died out in the country because birds could see it so easily. (In the photograph above, left, the normal moth below the black mutation is barely visible.) But as the Industrial Revolution poured its soot over the countryside, the smoke-begrimed regions (black on map at left) favored the freak. The less-resistant caterpillars of the normal moth were often poisoned by the chemicals that fell from the air on their food. For those who survived that fallout, their whiteness emblazoned against the sooty black tree trunks beckoned to hungry birds' beaks, while their freakish brothers found an all-over blackness as good a protection as night itself.

Juggling Mutations in the Lab

In a thousand-year-old Chinese manuscript, the anonymous author tells how one day, into the school of black crucian carp in his fishpond, a red freak was born. No one really explained the phenomenon until 1914, when Dr. Yoshiichi Matsui, the renowned Japanese geneticist, set out to prove that every goldfish alive today is a descendant of that first red mutation— or others like it.

In the next 20 years Dr. Matsui crossbred about two million goldfish in thousands of experiments before he ultimately proved that every species of modern goldfish is a mutated descendant of the black crucian carp of old China.

How does a mutation-maker feel about juggling living genes? Dr. Matsui tells how he once accidentally bred a one-eyed mutation which ended up on sale in the marketplace. Sometime later, he said, "I recognized the monster fish as my own creation, and I felt guilty before God."

MUTANTS CUTE AND PRICELESS
Dr. Yoshiichi Matsui *(right)* examines two ugly one-pound, lion-head goldfish, a mutation prized by Japanese breeders for its "cuteness." Unlike normal goldfish *(above)*, the mutants' genes produce a bloated head which breeders further enlarge by feeding a high-fat diet. Although he considers them "priceless," the breeder of this pair puts their market value at $180 each.

4

The First
Living Thing
on Earth

THE BASIC ENIGMA OF LIFE is posed in one short question. How did it start? How could something as exquisitely organized as a living cell come into being in a world of attenuated gases and volcanic fumes and hard, crystalline rock? In many ways, the appearance of biological cells in a barren and hostile world is more improbable than the subsequent development of primitive cells into dinosaurs and primates. Given life, everything is possible. But is there any logical explanation that accounts for the development of life from the dead, inanimate stuff of a newborn planet?

Science accepts certain major features of the story of life's appearance on earth. In the words of one investigator, "time is the hero of the plot." The transition from nonlife to life on earth was almost certainly a gradual process. All indications point to an exceedingly slow and undirected development of the organization of matter in past ages. Time stretches out behind us like an infinite wake, receding to events about which we can only speculate.

The first rational theories concerning the genesis of life came from the early Greeks. Six centuries before Christ, the Ionian philosophers held that living organisms originated in sea slime through the action of heat, sun and air. While this sounds deceptively like the modern hypothesis that life began in the warm, soupy seas of the early earth, these ancient philosophers were a world removed from scientific thought. The Ionians believed that everything in the universe was alive and their choice of sea slime as a starting place was purely fortuitous—it looked like an appropriate place for the seeds of life (which they thought were floating like dust motes in the air) to settle and begin to produce the viable and visible organisms that comprised the Greek world. The Ionians were almost right but for the wrong reasons.

Aristotle, who followed the Ionians by several centuries, added observation to this early speculation to produce a whole philosophy of natural science. Aristotle held that animals arise not only from other animals but also from lifeless matter through the intervention of a "soul" which is the property of the four elements, air, water, fire and earth. In substance, Aristotle was saying that life could arise from slime or any other apparently lifeless matter if it was worked over by the elements. Here again, the argument produced but did not justify a conclusion that approximated the truth as we now see it—and when Aristotle descended to details and traced the generation of fireflies to morning dew and the birth of mice to moist soil he launched a school of nonsense which persisted for almost 2,000 years.

Throughout the early and middle ages of the Christian era, attempts to account for life's beginnings ranged from the reverent to the ridiculous. Churchmen in general accepted Aristotle's views, adding an ele-

INSPECTING THE SPARK OF LIFE
A tiny spark arcs into a laboratory mixture of water vapor, ammonia, methane and hydrogen in a re-creation of what may have been the first steps toward life on earth. This "Miller experiment" is named for the scientist who proved that a spark, such as lightning, could convert the gases of the world's primitive atmosphere into amino acids, the building blocks of life.

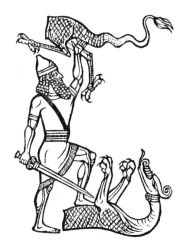

A BABYLONIAN BEGINNING

The ancient Babylonians concocted their creation legend from the heroic tale of Marduk, a mighty god who became one of their chief deities. Marduk attacked and killed a mammoth dragon, Tiamat, who was the embodiment of pre-creation chaos. After his colossal victory, Marduk created order from chaos by cleaving the dragon's carcass into two pieces. From one half he fashioned the earth; the other half became the heavens.

BLOODTHIRSTY NORSE NATIVITY

The mythology of primordial Scandinavia told of an unusual meteorological phenomenon: fiery clouds from the south united with icy gusts from the north, and from the resultant mist were created Ymir, the first giant, and a bevy of beautiful Frost Maidens. Their mating eventually led to three grandsons who, in a fit of ingratitude, hacked Ymir into several chunks. His blood became the seas, his body the earth and his battered skull the heavens.

ment of Divine Intercession to reconcile them with dogma. Naturalistic philosophers embellished Aristotelian logic with all manner of fanciful inventions—trees which produced birds and lambs, and wheat kernels which, when properly activated by human sweat, gave rise to mice. Early in the 16th Century the famous physician Paracelsus claimed he could produce the embryo of a little man (which he called the homunculus) by manipulating the proper elements in a special container.

Many eminent thinkers of the 17th and 18th Centuries—among them, Descartes and Newton—accepted the theory that, through spontaneous generation, life could arise from lifeless matter. A dissenting voice belonged to William Harvey, the physician and anatomist who discovered the circulation of the blood, when he announced that all life derives from the egg. This concept heralded the beginning of a complete change in the theories concerning the creation of life.

No maggots came to dinner

One of the first laboratory attacks on the theory of spontaneous generation was made by an Italian physician named Francesco Redi during the middle 1600s, when he protected decaying meat from flies by a muslin covering. No maggots appeared in the meat. This indicated that life did not arise spontaneously from decaying matter, as was commonly supposed. But spontaneous generation won a reprieve when the early Dutch microscopist, Anton van Leeuwenhoek, discovered microorganisms, or "animalcules," in decaying organic substances. Many observers claimed the animalcules were spontaneously generated from the substances. (Interestingly, Leeuwenhoek himself did not accept this reasoning: he claimed that the organisms were present in the air.)

The ensuing 200 years saw a continuing battle between experimentalists over the question of spontaneous generation. A French biologist, Buffon, and a Scottish cleric, Needham, declared that Leeuwenhoek's newly discovered microscopic organisms were a "special force" that vitalized life—a concept that came to be known as the vital-force theory. A Frenchman named Puchet wrote a 700-page book proving that spontaneous generation was possible. Controversy raged and all shades of opinion surrounded the question of how life arose from the apparently lifeless matter of the world. In 1860, the French Academy of Sciences offered a prize for exact experiments which would settle the question.

Louis Pasteur, a chemist who had won renown by demonstrating that fermentations are caused by living microorganisms, accepted the challenge. Pasteur approached the problem in three steps. He first demonstrated that microorganisms did exist in free air, as Leeuwenhoek had suggested. He then proved that when solutions of organic materials were boiled they did not lose their capacity to sustain microorganisms; this indicated that if there was a life-creating vital force, it was not vitiated by life-killing heat. In a third and conclusive step, Pasteur exposed a flask containing a boiled solution to free air from which all microorganisms had been filtered. The results showed incontestably that if rigorous techniques kept the solution free of contamination (even though it was exposed to the filtered air), no life arose within the flask. Apparently there was no such thing as spontaneous generation. Life could not arise from nonlife. Pasteur won the prize.

The mystery of life

Since Pasteur's experiments, there have been spectacular advances in our knowledge of the inanimate world and the life processes of organic matter; nevertheless the essential scientific question of how life began remains unsolved. Cell research on the molecular level has revealed many of the processes by which living matter reproduces itself, develops in complexity and evolves into different forms. But the great gulf between life and nonlife remains an enigma. Science can only conjecture about the basic steps of the process.

One principle has guided recent thinking about the origin of life. It is generally agreed that life did not appear in a melodramatic flash but that, in a sense, it crept quietly upon the scene. The stage was set, according to current estimates, some five billion years ago, when the earth was a newly formed planet. The earth's original atmosphere was probably composed chiefly of hydrogen and its compounds, such as water and ammonia, and the carbon-containing substance, methane. These ingredients were undoubtedly among the primary raw materials fed into the long process that would eventually bring life to a sterile world.

Laboratory studies indicate the possible nature of the early steps in this process. In 1952, an American graduate student in chemistry named Stanley L. Miller assembled a simple apparatus which stood about two feet high and included glass tubing and a globular flask. Miller circulated through this apparatus a sample of a hypothetical early atmosphere—a mixture of water vapor, hydrogen, ammonia and methane.

Miller wanted to find out how these substances might have combined to yield more complex materials. He knew they combine very slowly unless there is some source of energy to stir up chemical activity. Electricity was one likely source of such energy: in the early history of the world it would have been available in the form of lightning bolts.

To duplicate these conditions, Miller created a miniature lightning storm—a 60,000-volt spark—inside his apparatus. He arranged his equipment so that the mixture of water vapor and gases drifted continuously through the crackling spark. After circulating past the spark, liquid condensed from the vapor drop by drop in the flask and gradually collected

GREEK TALE OF GENESIS

Ancient Greek thinkers conceived a highly abstract creation myth. According to the account attributed to Orpheus, the heavens and the earth were spun from chaos by the force of time. Chaos was a formless mass of disorder—night, mist and fiery air drifting in aimless anarchy. Time imposed order; the mass began to spin, eventually assuming an egg shape cosmic in proportions. The mass flew apart and the universe came into being.

at the bottom. Miller let the mixture circulate for about a week. When he analyzed the solution which had accumulated he made a significant discovery. Though biologists had not suspected that such a simple and straightforward experiment would produce an assortment of chemicals which play important roles in the growth of living cells, that is precisely what had happened. The synthesis-by-electricity had produced an impressive list of carbon-containing organic compounds—substances that exist in nature as constituents of living organisms. Miller's simple experiment had reintroduced the concept of spontaneous generation.

Perhaps the most important of Miller's findings was the identification in the solution of amino acids, the building blocks of enzymes and other proteins. Four different kinds of amino acids had been synthesized during the experiment, together with more than half a dozen other compounds of biological interest. There was also evidence of the synthesis of polymers, long-chain molecules made up of identical or closely related chemical groups hitched one to the other.

Light makes the gases dance

Soon after the announcement of these results, investigators at other laboratories, theorizing that solar radiation could have been as effective as lightning in promoting chemical synthesis, managed to produce amino acids and many other organic compounds by using ultraviolet light (a component of sunlight) instead of an electrical discharge.

The processes involved in both forms of this experiment can only be surmised. Apparently, the spark or the ultraviolet light jarred the molecules in the flask into violent motion, making them highly reactive and causing them to combine readily with one another to form more complicated compounds. There is no way of proving that the experiment actually did duplicate the general conditions existing in the atmosphere during the early period of this planet, but if it did, then similar naturally occurring reactions probably produced not only one but many organic or carbon-containing compounds during those pre-life times.

Scientists reasoned that this sort of naturally occurring synthesis was most likely to change simple substances into complex compounds in the upper atmosphere of the primitive planet; they also assumed that a reverse process may have taken place near the surface of the hot young earth. Winds and storms could have stirred up the gases at the higher levels, and temperature variations could have siphoned their load of complex compounds down to the earth's surface. Here, the extremely high temperatures of the primitive planet could have split the compounds back to their simpler components.

These changes from simple to complex to simple represent the beginning of a massive cycle, a cycle promoted by the circulating tides in the atmosphere. Turbulence swept the simpler substances upward and away from the surface—and solar radiation, or perhaps lightning, put the pieces back together, creating quantities of new organic compounds. In this apparently pointless round of synthesis and destruction are the foreshadowings of the carbon cycle, the combination of photosynthesis and respiration that keeps life flourishing in today's world.

The formation of carbon compounds was only a harbinger of life. The amino acids which may have existed in that early period are not the proteins which are necessary to life, and anything even faintly resembling a cell lay far in the future.

The long rain

During these early eons of the earth's history, the first and greatest deluge was in the making. Violent disturbances shook and cracked the surface of the infant earth. Seas of lava flowed out of many thousands of volcanoes; earthquakes were common. Later the surface cooled, preparing the way for a new phase of evolution—the formation of oceans. Waters originally trapped beneath the earth's surface and within mineral crystals escaped through vents, hot springs and geysers, and spurted into the skies, to remain suspended in the form of enormous clouds.

It has been estimated that a few million years after the formation of the earth, the water suspended in the atmosphere amounted to some 200 million billion tons—about a tenth of all the water in today's oceans. As yet no oceans existed. Then the rains came, incredibly intensive rains. The oceans literally fell from the skies throughout a period which may have lasted millions of years.

The earth was a strange and comparatively peaceful place after the rains. The sun, so long obscured by clouds, now gleamed bright in an atmosphere which consisted chiefly of nitrogen, methane, some carbon monoxide and carbon dioxide. This mixture of gases absorbed more color from sunlight than does the present-day atmosphere, which includes oxygen produced by living organisms. The post-deluge skies were probably a vivid greenish blue. An observer might have seen intermittent red, yellow, orange and green flashes in the atmosphere, fluorescent effects resulting from the action of ultraviolet light on gas molecules.

One conception of the young earth pictures a planet awash in its own oceans. Here and there, waves broke on the bare gray rocks of isolated islands, but nothing else existed to relieve the monotony of vast stretches of ocean. In a sense, things had settled down for the long haul. The recombination of the elements, the formation of substances and compounds continued, but at a greatly reduced rate.

The compounds formed in the atmosphere were now accumulating in the oceans, being washed down with the rains. As this leaching of the

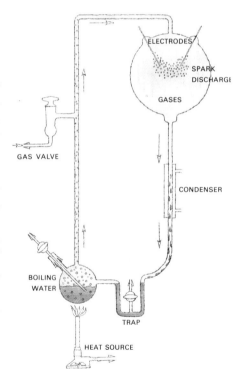

CONCOCTING LIFE'S CHEMICALS

Above is the apparatus used by Stanley L. Miller in which he synthesized the basic components of life under simulated conditions. A mixture of vapor from boiling water *(lower left)* plus the gases methane, ammonia and hydrogen, introduced through the valve *(upper left)*, was subjected to a spark *(upper right)*. After condensing, Miller found four amino acids—and with improved techniques, 10—in the trap.

atmosphere continued, increasing quantities of organic compounds came to rest in a dilute solution in the seas.

In this molecular soup, over long periods of time, the organic compounds became increasingly diverse and complex. With complexity there developed a form of competition: through chemical reactions the large molecules tended to incorporate the smaller molecules, sweeping them up from the primitive atmosphere. Another step in the organization of organic matter was now under way.

With this formation of ever-larger molecules, nature had inaugurated a process of selection and survival that was probably the primitive beginning of evolution. The creation of increasingly complex molecules may also have occurred in regions of volcanic activity, where temperatures hovered between 200°F. and 300°F. Experiments with organic compounds at these temperatures at Florida State University suggest that the development of life could have been an almost inevitable process. Researchers there have proved that heating a mixture of amino acids results in the synthesis of large proteinlike molecules, polymers which may contain 50 or more amino acids linked together. Similar results can be obtained with lower temperatures by adding certain phosphate-containing compounds to the solution—an observation of special interest in view of the importance of ATP and other energy-yielding phosphates in living cells. It has been found, furthermore, that when the proteinlike substances are dissolved in hot water and the mixture is allowed to cool, myriads of tiny spherical globules condense out of the solution. Their walls have many of the properties of cell membranes.

World without life

Though experiments such as those carried on by the Florida investigators do not explain how life actually arose from inanimate matter, they suggest another step in the journey toward life. Matter was now appearing in the form of units with a specific chemical character. A new feature—a tendency toward order—was being added to the factors of complexity and size in the development of molecular compounds.

During the ages which saw the gradual development of large molecules of organic matter, the earth's contours were changing. The earth's surface gradually cooled and became wrinkled. Thermal disturbances took place under the water and deep beneath the crust. Continental masses rose out of the seas, mountains formed and erosion gradually shaped the land. The result was that the earth of four billion years ago probably had certain features, such as streams and rivers and lakes and valleys, which would be recognized today. But there was no life. It was a desolate world, where the only sounds were those of moving waters and winds, punctuated by an occasional explosion or eruption.

AN ANCIENT IDEA THAT SLOWED SCIENCE FOR CENTURIES

"SPONTANEOUSLY GENERATED" VERMIN

AN OPEN-AND-SHUT EXPERIMENT

In his classic manner of all thought and no experiments, Aristotle adopted the primordial idea that certain forms of life generated spontaneously from decomposing matter. In 1668 Francesco Redi, a Florentine physician, challenged this idea, which even Isaac Newton had accepted. Redi put meat into two jars, covered one, and watched ordinary flies lay eggs in the other. Meat in both bottles putrefied, but only the open bottle spawned any flies.

REDI'S THEORY-SMASHING APPARATUS

NO WORMS, NO FLIES; A DOGMA DIES

The complex compounds which had developed in the oceans now had a chance to accumulate in exposed places near the edges of the new seas. During storms and high tides, water flowed into pools and later evaporated under the hot sun, leaving scattered residues of organic compounds along the shores. The wind blew these compounds over the land.

With this distribution of organic compounds, the stage was set for a further development of the precursors of life over wide areas of the planet. Some of the most interesting speculations concerning this continuing development appear in a recent study by Gösta Ehrensvärd, a biochemist at the University of Lund in Sweden. Here is his interpretation of a part of the evolutionary process as it may have taken place three billion years ago, in a spot where chemical brews were simmering.

A small crater lake, fed by thermal springs, rests like a mirror in a setting of gems. On the shores are minerals of all colors, which have crystallized out of molten rock. These mineral layers also form the floor of the lake. The lake water is brownish green, deep and still. Areas of chemical activity are marked by blurred or turbid spots on the lake surface. From the water comes a smell like that of rotten eggs as bubbles of hydrogen-sulphide gas rise and break at the surface.

HOCUS-POCUS: HOMUNCULUS
Alchemists in the dark ages of pseudoscience tried in vain to create human life in their laboratories. In *Faust,* Goethe describes a scene in which Faust's assistant Wagner *(above)* makes a homunculus, or little man, in a glass alembic. Goethe describes the man as a "pretty manikin, moving, living, seeing." Unfortunately, Goethe did not list the ingredients, except to say that "many hundred substances" must "gently be compounded."

Revolution in a lake

In this quiet, odorous scene, major chemical transformations are under way at the molecular level. Proteins and other long-chain molecules are being formed. The first primitive enzymes—crude substances, but compounds which nevertheless accelerate chemical reactions—take shape and speed other reactions. Other processes yield stable, flat molecules, chemical relatives of the compounds that will appear in later ages as the red blood pigment, heme, and the green plant pigment, chlorophyll.

The quiet lake is also the site of the evolution of a very special kind of process. As compounds react with one another, forming larger and more complex molecules of organic matter, they tend to form self-feeding cycles, each step in the cycle being accelerated by a primitive enzyme. Such cycles introduce a repetitive pattern into the hitherto random processes taking place in the lake.

These self-regenerating cycles herald a quiet revolution, a kind of organic declaration of independence. Life has not yet appeared, but the precursors of biological substances are no longer being formed by merely fortuitous forces. Where the environment once influenced the synthesis of organic compounds, the organic compounds are now beginning to influence, to organize, the environment. In the words of Ehrensvärd: "The sedimentary slime has become more aggressive chemically . . . the actors are taking over the stage management."

One sign of this epochal change is that chemical processes no longer depend entirely on the chance presence of complex intermediate compounds. Various processes now produce the intermediate compounds they need from simple and readily available substances. Many of these regenerating cycles yield carbon dioxide gas as a by-product. This gas accumulates, becomes a relatively common ingredient of the atmosphere and later serves as a basic raw material in the synthesis of organic compounds. Life is coming closer with each millennium. Somewhere along the line, blobs of jellylike material appear, systems of active regenerating cycles enclosed in membranes, the remote ancestors of cells.

The genesis of life

Sometime within these millennial spans, in some manner not understood, in some long-vanished site on the young earth (in the quiet lake, perhaps, or in the seas), the climactic event of creation occurred. This was the formation of the first compound which could reproduce itself. This act of replication is the generally accepted evidence of life. Though we can only guess at the exact nature of the substance which embodied this unique and portentous development, present knowledge suggests that it might have been some arrangement of DNA-like strands, with the collateral enzymes necessary for replication.

Whether the appearance of a self-replicating compound was a once-only happening which persisted or the result of countless trial-and-error reactions at countless sites over the ages, the step marked the turning point of evolution. For now sheer chance was replaced by organization, accidental structure by design. The self-duplicating compound could help itself; in the very process of its survival from generation to generation, it introduced a new and mercilessly efficient element of competition into the struggle for the limited supply of raw materials available.

Chemical evolution must have been an uneven and an uncertain process. Organic compounds undoubtedly approached the complexity of living matter in a halting fashion. The waters of a crater lake probably seldom remained undisturbed for long; chemical systems which developed during the quiet periods would be wiped out as new disturbances rent the waters. As always, it was time that saved the situation, eons of time and a planet that offered countless brewing sites for all manner of chemical aggregations. At any moment, something was sure to be fermenting somewhere.

Biologists believe that when life first appeared in cellular form it did so in structures closely resembling present-day bacteria. The bacteria of today may be direct descendants of primitive strains similar to those which still exist in waters rich in iron and sulphur. These crude forms still get their energy from inorganic matter; they have never learned to use the more complex substances of the organic world. Bacteria in

CELLS—EXTRAORDINARY AND EXTRATERRESTRIAL

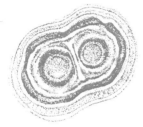

PSEUDO-CELL: ANCESTOR OF ALL LIFE?

FROM SCIENCE, SPACE AND PAST

Modern science has not only shown that life may exist beyond the earth, it is also on the verge of demonstrating how life might have originated. Lifeless but lifelike in appearance, pseudo-cells *(above)* have been produced in laboratories, and scientists believe that natural forces could have imparted life to such pseudo-cells by aimlessly combining atoms until an "Adam molecule," capable of growing, was formed. Cell-like fossils *(below, left)* have been found in meteorites— sometimes 40 million to a cubic inch. This is a startling indication that life might have been much more prolific on other worlds, since cell fossils from the early earth *(below, right)* are far less concentrated than those from space.

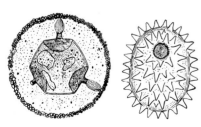

CELL-LIKE FOSSILS IN METEORITES FROM SPACE

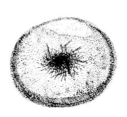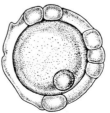

FOSSILIZED CELLS FROM THE PRIMITIVE EARTH

general are likely examples of early forms of life because they are built along relatively simple lines. They have fewer special parts than other cells. Such structures as true nuclei and mitochondria, found in other organisms, were apparently products of later stages of evolution.

The arrival of life on earth is difficult to date. Among the oldest traces of living matter are fossils discovered some years ago on the Canadian shore of Lake Superior. A geologist was conducting a microscopic examination of thin sections of rock collected from iron-bearing deposits when he observed what appeared to be fossil cells. Later, a biologist identified the cells as a blue-green algae, similar to existing organisms. Recent studies have confirmed that these cell remains are some two billion years old. Compared to bacteria, algae are advanced organisms and their presence so many years ago suggests that life must have appeared in the still more remote past, perhaps more than three billion years back.

Progress through error

All evolutionary advances are the result of changes in the genetic apparatus of the cell. The fact that DNA is not an unalterably perfect duplicating molecule makes it, paradoxically, an ideal medium to serve evolution. For progress and for survival, the hereditary material must breed true, but not too true. A DNA molecule may manufacture faithful copies of itself a million times in a row. But a mistake or mutation may occur during the next replication and appear in the million-and-first reproduction.

Such rare events make evolution possible. If, for example, early bacteria had bred true, if their hereditary material had duplicated itself without errors, nothing higher than these primitive organisms would ever have appeared on earth. It happened, however, that because of genetic mutations some of the early bacteria differed from the rest. They could synthesize light-absorbing pigments, and these might have been the progenitors of algae which use photosynthesis. Later generations, perhaps, made use of water instead of hydrogen sulphide in some of their life processes. The errors, the changes, must always be relatively slight. Extensive changes prevent reproduction entirely and the species becomes extinct. The secret of evolution is a continuing series of small changes among large populations whose individuals are very much alike. Such populations are flexible and can survive by developing new strains or races in the face of changing environments.

A dramatic example of adaptation probably occurred after the rise of chlorophyll and single-celled plants. Photosynthesis became a large-scale phenomenon, increasing amounts of carbon dioxide were consumed and plants spread like green waves over the surface of the oceans. That probably happened about 800 million years ago. Ironically, this burst

A GREEK MYTH AND A SPECULATION ON SALINITY

A THEORY NOT WORTH ITS SALT

A popular Greek myth tells of the birth of Aphrodite from the foam of the sea *(above)*. In a theory remarkably reminiscent of the Aphrodite myth, A. B. Macallam stated in 1903 that there was a causal relationship between the salinity of the sea and the salt content in blood plasma—a direct reflection of our ancient emergence from the sea. The ratio between the different kinds of salt is about the same, but Macallam's theory was rejected after scientists showed that a sample of sea water holds more than three times as much salt all together as an equal amount of blood. Even hundreds of millions of years ago, when vertebrates first appeared, the sea was twice as salty as blood plasma is today.

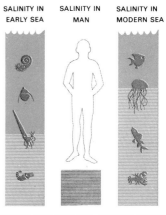

RELATIVE SALT CONTENTS: A THEORY DEBUNKED

of life threatened to bring about its own extinction. Millions of tons of oxygen, a by-product of photosynthesis, were poisoning the air. Over a span of thousands of years the concentration of oxygen rose from a trace to its present level of about 20 per cent of the atmosphere.

The threat to living matter during this period resulted from the fact that cells adjusted to extremely low oxygen conditions will die if their oxygen wastes accumulate in the environment and are not removed. It was a sink-or-swim situation and many species undoubtedly sank without trace. But other cell species arose which not only required oxygen for their existence (thereby preventing a potential poison from accumulating above a certain level) but also produced carbon dioxide wastes, which plants use in their life processes. In this way, as oxygen-dependent animal cells developed, the great balanced carbon cycle established itself and life was ready for another series of developments.

If the earth, throughout its history, had been inhabited only by photosynthetic organisms, single cells might still represent the most advanced forms of life. But energy resulting from the use of oxygen by animal cells made possible the rise of a long chain of active organisms from fish to primates. This use of oxygen spurred the organization of matter into increasingly complex forms and evolution continues the process of complication in its latest production—man.

The Awesome Mystery of the Beginnings

The origin of life, like the origin of the earth, is a mystery. Man's approach to this mystery has been a mixture of thoughtful conjecture and continuing awe. What is presented here, in text and a series of evocative photographs by Gordon Parks, is conjecture—an attempt to give to mystery sequence and shape. "In the beginning," says Genesis, "the earth was without form, and void." It was, according to most modern scientists, part of a huge, swirling cloud of gas and dust which slowly condensed under pressure of starlight and of its own gravitational action. Part of that revolving cloud became the sun. Thickening clusters of the cloud became the nuclei of the earth and other planets. The formation of the earth is estimated to have taken place about five billion years ago. And enveloping the new planet was an atmosphere rich in compounds containing carbon and hydrogen—ingredients essential to the future development of life itself.

DISTANT DYNAMO OF THE SUN

In the beginning, as now, it was the steady flow of energy from the sun that made life possible on earth. From 93 million miles away, its power reached down to initiate chemical reactions that formed the primitive stuff of life. And on the newly formed and barren earth, the warming sunlight provided a steady climate mild enough to encourage the experiment of living.

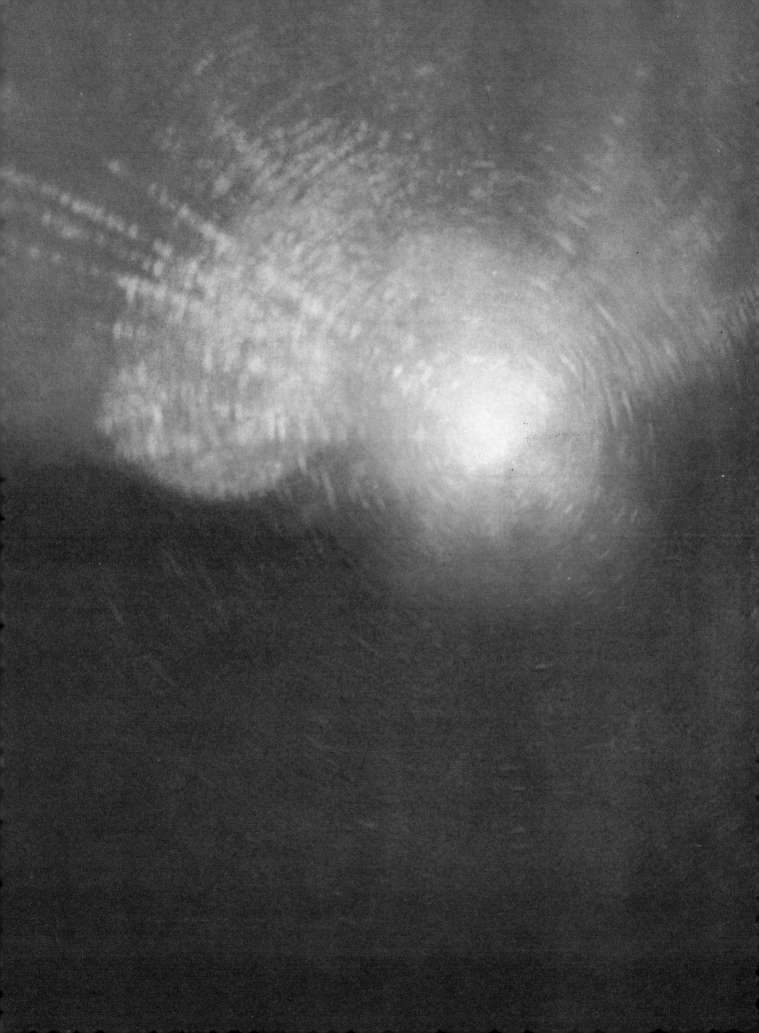

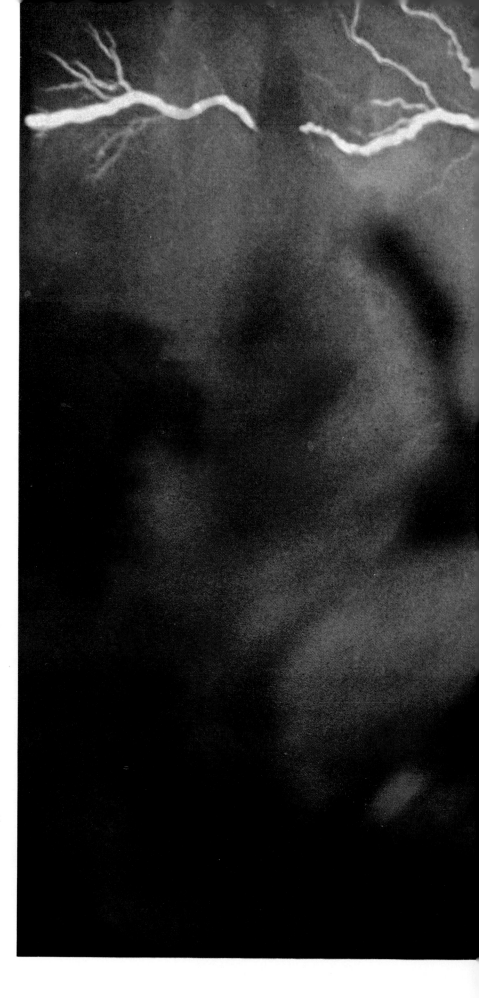

THE VITAL SPARK
AND THE CHANGES IN
THE ATMOSPHERE

In the atmosphere, strong creative forces
were at work. They were the ragged
bolts of lightning that struck through the
sky and the ultraviolet radiation that
came from the sun. It was these sources
of energy, probing the heavens above
the new world, that altered the
atmosphere, turning its stable mixture
of gases into highly reactive compounds.
Rent by electric discharges *(right)*
or bombarded by solar rays, the earth's
primitive atmosphere yielded amino
acids—the compounds basic
to the development of life. These
would serve as the minute, simple
building blocks for the more complex
combinations to come. Yet, just as it had
taken millions of years for the cosmic
cloud of whirling dust and gas to
condense into the world, so too it would
take eons for the first organic compounds
to merge and organize. The smallest
changes required uncounted centuries.

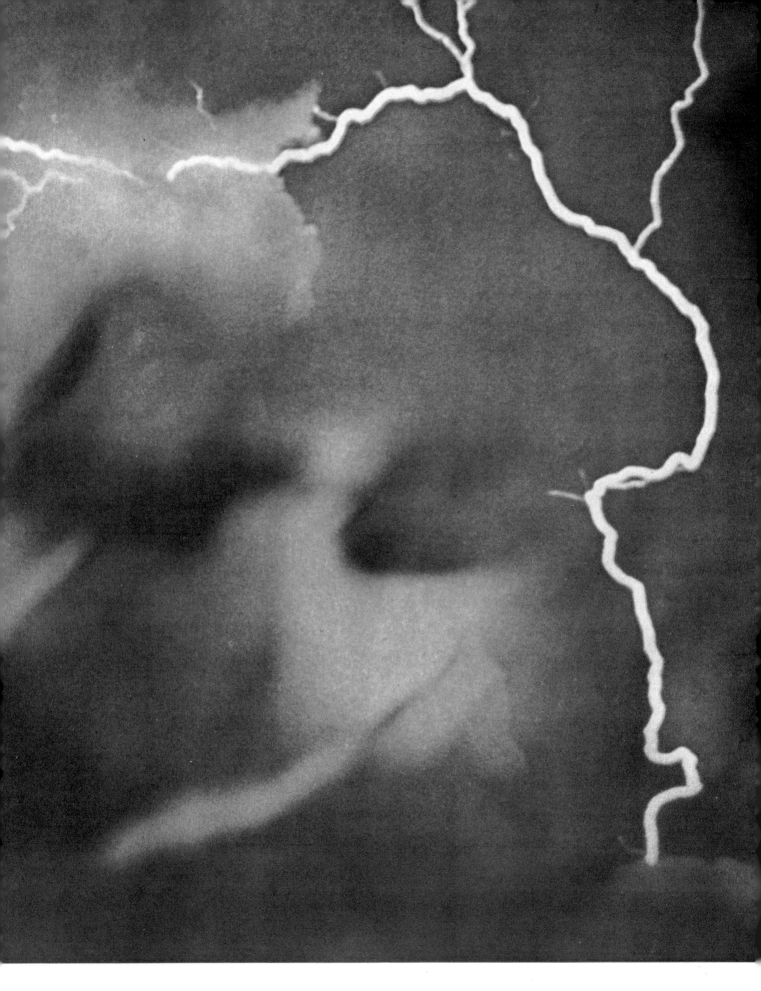

CENTURIES OF RAIN AND THE RISING OCEANS

From beneath the cooling surface of the earth, water that had been trapped in rock spewed upward in vast eruptive showers. And the atmosphere was saturated with vapors. Falling on the hot earth, rain turned to steam. It rose again to fall again *(above)*, each time further cooling the planet. Then at last the water no longer hissed away as steam, but stayed where it fell. Now, as the rains fell from the high atmosphere, bringing down the lightning-synthesized compounds, the deeps of the planet became its seas *(opposite)*. For unrelenting centuries the deluge continued. The warm and ever-rising seas held, mixed, combined and nurtured the materials essential for future growth.

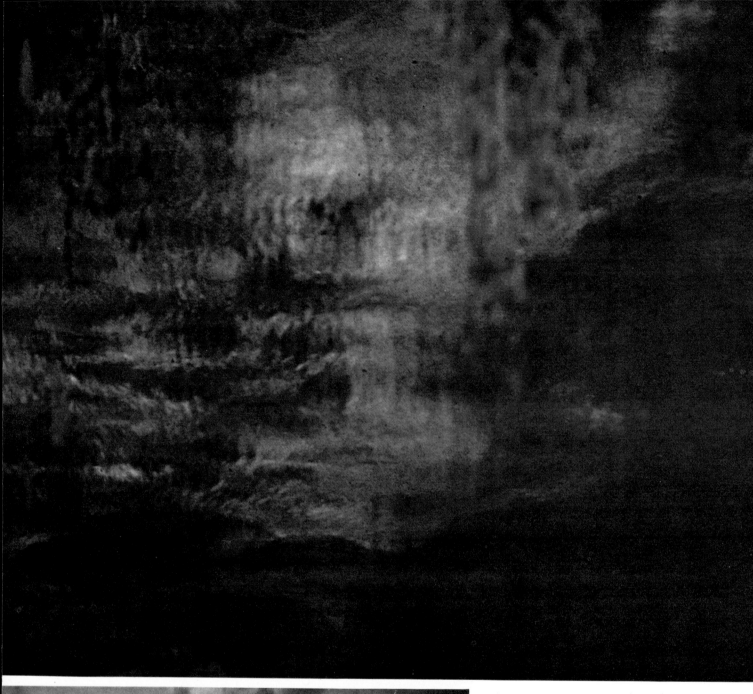

SIMMERING CALDRONS WHERE LIFE BEGAN TO BREW

Shrouded in steam, a vast volcanic pool seethed on the still-heaving, still-eruptive surface of the earth. Jets of steam shot into the sky, releasing further supplies of water and further warming the surrounding sea. Such simmering pools as the one at left, scientists believe, may well have served as the creative caldrons in which a rich variety of compounds attained new complexity. It is thought that, along protected shores or in inland seas and brackish marshes, evaporation thickened the early brew of matter.

Recent experiments have thrown some light upon this dark portion of our origin. They have shown that, in a boiling solution, amino acids do indeed synthesize into large, proteinlike molecules. These molecules, in turn, dissolving and cooling, condense into a myriad of globules whose structure foreshadows that of the cell.

IN PRIMORDIAL WATERS
A PRIMITIVE URGE
TO UNITE AND FLOURISH

Not in one pool but in millions of seaside
shallows and inland marshes
did the long process of blending the
shapes and energies of existence occur.
That process appears to have been as
relentless as it was tenuous.
Infinite combinations must have taken
place, and an infinite number must have
dissolved and vanished. Only time
and the continual accretion of compounds
washed down from the sky or from the
barren continents assisted the experiment
to combine and grow. It may have been
in such pools as that shown at right
that molecules, protected and
warmed, first began to cluster
and thrive. Here, perhaps, the first clumps
of organic matter—midway between
fluid and solid—united. There, in what
some scientists pragmatically call
"the primordial soup," such
unions repeatedly advanced toward
the distant achievement of life itself.

98

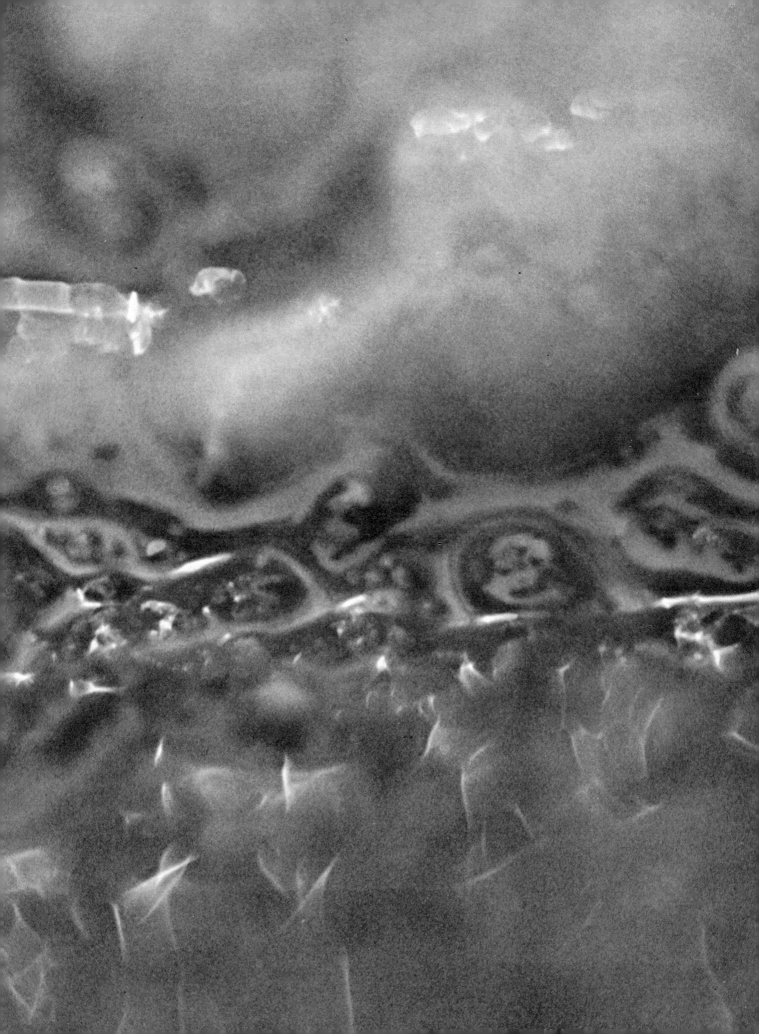

5

Cell Division and the Marvel of Reproduction

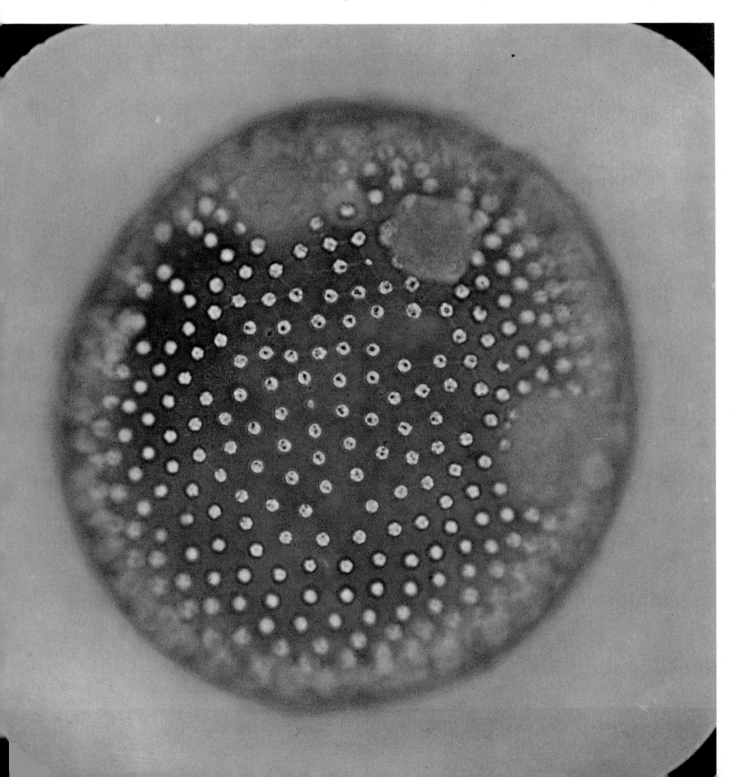

ONE OF THE WONDERS OF LIFE is the way in which a few identical cells can multiply, diversify and organize to form all the different sorts of tissues which make up the higher organisms. The study of these transformations and building processes, which take place before birth, is known as embryology. The question of how one fertilized egg cell can beget organized clans of widely varied descendants—as different as yard-long nerve cells, the microscopic globules which are fat-storage cells, whiplike sperm cells and fibrous muscle cells—introduces problems which have made embryology one of the most challenging areas of science.

Most cells in the higher organisms—which include just about everything visible in the plant and animal kingdoms—belong to one of many groups of specialists. In these groups, surrounded by their own kind, specialist cells limit themselves to a specific type of work benefiting the whole organism. It is through the grouping of these specialized cells that nature has achieved the fantastic level of complexity found in multi-celled organisms.

The basic challenge in current embryological research is to explain in molecular terms the changes that occur in successive cell generations. Embryologists would like to know, for example, how cells become specialized and at what stage of development the irrevocable changes take place. This investigation must start with the original fertilized egg cell. This fertilized ovum is clearly no specialist, since it produces all the many types of cells needed to make a complete organism. The first step in the development of the embryo is the division of this fertilized cell into two daughter cells, which in turn divide into four cells and so on. During this so-called cleavage period of rapid division, the cells remain clumped in a ball (which does not increase in size while undergoing this subdivision) and show no appreciable signs of differentiating.

In the frog, this first stage of growth, the cleavage stage, may last through seven or eight cell generations, by which time the ball is composed of hundreds of cells that have become progressively smaller with each division. It is at about this point in the development of the embryo that irreversible changes begin taking place in the cytoplasm of the cells and they start on the long road toward complete specialization.

Important evidence concerning the stages at which these changes occur in a frog embryo comes from the microsurgeons, biologists who perform delicate operations on a single cell. In a typical experiment, these scientists remove the nucleus, a speck of matter about six ten-thousandths of an inch in diameter, from an unfertilized, mature frog egg and replace it with a nucleus obtained from a frog embryo at the stage when it contains 16,000 cells. The egg, despite its alien nucleus, develops normally—indicating that the embryo's nuclei at the 16,000-cell stage are all alike, each being an unchanged copy of the nucleus of the original

LIFE IN THE COLONIES
A primitive form of specialization is set up by *Volvox*, free-living, one-celled organisms which collect themselves into a spherical colony. The three round shapes at the upper right of the sphere shown here are daughter colonies produced by specialized cells which have taken on sexual roles. When the parent group dies, the new generation will be sent out on its own.

egg. Shortly after the 16,000-cell stage, the nuclei of the cells begin to change and they lose their capacity to produce complete organisms.

In the human embryo, the first step in specialization results in the production of three different types of cells. Ten or 11 days after fertilization, the embryo is a hollow ball, smaller than the head of a pin, containing these three cell types grouped into inner, middle and outer layers of tissue. These cells have now embarked on a course from which there is no turning back; their descendants can only become more specialized as the development of the embryo continues. Future cell generations derived from the middle-layer tissue, for example, contribute to the formation of bones, muscles, cartilage and blood vessels, while cells in the outer layer will have descendants that form epidermis and the nervous system.

The main problem posed by this progressive differentiation stems from the fact that all cells have the same beginnings. All cells of an embryo carry exactly the same hereditary material; in reproducing, they pass on to their daughter cells the same set of DNA molecules made up of the same set of genes—sections of a DNA molecule which dictate particular traits. How does nature achieve variety from this sameness?

The keys to change

Current research indicates that the development of specialized cells is the result of some sort of chemical mechanism which controls the action of the gene. If this is the case, the complete and identical set of genes each cell of an embryo possesses can be thought of as a kind of keyboard. The pressing of different keys would activate different genes, directing the cell to develop certain characteristics.

To show how an "uncommitted" cell becomes specialized, suppose that in the first step of differentiation a set of keys is pressed calling for the development of outer-layer cells. The appropriate genes go to work and begin to promote the manufacture of enzymes and other proteins unique to that particular layer of tissue. This commits the cell; it has taken one road of a three-branched fork. It can no longer become an inner-layer or a middle-layer cell. It contains the genes for these tissues, but they remain forever inactive in this cell and its descendants. Thus the number of alternatives open to the cell has been reduced.

This narrowing of opportunities continues among subsequent generations of the cell. Outer-layer cells can develop along many lines. They may form, among other things, part of the inner ear or skin or nervous system. If a particular outer-layer cell becomes rudimentary nerve tissue, however, all other possibilities are automatically canceled, although considerable variety is possible even within the new limitations.

Cells in which nervous-system genes are active will, in turn, produce

THE CELL FROM EGG TO BONE

The flow chart below shows the development of a single cell of the trillions that make up a human body. As the embryo grows, its cells receive increasingly specialized orders to differentiate into inner, middle and outer layers and then into more specific kinds of tissues. This cell is destined for the body's bone structure—it cannot become part of a gland or the brain or the heart or anything else. In fact, it is not only a bone cell: it is specifically earmarked for a particular location in a particular bone.

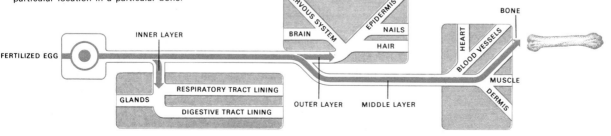

cells with active genes for any one of the many kinds of specialized nerve cells which make up the brain, the spinal cord or the other parts of the nervous system. At each step, the road narrows. The final product, after many cell generations, is a completely specialized nerve cell functioning in a specific manner at a specific location in the fully developed organism.

This is but part of the shaping process of the embryo. While outer-layer cells are being changed into nerve and other tissues, similar processes take place among cells derived from the inner and middle layers. The changes making up all three processes are neatly synchronized, the individual steps being timed so that they occur in the proper order within each process. Furthermore, development of the cells in each layer is synchronized with the development of the other two layers, for many organs are built of cells derived from different layers.

How nature builds an ear

The precision involved in building specialized tissue is illustrated in the series of interactions which takes place between the primary layers of cells in producing certain parts of the inner ear. During the third week of life of the human embryo, a growing group of middle-layer cells comes into contact with a part of the outer layer of cells. This meeting of the two layers results in the transfer of a chemical substance which directs the affected outer-layer cells to become nerve cells.

In the later stages of the embryo's development, parts of this newly created nerve tissue become primitive brain tissue. This tissue subsequently interacts with an area of skin tissue, which becomes the labyrinth of the inner ear, and this structure, through a chemical mediator, stimulates a surrounding group of middle-layer cells to produce cartilage as a protection for the inner ear.

Such a series of interactions indicates the presence of a communication system. When cells produce specific changes in other cells, some kind of message must pass between them. Many experiments suggest that the messages are chemical in nature.

Investigators at the University of Pennsylvania School of Medicine have traced the course of these chemical messages in chick cells growing in a nutrient solution. Using groups of middle-layer cells called somites, which can develop into either vertebrae of the spinal column or skeletal muscles, the investigators found that exposure to a piece of spinal cord caused the somites to become cartilage-makers, the first step in producing the vertebrae. When, in a second experiment, the somites and the spinal-cord tissue are placed in the solution and separated by a filter that permits the passage of molecules but not whole cells, the changes still occur in the somites. This indicates that the chemical

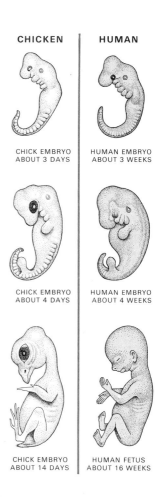

CHICKEN **HUMAN**

CHICK EMBRYO
ABOUT 3 DAYS

HUMAN EMBRYO
ABOUT 3 WEEKS

CHICK EMBRYO
ABOUT 4 DAYS

HUMAN EMBRYO
ABOUT 4 WEEKS

CHICK EMBRYO
ABOUT 14 DAYS

HUMAN FETUS
ABOUT 16 WEEKS

FROM EMBRYO TO ENTITY

In its first months a human embryo mirrors millions of years of evolution. On its way from being a fertilized egg to achieving its destiny as a human, the embryo passes through stages that resemble lower animals'. For instance, in the earliest stages of development, little difference is seen between a chicken *(left)* and a human *(right)*. But as the embryo grows, it becomes increasingly specialized. In eight weeks its role as a human is apparent.

messages are molecular units small enough to pass through the filter.

These same investigators have prepared extracts which contain a message-carrying compound from chick spinal cords. They found that the extracts alone are capable of converting somite cells into cartilage cells. Although the compound has not been fully analyzed chemically, its basic molecule seems to be composed of a number of amino acids. Other scientists studying different stages of development have worked with a number of other chemical compounds that may be significant in embryonic interactions.

The roles these various compounds play in the development of specialized cells again suggest the keyboard analogy. According to one hypothesis, such substances press the keys by reacting with certain genes, which then begin to direct certain cell processes. In other words, a gene may be inert until a "releaser" substance spurs it into activity.

The exact nature of the releasers remains a puzzle. But it is clear that they operate on a strict schedule, for the same genetic action may take place at different times in different cells. The gene controlling the manufacture of an enzyme involved in obtaining energy from glucose, for example, apparently starts working in human liver cells about 10 weeks after the fertilization of the ovum. In lung cells this same enzyme is produced one week later, in kidney cells three weeks later. These cellular processes must also *stop* working on schedule, for the manufacture of certain proteins ceases when they are no longer needed.

Right cell, right place, right time

The chemical substances which direct the development of a cell into a specialized unit would be of little use if cells of like character did not organize themselves into tissue. One of the most amazing features of embryonic development is that the right cells almost invariably manage to find their way to the right places in the embryo at the right time. The appropriate cells always seem to be available when interactions involving their development are scheduled to occur. To date, no one knows how this is accomplished.

A fundamental fact of cell life is that motion is the cell's natural state. Left to its own devices, it continues moving throughout its lifetime. This compulsion of the cell to keep moving is illustrated by the behavior of an amoeba placed in a circular track etched into the glass surface of a microscope slide. If the track (which must fit the amoeba snugly, so that it cannot turn around) is filled with water, the creature will propel itself around the circle at a fairly constant speed, like the second hand of a watch. This motion will continue for a single amoeba's entire lifespan. When the creature divides, after two days, its descendants will continue the endless journey.

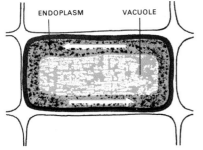

ENDOPLASM   VACUOLE

ENDOPLASM IN MOTION IN A STATIONARY CELL

MOTION, THE HALLMARK OF LIFE

Life is virtually synonymous with movement: although everything that moves is not alive, everything that is alive moves. In a plant cell *(above)*, the movement is internal—endoplasm flows around the cell's vacuole. In an amoeba *(below)*, the endoplasmic flow is internal but it also produces a forward motion in the free-swimming animal, allowing it to move about seeking its food.

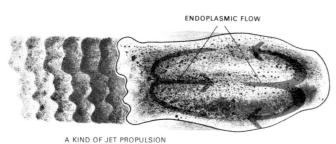

ENDOPLASMIC FLOW

A KIND OF JET PROPULSION

104

Though continual motion is the destiny of all free-living cells, there is one mode of cellular life which may be characterized by immobility. This occurs when cells associate to form the tissues of an organism. The problem facing biologists in this case is to discover what makes the mobile cell give up its wandering to settle permanently among its fellows.

Time-lapse motion pictures of human cells in tissue culture help provide an answer to this question. A light microscope reveals hundreds of extruding structures resembling porcupine quills on each cell. These "microspikes," as biologists call them, spring out from the cell surface, wave about in a groping sort of way and then vanish as new spikes form elsewhere on the outer membrane.

The microspikes do multiple duty: they are feelers, tentacles investigating the environment, and clingers. They sweep about until they make contact with the surfaces or with the microspikes of other cells of the same type. When this happens there may be a sticking together, a clustering of like cells. This clustering process continues until a tissue forms and the cells which are built into the tissue cease moving. No longer explorers, they have, in a sense, been tamed.

The immobilizing, or taming, of cells may be regarded as a social phenomenon of the cellular world. Specialized cells of the same type are clannish. The fact that they attach themselves exclusively to their own kind and ignore dissimilar cells suggests they must have some way of distinguishing like from unlike. Obviously, some sort of recognition system is built into specialized cells.

A purée that comes to life

The effects of such a recognition system may be demonstrated in the laboratory with the hydra, a tiny, green, fresh-water organism rimmed by long spidery tentacles. A hydra is made up of several different types of tissues and it can be broken into single cells and groups of a few cells by squeezing it through fine-mesh cheesecloth. If the resulting purée is poured into a glass of water, the individual cells reorganize themselves to form a brand-new hydra within a few hours. Other simple organisms, such as the sponge, will do the same thing. In fact, if the dissociated tissues of two species of sponge are mixed, the cells sort themselves out by species and form a number of rebuilt sponges.

The higher organisms cannot reconstitute themselves in this fashion. The ability to reshape a complete body has been lost with the evolution of increasingly complex species made up of many different types of cells and tissues; the basic recognition system used by cells has, however, been retained. Indeed, embryonic development would be impossible without it. The limb bud of a chick embryo, the part which will become a fully formed leg, consists of several hundred thousand cartilage, mus-

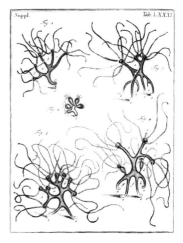

HYDRAS: PRODUCTS OF GRAFTERS

The hydra has interested scientists since about the middle of the 18th Century. Its cells are specialized enough to give it a definite form—a tubular body and a mouth surrounded by tentacles. On the other hand, a hydra's cells are *non*specialized enough so that parts of one hydra can be freely grafted onto another hydra, resulting in spidery grotesqueries like the ones concocted by A. J. Rösel von Rosenhof in 1754 *(above)*.

cle and skin cells. If a batch of these cells is placed in tissue culture, the result is not a rudimentary limb, but the cells do cluster by type. They may even form a ball, with clumped cartilage cells at the center, a shell of muscle cells covering the cartilage cells, and skin cells forming an outside cover—the same general arrangement of tissue found in the original limb bud.

The aggregation of specialized cells to form tissue is not yet fully explained. It is known that some slime-mold cells emit a substance called acrasin that attracts other slime-mold cells. Similar chemical messages may attract other types of like cells to each other. Once they have been drawn together, like cells apparently employ a chemical tie to bond themselves together into tissue. It is thought that molecules on the surface of one cell react with the molecules of a neighboring cell, establishing a firm bond between the two.

The tie that binds

Though they are bonded together, tissue cells, except those of certain muscles, do not fuse or even come into actual contact with each other. The space between them seems to be filled with some sort of a cementing substance—like the mortar that separates the bricks in a wall. Some cells also reveal clumps of spikelike structures that bridge the intercellular gaps and bind the two cell membranes together.

The formation of tissues is but a part of embryological development. At times, cells must break away from tissues in which they are incorporated in order to form new tissues. This breaking away is as significant a phenomenon as the clustering of cells. The mechanism responsible for this disruption has not yet been identified.

The investigation of the formation and disruption of cell groups is important not only to embryology but also to cancer research. The bonding of cells seems to be partially ineffective in the case of cancer cells; they stick together less firmly than normal tissue cells. This weakened bonding is crucial, since loosened cells can migrate and spread tumors. If some way could be found to combat this tendency, it might be possible to confine tumors to their original sites.

Many of the processes of normal tissue development are duplicated on a small scale when a wound heals. When you cut your finger, a fluid discharge covers the exposed region and forms a film over it. The film includes fibrous strands which stretch across the wound and probably provide guidelines for the migrating cells which form the new tissue. After the formation of the fibrous film, some skin cells become detached and are then free to wander about. This is a controlled migration of individuals—which is something like the movement of a herd of animals. Deeper-lying cells migrate to replace those that were destroyed by the

THE BASIC UNITS OF BEING

In sketches at the right are six kinds of differentiated cells that make up the tissues in the body. Nerve cells, sometimes more than a yard long, act as the body's communication system. Muscle cells, which shorten and extend, do the body's work. Epithelial cells cover the surfaces of the body, inside and out. Blood cells carry supplies and dispose of waste products. Skeletal cells build the body's structural frame. Connective tissue cells join other tissues.

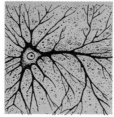

NERVE

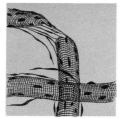

MUSCLE

EPITHELIAL

cut. New capillaries are formed. At the same time, other cells advance from the edges of the wound, perhaps following the fibrous guidelines, and bridge the surface of the wound. Bit by bit, the tissue is restored to normal.

There is a final act in the healing process. The tissues of a wound not only grow when needed; they stop growing as soon as healing is completed. This illustrates another major feature of tissue development, an influence which is at work not only during embryonic existence but throughout the course of life. In the shaping of new organs and in replenishing the tissues of organs already formed, the phenomenon of growth is under strict control at every stage. Cells of all types increase in number and size until various structures are completed; then they stop growing as if turned off by a switch.

The study of cell development does not stop with the embryo or even with the shaping of the adult organism; it includes the full sweep of life from beginning to end. The fact that cells change with age must be regarded as part of the development process—which is why embryologists are among investigators most actively engaged in research on aging. Cellular aging intimately concerns every human, for as a man's cells age, so he himself grows older. The death of an organism is actually a requiem for a critical number of the cells that are vitally important to its survival.

The death of a cell

What is meant by the aging and the death of a cell? The fact that all cells carry a complete set of blueprints for their replication and that most cells can divide and reproduce frequently enough to replenish tissue suggests that an organism should be continually supplied with fresh, new parts. This is the case in young, healthy organisms, where many cells divide at a rapid rate. As an organism ages, however, the cell processes deteriorate and the ensuing generations may be either imperfect or in short supply.

No cell lives forever, though the essence of a cell—its "livingness"—can endure through a vast number of generations if the multiplication process is not disrupted. As specific, identifiable units, however, cells have varying life-spans. For example, an epithelial cell from the intestinal lining lives about a day and a half before it dies and is sloughed off. White blood cells, on the other hand, live about 13 days and red blood cells about 120 days. Liver cells rarely divide unless part of the organ is removed. Nerve cells can live a hundred years—which is fortunate, because they are irreplaceable.

As an organism ages, changes characteristic of aging appear in the cells that form its tissues. The capacity of the cells to reproduce, grow

BLOOD

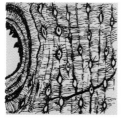

SKELETAL

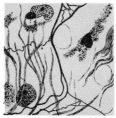

CONNECTIVE

and repair themselves diminishes—accounting for the fact that an older person's body cannot repair a wound as rapidly as a younger person's. Sometimes the cell decreases in size, there is a slowdown in protein production and the Golgi complexes become fragmented. The mitochondria may break up or become elongated, further affecting the vital processes of the cell. Furthermore, both the genetic material and the enzymes may vary in quantity as the cell grows older. These changes may not only lessen the reproductive rate of the cell, they can threaten the very existence of the cell itself.

Several studies suggest that aging is a complex process that is brought about by interaction among the various cell types. There also are a number of theories which attempt to account for the invariable and apparently inevitable aging process within the cell—and therefore within man himself. None of them is definitive, none generally accepted. Modern medicine has lengthened the probable life-span of the organism. In this century there has been a notable increase in the number of people living into their seventh, eighth or even ninth decade. Interestingly, there has not been a proportionate increase in the number of centenarians. This suggests that there may be a species-wide, genetically determined limit to the life expectancy of both cells and the organism they constitute.

A Finer and Finer Division of Labor

In nature, specialization is the key to progress. From the primitive slime-mold colonies (opposite) to a fully developed human fetus, organizations of cells—living things—show a finer and finer division of labor in meeting their increasingly complicated destinies. But specialization is achieved only at the sacrifice of versatility; as cells associate into tissues, as tissues are subordinated into organs, the ability of cells to be now part of one tissue, now part of another becomes more and more limited. The following pages sample the organization of life at several levels: the Robinson Crusoe level (a solitary slime-mold cell); the loose cooperative with beginnings of individuation (red alga, the slime-mold colony); the cellular small town where everyone knows about everyone else's business and occasionally does it (the hydra); and the various metropolis of the human embryo, itself the record of a supreme differentiation from a single parent cell.

A START TOWARD SPECIALIZATION
In this photomicrograph, eight slime-mold reproductive structures rear in the air like cobras. The stems bear spore houses from which the spores of future colonies will be scattered. Several stages are visible here: the extended sluglike mass of the slime mold (center, fifth from left); further development of the stalk (third from left); and the fully evolved "fruiting structure" (second from left).

Nomad Cells
Form a Cooperative

In the four-day saga of the life cycle of *Dictyostelium discoideum*, the slime mold pictured on these pages, may be seen a sort of parallel to the social history of mankind: nomad hunters come together in a pack *(below)*, unite to form a cohesive colony *(center)* and then raise their temple *(opposite)*.

Slime molds are colorless amoeboid cells which group together to form now plantlike, now animal-like organisms. They are direct descendants of the earth's first living units. The individual cells of the species shown here cluster when certain of them secrete a chemical called acrasin, which has a powerful attracting effect, causing others to aggregate into a clump around the secreting cells. A typical colony would be composed of 50,000 single cells; each retains its outer membrane and its individuality, yet all "work together" to forage for food. The sluglike mass represents the high-water mark in cellular interrelationship among amoebae.

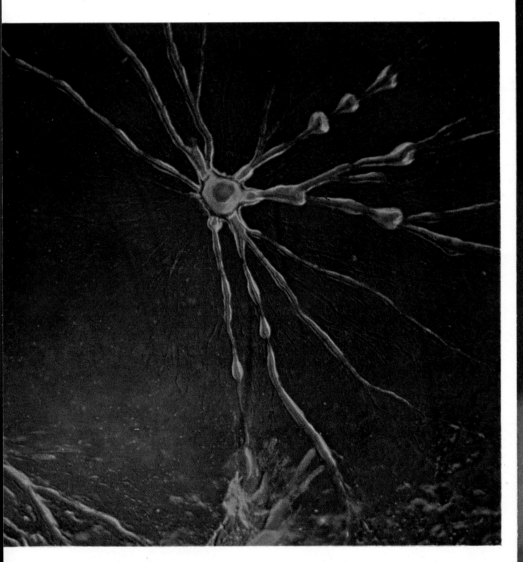

A CELLULAR MASS MIGRATION

As soon as the local food supply—bacteria—gives out, the "fruiting phase" of the slime mold's life cycle begins. Certain cells secrete acrasin, which stimulates the others to migrate toward them. Eventually, all the individual cells in a population flow toward the acrasin-secreters in a radial pattern of streamlets, and a sluglike agglomeration then begins to take shape.

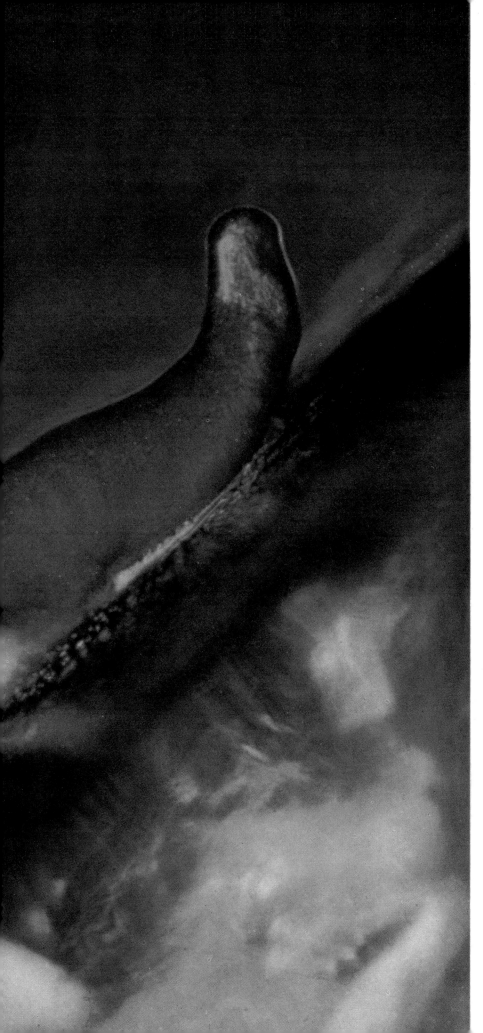

A COOPERATING MULTITUDE

As more cells are attracted by the chemical secretion, a bullet-shaped colony about a half inch long begins to form *(left)*. The cells of this structure remain undifferentiated and can still respond and move individually. But they do cooperate when the organism moves in search of food: a thin slime is secreted on the supporting surface, over which the "animal" glides.

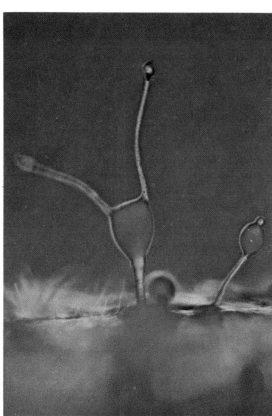

A COLONY AT ITS ACME

A colony completes its life cycle by sending up the seeds of the next generation *(above)*. The individual cells, originally alike, now differentiate into stalk-forming and spore-forming types. Migration stops when the organism culminates its four-day life cycle with the formation of this fruiting structure. The terminal bulge contains spores which hatch free-swimming amoebae.

Divergent Paths to Two Kingdoms

One of the most extensive experiments in cellular differentiation occurred eons ago, as life in the ancient seas slowly explored the myriad possibilities of new forms. Some cells and cell communities developed plantlike characteristics, while others became animal.

The earliest cells with chlorophyll were the algae (below). There are now some 18,-000 species in the oceans, in ponds and streams, in snow and ice, in near-boiling springs, on the bark of trees and under the ground. The smallest algae are single cells barely a twenty-five-thousandth of an inch in diameter, while the largest are sea gardens longer than a blue whale. The hydra (opposite) is a simple animal, yet, intellectual achievements aside, it can do almost everything humans can. In addition it can grow a new foot or a head.

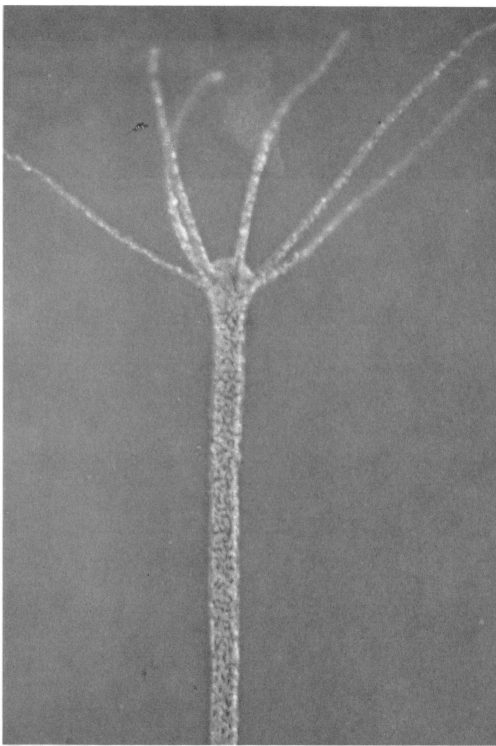

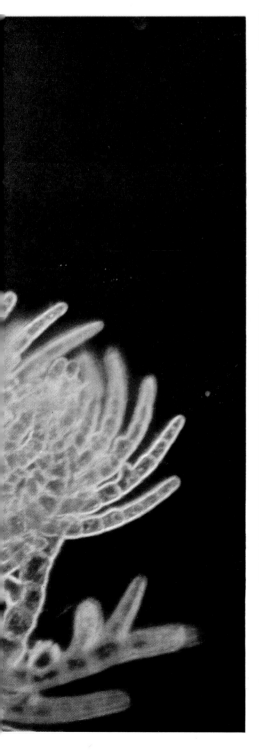

THE FEATHERY BODY OF AN ALGA
Red algae are called "sea moss" because of their delicate appearance. The red pigment is predominant over all the others, including the green chlorophyll. *Antithamnion plumula*, the species shown magnified here 300 times, is found along the British coast. The individual cells link together to create regular branches remarkably similar to those of higher plants.

PULLING IN A MEAL
Hydra viridis, seen here under 60-fold magnification, waves its crown of tentacles in the eternal food-getting effort. Hydras have reached the tissue and organ level of organization: both the mouth and the tentacles surrounding it are true organs. This animal's coloring comes from green algae parasites it harbors. Others are brown, black or red, depending on their last meal.

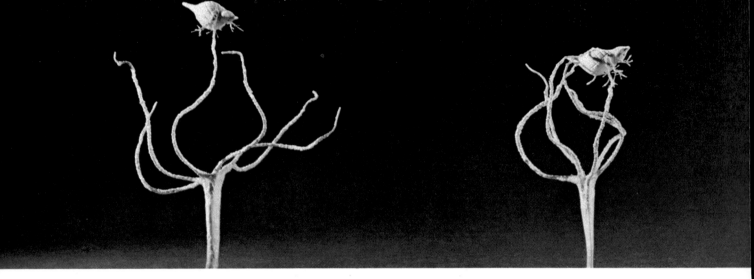

These models show how a hydra catches the water flea *Daphnia* by snagging it with one tentacle. The other tentacles are then brought into play for

Working Plans for a Tiny Animal

The hydra is a fresh-water animal about half an inch long that goes places by turning somersaults on its tentacles. Compared with the alga, the hydra represents a sophisticated level of cellular organization.

The hydra's body is made up of two specialized layers of cells—the outer ectoderm, which is primarily protective, and the inner endoderm, which is primarily digestive. These layers form a pocket: the animal kingdom's original gut. A measure of the hydra's anatomic sophistication is its possession of true organs—its mouth and tentacles—which are organized tissues constructed from organized and specialized cells. The hydra reacts promptly to stimuli because it possesses sensory and nerve cells. The hydra's reproduction is both asexual and sexual; its asexual reproduction produces a bud on its body, the bud develops mouth and tentacles and breaks off to become a new hydra.

THE HYDRA EXPOSED

The diagram of the hydra's gross anatomy at right shows a mouth *(top)* surrounded by a number of tentacles, six in this case. Protruding from the body, but within the outer cell layer, or ectoderm, are a testis containing sperm cells *(upper left)* and an ovary containing one egg cell *(lower right)*. Some hydras are hermaphroditic, with both testis and ovary. An asexually produced bud is shown *(below testis)*. The primitive nerve net is carried between the ectoderm and the endoderm. The net carries nerve impulses randomly in every direction.

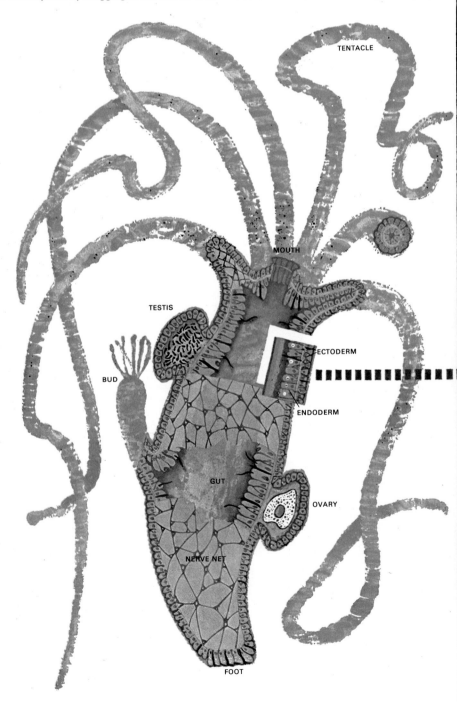

TENTACLE

MOUTH

TESTIS

ECTODERM

BUD

ENDODERM

GUT

OVARY

NERVE NET

FOOT

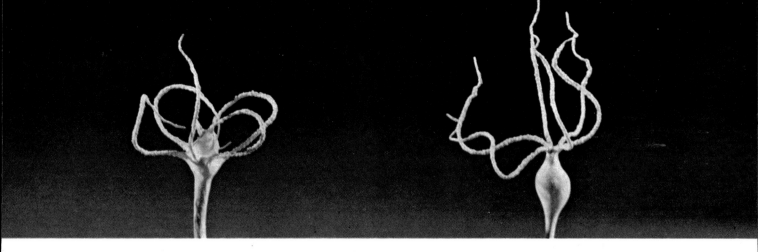

a firmer grip on the flea. The hydra swallows it and digests it in the hollow gut, where various cells dissolve it and finally convert it into energy.

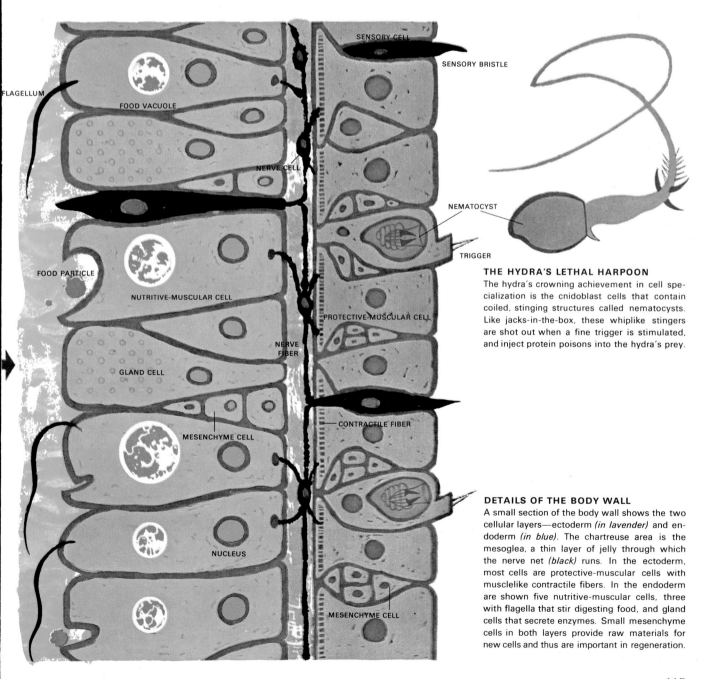

THE HYDRA'S LETHAL HARPOON

The hydra's crowning achievement in cell specialization is the cnidoblast cells that contain coiled, stinging structures called nematocysts. Like jacks-in-the-box, these whiplike stingers are shot out when a fine trigger is stimulated, and inject protein poisons into the hydra's prey.

DETAILS OF THE BODY WALL

A small section of the body wall shows the two cellular layers—ectoderm *(in lavender)* and endoderm *(in blue)*. The chartreuse area is the mesoglea, a thin layer of jelly through which the nerve net *(black)* runs. In the ectoderm, most cells are protective-muscular cells with musclelike contractile fibers. In the endoderm are shown five nutritive-muscular cells, three with flagella that stir digesting food, and gland cells that secrete enzymes. Small mesenchyme cells in both layers provide raw materials for new cells and thus are important in regeneration.

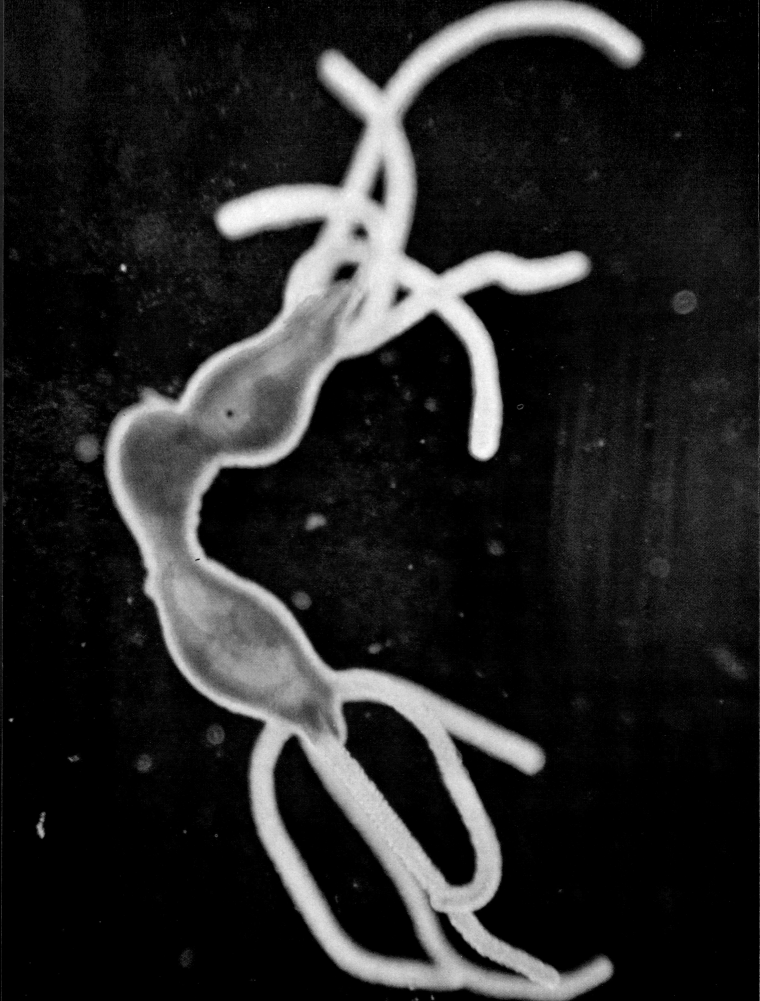

Living Up to a Famous Name

That the hydra is famous for its regenerative capabilities is evident from its name: Hydra was the nine-headed monster that grew two new heads each time Hercules chopped one off.

Not only can a maimed hydra quickly replace a lost part, but a maimed part can often replace a lost hydra. In experiments in which hydras are chopped up and sieved through fine cloth, one or more complete animals can be reborn from the pulpy mash. This means that cells that previously performed one function and had one location in the body assume new functions and positions. When hydras are simply cut in half, the bottom half grows a new mouth and tentacles while the top regenerates a foot.

Moreover, a hydra's cells are so highly mobile that when an animal is turned inside out, the two layers can flow through each other and resume their original positions. Finally, when two pieces each longer than half a hydra are joined together to form one animal a little longer than normal, the organism undertakes to correct the abnormal length by developing tentacles in the middle and breaking apart to form two hydras of normal length.

All these instances of regeneration, reassembly and mobility are possible because the hydra's cells, while specialized, have not become *too* specialized. Just how the cells know how to regenerate and know which is the top and which the bottom is still a central question in biology.

A LIVING EXPERIMENTAL MONSTER

The freakish animal created by the operation *(opposite)* is a living, man-made, two-headed hydra with no foot. The fate of this strange animal is difficult to predict: it is possible that it may survive the surgery as is, or it is possible that the middle part may differentiate into two foot-ends, the graft break, and two completely normal hydras be "born" of the surgical splicing.

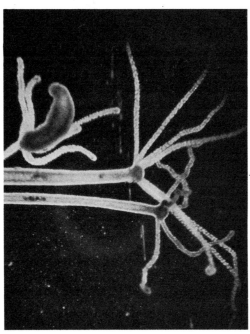

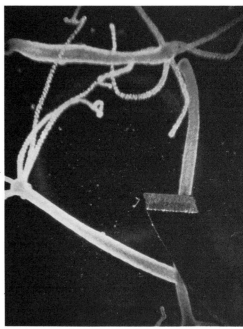

1 Three hydras are assembled for the "operation."

2 Hydras are cut with a razor blade.

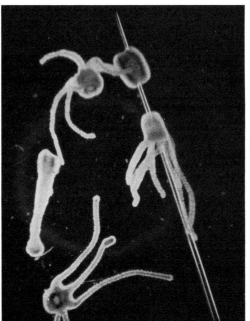

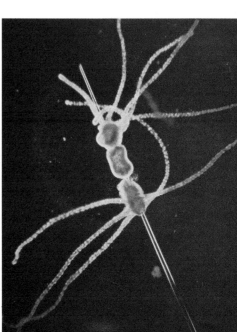

3 The freak hydra is strung together on a needle:

4 The needle allows parts to knit.

MICROSURGERY CREATES A FREAK

These photomicrographs show the surgical procedure whereby the composite freak hydra on the opposite page was manufactured. At upper left are shown the three hydras used in the experiment. The top one is stained with methylene blue so it can be distinguished later on from its pinkish-brown fellows. Upper right: the hydras are sectioned with a razor blade. One is trisected to provide a middle piece and the other two are bisected to provide two head-ends. At lower left, the end of one hydra and the middle section of the other have already been skewered on a thin glass surgical rod. Lower right: all three parts are in place and now the graft must be given time to knit. The pieces will be left in position on the needle for 24 hours.

For Mankind, Limited Renewal

Man, the very pinnacle of cellular differentiation and specialization, is also the animal kingdom's most inept restorer of damaged tissue. The spectacular feats of organ and tissue repair of the hydra and other lower animals are far beyond him. He is able to renew tissue in a limited way only—although such massive feats of cellular regeneration as that shown here occasionally startle medical science.

Some human tissues do have a degree of regenerative power—liver tissue, skin, connective tissue, fat, bone, cartilage and some nerve fibers. Muscle tissue has little regenerative power, and the central nervous system and heart muscle have none.

Peripheral nerves—those outside of the body's central nervous system—regenerate in a series of intricate moves. When the fiber of a nerve cell is severed, the stump nearest the cell body remains alive, while the farther part starts to die off after three or four days. After about a week, regeneration starts. Specialized cells forming a sheath about the fiber bridge the gap of the cut and blaze a trail all the way out to the end. The nerve fiber then grows out along the guidelines thus laid down.

Doctors examine a three-year-old Washington, D.C., boy who is so severely burned that only a miracle of cell regeneration can save him.

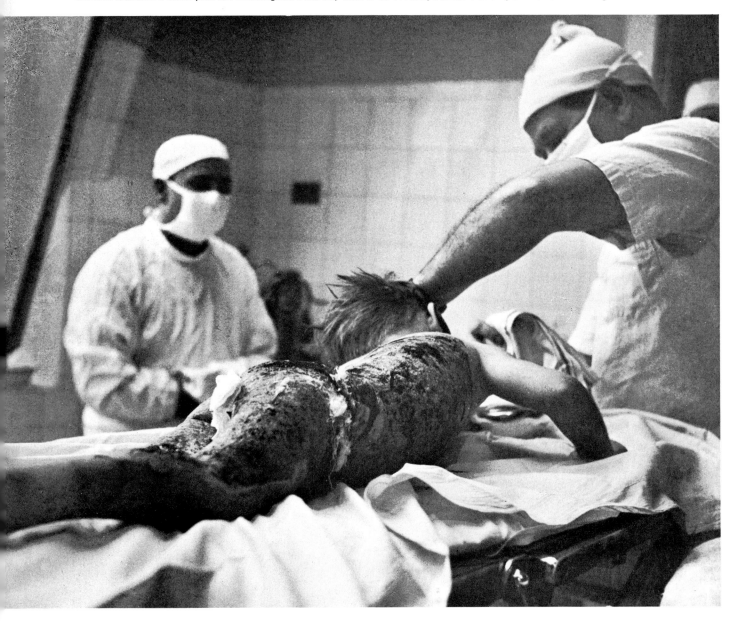

THE MIRACLE ACCOMPLISHED
In a picture made about a year after the one at left, the little boy, now almost fully recovered, is surrounded by the doctors, the medical equipment and the skin donors who helped him regrow nearly three quarters of his skin. Skin transplants from donors cannot "take"—the body's skin cells reject the outsiders—but they protect the body while its own cells regrow.

119

Complex Wonder in Human Embryos

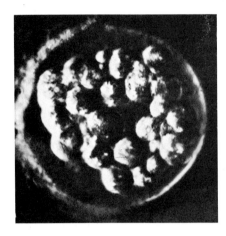

HUMAN EMBRYO AT THREE DAYS

Photomicrograph of a human embryo at three days shows the cluster composed of the first five generations, or 32 cells. The cells are noticeably different in size, yet the embryo itself is smaller than the period ending this sentence.

To trace the development of the human fetus from its beginning as a single fertilized egg within the mother's body to its completion as a baby made up of billions of cells—skin cells, blood cells, bone cells, muscle and connective cells, nerve cells, gland cells—is to trace the phenomenon of cellular differentiation in all of its wonder and complexity.

The fertilized egg, a single cell, first gives rise to a large number of cells. This is achieved by repeated divisions following each other in quick succession. The divisions begin in synchronism, each cell splitting when its sisters do. Later, the process falls out of pace, some cells splitting rapidly as others lag behind. At first the cells seem all alike, but soon differences arise, even though each daughter cell has inherited and will bequeath un-

altered the entire genetic master plan of the original cell.

As the generations of cells pile up, individual cells hew more and more to their own select parts of that master plan. As the ever-increasingly differentiated cells congregate into tissues, as the tissues themselves differentiate and interact to form organs, as the organs systematically intermesh in their functioning—the whole creature itself becomes more sharply differentiated from other animals. What at nine or 10 hours might just as well be a starfish, what at 26 days might still pass for a chicken, becomes irrevocably, at full term, a unique human being. The embryonic period in humans extends from fertilization to between 55 and 57 days, when the body structure is completed. Thereafter, the embryo is known as the fetus.

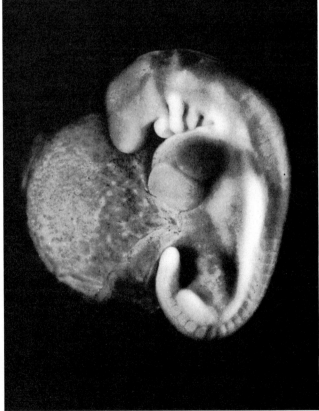

THE EMBRYO IN THE FOURTH WEEK

Encased in the transparent "bag of waters," the fourth-week human embryo is shown head down *(left, above)* and in a side view *(right, above)*. It is now about one fifth of an inch long and weighs seven ten-thousandths of an ounce. The ballooning yolk sac, the body stalk by which it is attached to the uterus, the arm buds and the primitive spine can be seen. Eye lenses are forming, and organs of hearing and smell are present in rudimentary form. A sixth-week embryo *(opposite)*, shown magnified five times, is already beginning to resemble a human adult.

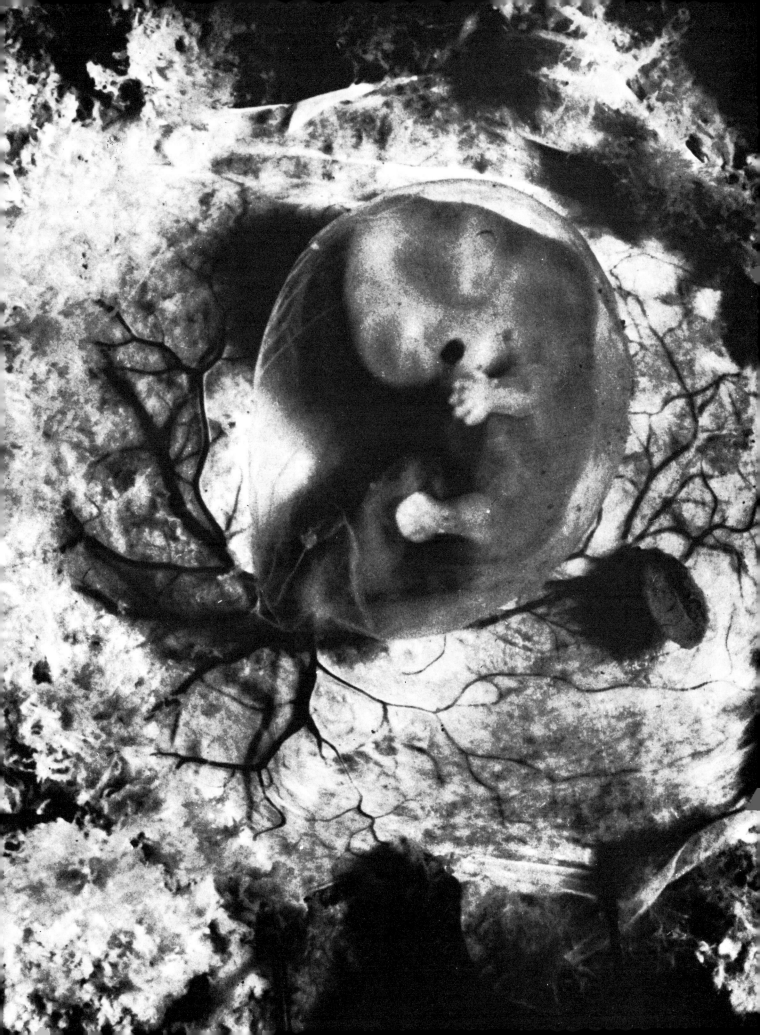

6

The Mechanics of Muscle Power

CELLS THAT WORK AS A TEAM
The word "muscle" usually conjures a picture of the sinewy torso of an athlete. But muscle may be a boxer's biceps or a baby's heart. In either case, it is one of the most specialized types of tissue in the body. A signal from the brain can convert relaxed bundles of muscle cells into a regimented army pulling together to keep the body and its parts moving—an essential of life.

CELLS MOVE IN MANY WAYS. Some single-celled organisms, such as the paramecium, move by the beating of hairlike extensions called cilia. Amoebae creep along by extending the cell wall and the cytoplasm within it. The sperm cell moves by strokes of its whiplike flagellum.

All these forms of locomotion apparently result from interactions at the molecular level. In the larger organisms, the movement of muscle cells also involves some of the most sophisticated and ingenious processes found in nature.

Muscle is one of the most remarkable of all the body's specialized tissues. Few of us realize how strong we actually are. Several years ago in Tampa, Florida, a boy was working under the rear end of the family station wagon when the jack slipped, pinning him under the car. His mother, a small woman, grabbed the rear bumper and lifted the 3,300-pound auto off her son; he suffered nothing worse than a few bruises. In the emergency the mother had tapped a source of strength far greater than any she uses in normal situations.

This reserve of power is but one of several unusual properties built into muscle. Muscle tissue is also remarkably adaptable. You exert a force of a fraction of an ounce in picking up a pin or paper clip, about seven pounds in holding a heavy book, and 20 pounds or so on the handle of a lightly packed suitcase; the same muscles can apply a maximum right-handed squeeze of more than 150 pounds.

The structure of a muscle is altered repeatedly during the routine actions of everyday living. In its completely relaxed state, muscle is unimpressive—a jellylike substance which hardly looks like the structural material for the prime movers of the body. This slushy tissue, however, can undergo a drastic and rapid transformation when it is called upon to contract and exert force. In a few hundredths of a second it can change into a hard, tough, elastic material with dynamic characteristics that intrigue engineers and physicists as well as biologists.

Despite its unique characteristics, muscle tissue has a structural basis not unlike that of other body tissues. If a mass of muscle fiber is minced, wrapped in cheesecloth and squeezed in a press under high pressure, a fluid called "press juice" can be extracted. Analysis of the solid residue and the juice shows muscle to contain: about 78 per cent water, 20 per cent protein, 1 per cent carbohydrate and some fat and salt. The same contents and ratios could be used to describe most other forms of body tissue—so the unusual capacities of muscle must result from the organization of its parts, rather than its basic material.

Muscle could be defined as a tissue of cells which enables an organism and its parts to move. The basic mechanical process involved in all muscle action is the contraction of many closely bound muscle cells, or fibers. While all cells can contract to some extent, contraction is a specialty of the muscle cell. The formation of the highly specialized muscle fiber begins during embryological development, when a great many similar cells from the middle-layer group come together. The outer membranes of the cells seem to fuse at the contact points, forming a single unit enclosed in a continuous membrane. The resulting fiber may contain hundreds or even thousands of nuclei—one from each of the original cells. The average muscle cell, or fiber, is a long cylinder which measures about one five-hundredth of an inch in diameter and several inches in length.

Matching muscle to the load

An individual muscle cell contracts when it receives a stimulus from the appropriate motor nerve. The degree of stimulation must be above a certain minimum level, or threshold, before the muscle fiber will react. When the fiber does react, however, it contracts to its maximum ability. Scientists call this an "all or none" type of response. In order to keep the entire muscle from responding in this fashion, not all the cells are alerted at once, except in rare cases. Just enough impulses are sent to match the force to the load—a few to pick up a paper clip, many for a suitcase.

The process of matching the response of a muscle to a specific load suggests a feedback system similar to that used in many modern electronic devices. Muscle action will increase as the load increases, just as a tractor engine is so made that it speeds up automatically when the plow hits heavy ground. Without such a feedback control in our muscular system, we would expend as much energy in lifting a spoon as we would in raising a heavy stone.

Unlike many other types of body cells, the muscle cells cannot divide and therefore cannot reproduce themselves in the conventional manner. In man (and most other mammals), however, new muscle cells can be formed to replace cells damaged in adulthood; the intricate process involves the assembling of structures already floating in the cell fluid and can be likened to rebuilding an old car from scavenged parts of a number of wrecks. Such replacements help maintain a certain level of muscle ability, but they cannot for long offset the attrition which is the result of dying cells. Indeed, the weight of some muscles may drop as much as 30 per cent between the ages of 30 and 75. This does not mean, of course, that muscles cannot grow in size and capacity during these years; but the bulging biceps of a boxer do not indicate an increase in the number of muscle cells in the arm—they are rather a sign that the individual cells or fibers have grown larger.

The exact relationship of muscle growth to exercise is as yet undetermined. It is thought that muscle growth may be correlated to the level of activity of the individual muscle fibers. It is known that when a nerve is destroyed by disease or accident and the nerve impulses to the

AN EARLY LOOK INTO THE BODY
Until the 14th Century, man's knowledge of his own muscles—and, indeed, his whole anatomy—was a mixture of haphazard speculation and inspired insight. Then, working in defiance of papal law, scientists began performing autopsies on humans (above) and exploring the body's muscular structure. This beginning was a first step toward a finer examination of all body tissues, a search which continues today on the molecular level.

fiber are thus cut off, the muscle fiber becomes inactive, shrinks and may eventually disappear and be replaced by connective tissue. Presumably, if the situation is reversed and the muscle is highly active, it will increase in size and power; muscular development may thus be looked upon as a direct product of muscle use.

All of the skeletal muscles of the body, such as the biceps, are composed of muscle fibers which are striated, or banded—the striations indicating that they are made up of a chain of shorter sections. In addition to striated muscle, which is responsible for most of the voluntary movements of the body, there are smooth muscles, which activate the internal organs, and the unique heart muscle, which works ceaselessly throughout the life of the body.

A single striated muscle may be made up of many hundreds of thousands of muscle cells or fibers packed together to form a kind of living cable. This cable pattern is repeated down to the molecular level. In turn, each of the many fibers in a muscle consists of some 1,000 to 2,000 smaller strands called fibrils, which run parallel to one another and represent the contracting elements—the parts that do the actual work. The fibrils are about one twenty-five-thousandth of an inch in diameter. The spaces between them are filled with the fluid, or cytoplasm, of the cell.

Muscle's mighty mites

There is still another set of cables in the muscle cell. Packed inside each fibril are hundreds of filaments, the smallest component of muscle. The filaments come in two sizes, a thick form and a thin one. When a cross section of a fibril is magnified about 200,000 times by the electron microscope, these superfine filaments are seen to be arranged in a geometric pattern in which thick and thin filaments alternate.

Research thus reveals striated muscle as a system of fibers, each of which is a bundle of fibrils, with each fibril being a bundle of filaments. These structural details are meaningful, however, only insofar as they explain how a muscle works.

As a muscle fibril contracts, the filaments do not seem to become shorter. This suggests that the thin filaments may be arranged so that they slide between the thick filaments. This theory might be illustrated by imagining two wooden disks studded with projecting needles. As the disks are brought closer together, the two strands of needles mesh and slide past each other, and the space between the disks decreases without any contraction of the needles. The limit of contraction is reached when the needles studded in each disk touch the opposite disk.

Any description of the mechanics of muscle action would be incomplete if it did not account for the power supply which enables a muscle to contract. Muscle is no exception to the rule that doing work requires energy.

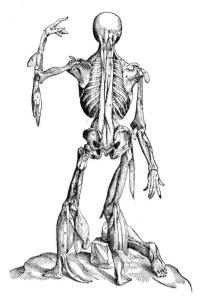

A MASTER OF LIVING ANATOMY
By the 16th Century, anatomy was an established science, although cadavers were hard to come by and anatomists had to perform their autopsies on criminals and paupers. The era produced Andreas Vesalius, who in 1543 published his monumental seven-volume work, *On the Fabric of the Human Body*. So much importance did he attach to his work with muscles *(above)* that he devoted one entire book to the subject.

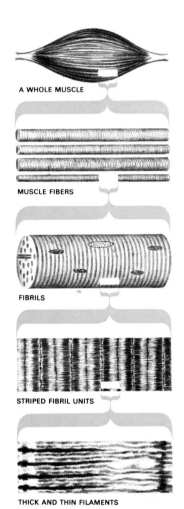

A WHOLE MUSCLE

MUSCLE FIBERS

FIBRILS

STRIPED FIBRIL UNITS

THICK AND THIN FILAMENTS

THE MAKINGS OF A MUSCLE

These progressively magnified diagrams show the component parts of a muscle—the cell tissue that translates energy into motion. The top drawing is an entire muscle with connective tendons. Next are the heavy strands called muscle fibers. The fibers are like a cable made up of many smaller wires, or strands; they are the fibrils. The light and dark striations are caused by varying densities of filaments *(bottom)* which compose the fibrils.

The generation of muscle energy, like that produced by an automobile engine, calls on electrical and chemical forces.

The "firing" of a muscle fiber—the contraction, or twitch, which occurs when the muscle cell is properly stimulated—begins at a point where the associated motor nerve is joined to the outer membrane of the muscle fiber. The resting muscle cell, which is charged with energy, goes into action when this nerve delivers a signal which "tells" it to contract. The transmission of this message involves two sequences of electrical activity and an intervening chemical event.

The action begins with a series of electrical pulses flashing along the various nerve fibers from the brain to the nerve-and-muscle junction on the muscle-fiber membrane. When the pulses reach this junction they initiate a chemical reaction which releases a squirt of a substance known as a neurohumor. The neurohumor somehow changes the properties of the muscle cell's outer membrane so that the cell releases its pent-up electrical charge. This electrical discharge spreads over the surface of the cell.

With this discharge the muscle fiber is almost ready to contract. The second sequence of electrical activity then occurs. An action message is transmitted from the surface of the muscle fiber to the innermost contracting elements, the fibrils. This takes several thousandths of a second. When this message is received, the fibrils contract. The total time for a single muscle-cell twitch—for stimulation, contraction and subsequent relaxation—is about a tenth of a second.

The electricity of the muscle

The electrical changes within the muscle fiber start when the neurohumor spreads over the surface of the resting cell. In this state the cell or fiber is a charged battery carrying 0.09 of a volt—a so-called resting potential which is maintained by the structural integrity of the cell's outer membrane. The neurohumor apparently changes the structure of this membrane temporarily so that there is a two-way flow of sodium and potassium ions (an ion is an atom which is in an electrically charged, rather than a neutral, state) between the cell and the fluid which surrounds it. As these ions pass through the membrane and redistribute themselves, the electrical balance of the muscle fiber changes and it becomes temporarily discharged. In this discharged state, the muscle fiber is ready for contraction.

All muscular effort requires a series of intricate reactions taking place at many sites simultaneously. Every body activity mobilizes millions of muscle fibers. Electronic interactions take place incessantly as electricity flows back and forth through the cell membranes and along pathways within the fibers. The pacemakers which control this activity are the nerve signals that release the squirts of neurohumors at millions of nerve-muscle junctions.

The critical importance of the reactions which occur at the junction of the nerve and muscle fibers is underscored by the immediate and far-reaching effects of any interference with the work of these junctions. The lethal toxin of botulism and other poisons such as strychnine, cocaine and curare all work by blocking the chemical activities at the nerve-muscle junctions. Myasthenia gravis, a rare disease in which patients suffer from abnormal fatigue and muscular weakness, is also the result of an as yet unidentified defect in the workings of nerve-muscle junctions.

Fuel for the muscle engine

Muscle-triggering neurohumors can be compared to the sparking mechanisms of an internal-combustion engine. The next line of inquiry concerns the operation of the engine itself. Once a muscle fiber has been stimulated, it requires energy to perform its work. ATP, the universal fuel of all plant and animal cells, supplies this energy. Muscle fiber, being an animal cell, makes some of its ATP by breaking down glucose molecules through a sequence of reactions called glycolysis.

This preliminary step in energy-making sets the stage for ATP production on a large scale by the Krebs cycle, described in Chapter 2. The assembly lines are located in mitochondria, the cylindrical bodies which serve as power plants and which lie packed in the fluid filling the spaces between muscle fibrils. Here the Krebs cycle takes place. The final steps involve the flow of electrons through molecules thought to be arranged in definite patterns on the walls of the mitochondria. Because of the high energy requirements of muscle, the muscle fibers generally contain many more ATP-synthesizing mitochondria than are found in most other cells.

Muscle can also produce ATP by another process which bypasses the Krebs cycle and takes place outside the mitochondria. The Krebs cycle requires oxygen and sometimes, during violent exercise, the body's oxygen demands exceed the supply. A trained athlete can inhale enough air to supply his blood with some eight pints of oxygen a minute. In order to distribute this oxygen during those 60 seconds, the heart must pump more than 20 quarts of blood to the tissues. This represents just about the maximum capacity of the heart-lung system.

When circumstances call for an effort which exceeds the individual's oxygen-providing capacity, the heart and lungs cannot supply enough oxygen to meet the energy demands of the hard-working muscle fibers. In this situation, the Krebs cycle is jammed up by lack of oxygen and the cell must produce ATP by glycolysis. When oxygen again becomes

A THEORY OF MUSCLE CONTRACTION

These diagrams illustrate the "sliding filament" theory of muscle contraction. In the first frame a single unit of a muscle fibril is shown at rest. The thin filaments are not joined in the middle, nor do the thick filaments touch the ends of the unit. In the second frame the thin filaments are coming together and the fibril is shortening. The fibril unit pictured in the last frame is fully contracted.

MUSCLE FIBRIL AT REST   CONTRACTION BEGINS   FIBRIL FULLY CONTRACTED

available, the Krebs cycle resumes operation and the accumulated products of the glycolysis reactions are then oxidized.

These particular reactions in the muscle cells are of special interest, since they show that all cells work according to common principles. While research biologists were unraveling the details of oxygen-free, energy-producing processes in muscle cells, they realized that these processes were similar to a series of reactions that occur in plant cells—alcoholic fermentation.

Fermentation wins the race

Louis Pasteur and his scientific successors had worked out the details of the fermentation process in the making of both wine and beer during the 19th Century. Fermentation takes place inside yeasts and other cells in a series of more than a dozen reactions which yields ethyl alcohol as one of the final products. Biologists concerned with muscle research discovered that most of these reactions were also involved in the working muscle fibers of the body. During periods of extreme exertion, a kind of fermentation takes place inside muscle cells. This process produces lactic acid, from which the energy-bearing molecule ATP is formed. The capacity of this supplementary system to produce energy without oxygen is, of course, limited and the body's accounts must be settled within a short time. That is why, after a strenuous event, an athlete breathes so deeply—he is settling the "oxygen debt" his muscle cells have incurred.

In the muscle cell, as in other cells, energy is bound up in the ATP molecule. Muscle research focuses attention on a problem that arises whenever the fuel is used, whenever a cell has to do work of any kind. This is the so-called "coupling" problem. ATP includes three phosphate groups linked together in a chain extending from the rest of the molecule. When the last link of the chain is broken, energy is released. Investigators would like to know how this energy is transferred or coupled to working materials in the cell. How, for instance, is energy passed to the muscle fibrils?

Though the answer to this question has not yet been found, it has been established that the energy transfer is carried on at the molecular level. Each muscle cell or fiber is a bundle of fibrils, each fibril a bundle of thick and thin filaments; it is now thought that these filaments are the site of the energy transfer. It is here that chemical energy is translated into movement.

The filaments of muscle cells are composed of bundles of long molecules. The thick filaments consist chiefly of the protein myosin; the thin filaments are made mainly of another protein, actin. As a muscle contracts and the thin filaments slide past the thick ones, actin molecules are sliding past myosin molecules.

Biologists have spent much time studying these proteins, which combine to yield a compound known as actomyosin. About a decade ago, Dr. Teru Hayashi of Columbia University conducted a classical experiment using a synthetic fiber which exhibits some of the properties of muscle. He prepared threads of actomyosin, suspended them in salt solutions and then added ATP. The threads contracted to half their length in 30 seconds or so. This contraction showed many of the characteristics of true muscle contraction. Furthermore, the fibers developed tensions great enough to lift several hundred times their own weight.

Other experiments have suggested a specific role for ATP in such reactions. It seems to weaken the chemical bonds that link molecules together to form compounds. Actin and myosin form extremely strong bonds when they join, but the presence of ATP is enough to loosen the structure to an appreciable extent. The energy required to produce this effect may come from the splitting off of the last phosphate group from ATP's three-phosphate chain. Another significant finding suggests that actomyosin contains a built-in ingredient for its own weakening, for myosin is an enzyme that can split a phosphate group from ATP.

The great muscle mystery

The same sort of chemical reaction may occur in the filaments that make up muscle fibrils. Cycles of relaxation and contraction may depend on the alternate loosening and re-forming of the bonds that link actin to myosin, so that the filaments are pulled past one another. If this is so, studies of muscle tissue indicate that the bonds in an active muscle must be loosened and re-formed some 50 to 100 times a second.

As these conjectures indicate, the coupling of ATP energy to cell processes is still a mystery; specifically, biologists do not know how the splitting of the ATP molecule affects the bonds linking the muscle proteins. It may be that water plays an important role in this biological phenomenon. The muscle proteins may be thought of as having a protective sheath of water that makes them relatively inaccessible to chemical action. Alteration of this water sheath, brought about by the splitting of ATP, may change the forces between adjacent muscle filaments in such a way as to cause them to slide past each other.

Some investigators believe future theories of the molecular basis for muscular contraction may derive from such a concept, but a great deal of research effort lies ahead. It is not enough to understand the detailed workings of animated fibers. Organisms are not simply collections of different kinds of tissues, they are coordinated systems which function as a whole—just as many cellular processes are related to chemical and electrical events under way in other types of cells.

As an example of this relationship, activities in cells of the nervous

SMOOTH MUSCLE

SKELETAL MUSCLE

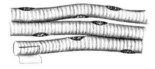

CARDIAC MUSCLE

TYPES OF MUSCULAR TISSUE
There are three distinct types of muscle in the body. Smooth muscle, which lines blood vessels, the alimentary canal and genitourinary areas, is made up of spindle-shaped cells, each with a single nucleus. Skeletal muscles, which control voluntary body movement, are striated ropes of elongated cells with many nuclei. Cardiac muscle, unique to the heart, has striations *and* central nuclei, resembling both smooth and striated muscle.

system may affect and be affected by the chemistry of myosin, actin and other compounds in contracting fibers of the muscle cells. Brain and muscle work closely with each other. Tests show that if a person imagines that he is lifting a heavy chair or climbing a tree, tensions are generated in appropriate muscles even though there is no actual movement. Your eyes move during dreams, under closed eyelids, and they tend to move up and down when the dreams involve rising or falling objects, and from side to side when objects move across your inner "field of vision."

The psychology of strength

It is common knowledge that feats of strength are partly a matter of psychology. Emergencies also add immeasurably to muscle performance. If the mother described at the beginning of this chapter had been asked to lift the rear end of the station wagon for the fun of it, she would almost certainly have failed.

The brain and nervous system are always adjusting and responding to the sliding filaments in millions of muscle fibrils. Every body movement involves a continual balancing of forces. Certain muscles, if uncontrolled, would flex your arms and legs in arcs; other muscles would tend to straighten your limbs and hold them stiff as ramrods. The body has many such pairs of opposing muscles, all of them in equilibrium and all of them monitored automatically by the cerebellum—a brain center located at the back of the head. Other brain centers control the complicated sequences of movements involved in walking, tying shoelaces and all the other activities which man has to learn once and then performs without conscious thought.

The investigations of muscle-fiber operation which have been discussed in this chapter have been limited to striated muscle, which moves the arms and legs and other members of the body. In striated muscles the fibrils and the filaments they contain are "packaged" into short sections. The end walls of these sections provide anchoring points for the contractive forces produced by the sliding action of the filaments.

In many other muscles of the body (such as those found in the stomach, throat and intestine) there are no striations, although there is evidence of filamentary structures. It is now thought that some sort of filamentary sliding mechanism is also responsible for contraction in these so-called smooth muscles. Though biologists cannot at present account for the "muscle" action which moves the amoebae, the cilia or the flagella, it is thought that these movements may result from a sliding action between protein molecules.

There are many medical considerations involved in the current research on muscle cells. In addition to the possibility of treating afflictions of the nerve-muscle functions, there is hope that further studies

THE WILLING COOPERATION OF OPPOSING MUSCLES

PULLING OR RELAXING ON THE JOB

Just as the lumberjacks below work as a team to support the tree or move it one way or the other, so human muscles work in pairs. Every muscle in the body has a counterpart, called an opposing muscle, and they do their job as a team: one muscle is contracting while the other is relaxing. In the tiptoeing leg above, the calf muscle is doing the pulling and the shin muscle is doing the loafing.

may indicate a way of making damaged muscles heal faster or even of replacing dead muscle with fresh muscle transplanted from another source. Such techniques could be particularly useful in heart surgery.

One current medical project involving muscle research concerns muscular dystrophy, a hereditary ailment which is characterized by the wasting away of muscle tissue. Muscular dystrophy affects an estimated 200,000 Americans, about two thirds of them children. Recent studies suggest that one important factor in the disease may be changes in the membranes of the muscle cells. Apparently the diseased membranes allow muscle proteins to escape from the cells. A new hormone preparation is being investigated as part of an experimental treatment which would inhibit this loss of proteins. This effort is one further example of the fact that medical advances in all areas depend increasingly on the research of biologists concerned with the workings of cells.

The search for a muscle machine

Investigators are studying chemical compounds that stimulate the behavior of muscle fibers. Their research represents the early stages of a long-term project to convert chemical energy into mechanical energy without intermediate steps. This problem is an old one in engineering. In an automobile engine, for example, chemical energy—released by the ignition of gasoline—must be changed into the heat energy of expanding gases, which then push pistons and move the car. In storage batteries chemical energy must be changed into electrical energy before it can run motors.

Muscle is far more efficient in changing energy from one form to another than are most man-made machines. Forty-five per cent of the energy fed into muscle can be translated directly into mechanical movement. This conversion process also produces heat, and whereas heat produced in engines is wasted energy, much of the heat produced in muscle contraction is used to maintain body temperature in mammals and birds that are exposed to the cold. The muscular movements associated with shivering have no significance in themselves; it is the heat liberation accompanying shivering which benefits the organism.

Using muscle as a model, researchers hope eventually to develop a rugged material which will stretch and contract hundreds of times a second, like the muscles of the wings of insects, and operate levers and other mechanical elements. A number of interesting but very primitive synthetic-muscle machines have resulted from the current investigations in this field. One of them incorporates five parallel strips of a transparent, rubberlike plastic which is chemically related to the plastics used to make synthetic textiles. This material contracts to about a third of its length when bathed in acid, and stretches back to its former dimen-

A MECHANICAL MUSCLE
Israeli scientists invented this machine to explain what goes on inside a muscle. In a living muscle, chemical energy is converted into work without having to pass through intermediate forms of energy like heat or electricity. The ropelike fibers in the machines contract in a saline solution and expand when fresh water is added. Here, their expansion causes the downstroke of a piston in a water pump *(right)*.

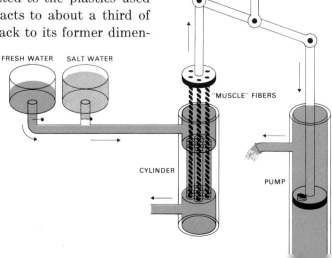

FRESH WATER   SALT WATER

"MUSCLE" FIBERS

CYLINDER

PUMP

sions when immersed in an alkali bath. When connected to a system of pulleys and subjected to the acid-alkali treatment, the five strips can lift weights of several pounds.

This material is inefficient and sluggish, contracting but half a dozen times a minute. Future advances obviously depend on finding superior methods and materials. Meanwhile, biologists continue to seek fundamental knowledge which may be applied by doctors and engineers in the future. There is considerable interest nowadays in broad aspects of the problem of how living things move. Is the same basic system used universally? Does movement in bacteria and other microorganisms, as well as in the specialized cells of higher species, *always* involve ATP and contracting proteins related to actin and myosin?

Preliminary answers to such questions may come in the not-too-remote future. Proteins similar to those found in muscle cells have been extracted from single-celled creatures. Moreover, accumulating evidence indicates that the proteins obtain their energy from ATP and that they may work by a sliding action among long-chain molecules. As in so many other cases, the evolution of cellular movement seems to consist of a continual refinement of properties inherent in the structure of the simplest cells. This is one reason why what we learn about muscle cells provides insight into the structure of all forms of living matter.

Probing the Innermost Secrets

The agelong attempt to comprehend the workings of heredity has, within this century, advanced from relatively simple studies of inherited traits to immensely complicated examinations of the chemicals that determine those traits. Genetics, the science of heredity, began as a study of complete organisms—the pea, the bean, the fruit fly. It proceeded, by narrowing the scope of investigation, to such single-celled organisms as yeast, fungi and bacteria. It narrowed further to the cell's nucleus—to the chromosomes, to the nucleic acids within the chromosomes and, finally, to one specific nucleic acid, DNA. Discovering the agent of heredity was a landmark in that search, but not its end. Throughout the world, scientists continue to probe the secrets of the nucleus. In the vanguard of this study is The Rockefeller Institute in New York; its scientists *(opposite)* are constantly devising new machines and new techniques to see into the nucleus.

THE BASIC TOOL OF RESEARCH

The light microscope being used opposite remains a basic tool in cell research. With its selection of lenses that bring greater or lesser power to bear upon the object under study, the light microscope is still the main device for observing living cells. The electron microscope is a newer and far more complex research tool, magnifying slices of dead cells up to 200,000 times.

Working Together to Isolate Nuclei

The Rockefeller Institute is "a community of scientific scholars . . . free to follow their interests in any field of scholarship." It is built around men who are distinguished in their fields. These scientists, provided with space, equipment and assistants of their own choosing, daily work to solve the intricate problems of their chosen specialties.

For instance, the laboratory shown on these pages has been established by Dr. Alfred E. Mirsky at the Institute. He has picked his own gifted and congenial crew of co-workers. Together they study the cell's nucleus and, particularly, the bio-

chemical processes occurring within the nucleus. A pioneer in this work, Dr. Mirsky was a codiscoverer of the RNA content in chromosomes. More recently he has contributed to the knowledge of how RNA-synthesis within the nucleus (page 72) is regulated. An initial step in much of this research is isolating the nucleus from the mass of the cell. After the nucleus has been isolated, systematic investigation can begin. It is this isolation of the nuclei and, later, the radioactive tracing of nuclear activities which are followed in the photographs and diagrams on pages 135 through 141.

A JOURNEY OUT AND A CUT IN

To collect the thymus gland from a freshly killed calf, a graduate student from the lab travels to a slaughterhouse in Brooklyn *(above)* about 6:30 in the morning. There, the gland is packed into a cold thermos jug. Brought back to the laboratory's "cold room"—a refrigerated area kept just above freezing temperature—the gland is quickly minced with scissors *(below)*. Only after it has been minced finer than hamburger will the gland be ready for the further mechanical stages of filtration and isolation shown in the diagram on the next pages.

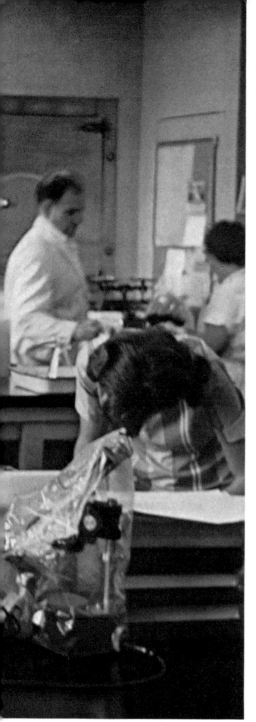

A CONCENTRATION OF SKILLS

In Dr. Mirsky's laboratory *(above)* at The Rockefeller Institute in New York, scientists work on different aspects of nucleus research. Projects vary, but many focus on one kind of cell—the cell of the thymus gland, extracted from calves. Thymus nuclei are preferred because they are large in relation to the over-all cell and survive well in laboratory solutions.

TO A FINAL ISOLATION

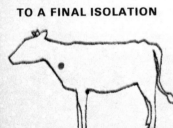

BEGINNING WITH A GLAND

The first step of the process shown here is obtaining a fresh thymus gland from the throat of a newly slaughtered calf. The aim of the study is to discover how and in what amounts amino acids enter a nucleus to be used in the synthesis of protein.

HOMOGENIZING THE TISSUE

After the gland has been finely minced, the process of isolating the nucleus proceeds with homogenization of the tissue. A blender used at relatively low speeds (1,000 to 2,000 rpm) breaks down most of the tissue without destroying the nuclei. Blending is carried out in a sugar solution. When this churned liquid is poured out, it contains about 60 per cent nuclei and 40 per cent cellular debris by volume.

SPINNING DOWN TO NUCLEI

The nuclear suspension is far from pure. Isolating the nuclei now continues through centrifuging. The centrifuge spins the mixture until the heavier nuclei settle as sediment and the lighter cytoplasm remains in an upper layer. Two spinnings give a 95 per cent pure suspension of nuclei.

STRAINING OUT THE DEBRIS

For the isolation needed in this research, all cell debris must be removed. Debris consists of cytoplasm, blood cells and connective tissue. Pouring the homogenized mixture through gauze *(above)* and then flannel will filter out much of that debris. But many other refined techniques will be necessary to finish the isolation.

MIXING THINGS UP AGAIN

At various stages in the process of isolation, the nuclei must be again suspended in a sugar solution. Otherwise both nuclei and the still-remaining cell remnants will cling together. An ordinary electric drill, adapted for laboratory use and fitted with stirring blades, mixes this suspension. Drills such as this, when fitted with different "bits," are useful in the laboratory for various research procedures.

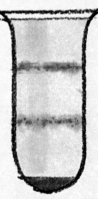

CHOOSING THE HEAVY ONES

One more step is often needed before the isolation is complete. A small volume of dense sugar solution is poured into a test tube. Then, a like amount of lighter solution is added and finally a like volume of nuclear suspension. Centrifuged, only the dense nuclei will press through the solutions to settle at the tip of the test tube.

Steps toward and into a Nucleus

Much of the work at the Mirsky lab involves separated nuclei of calves' thymus cells. The first step toward studying the nuclear processes by electron microscope or scintillation counter *(opposite)* is the physical isolation of the nuclei, accomplished by the processes shown on these pages. Progress in such research depends not only on knowledge and imaginative insight, but also on the machines and chemicals that implement that vision and knowledge. Even the basic procedure of nuclear isolation depends heavily on novel equipment and advanced techniques.

It is the controlled speed of the centrifuge that enables scientists now to spin

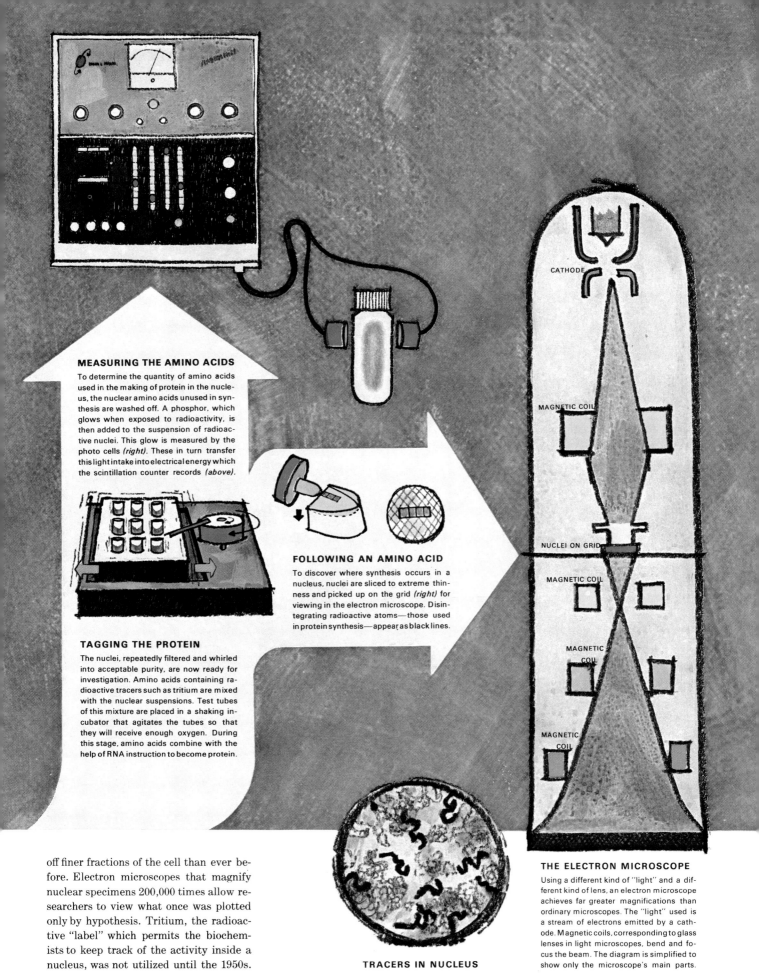

MEASURING THE AMINO ACIDS

To determine the quantity of amino acids used in the making of protein in the nucleus, the nuclear amino acids unused in synthesis are washed off. A phosphor, which glows when exposed to radioactivity, is then added to the suspension of radioactive nuclei. This glow is measured by the photo cells *(right)*. These in turn transfer this light intake into electrical energy which the scintillation counter records *(above)*.

FOLLOWING AN AMINO ACID

To discover where synthesis occurs in a nucleus, nuclei are sliced to extreme thinness and picked up on the grid *(right)* for viewing in the electron microscope. Disintegrating radioactive atoms—those used in protein synthesis—appear as black lines.

TAGGING THE PROTEIN

The nuclei, repeatedly filtered and whirled into acceptable purity, are now ready for investigation. Amino acids containing radioactive tracers such as tritium are mixed with the nuclear suspensions. Test tubes of this mixture are placed in a shaking incubator that agitates the tubes so that they will receive enough oxygen. During this stage, amino acids combine with the help of RNA instruction to become protein.

CATHODE

MAGNETIC COIL

NUCLEI ON GRID

MAGNETIC COIL

MAGNETIC COIL

MAGNETIC COIL

off finer fractions of the cell than ever before. Electron microscopes that magnify nuclear specimens 200,000 times allow researchers to view what once was plotted only by hypothesis. Tritium, the radioactive "label" which permits the biochemists to keep track of the activity inside a nucleus, was not utilized until the 1950s.

TRACERS IN NUCLEUS

THE ELECTRON MICROSCOPE

Using a different kind of "light" and a different kind of lens, an electron microscope achieves far greater magnifications than ordinary microscopes. The "light" used is a stream of electrons emitted by a cathode. Magnetic coils, corresponding to glass lenses in light microscopes, bend and focus the beam. The diagram is simplified to show only the microscope's main parts.

Giving the Nuclei a Rough Ride

SPUN INTO SEPARATE ORBITS

A centrifuge, shown in the diagram on the preceding pages, is here being filled with test tubes *(left)*. At this early stage of the isolation procedure, the cellular mash is heavily mixed with the nuclei in suspension. Centrifugal force will drive the heavy nuclei to the bottom of the tubes, where they will cling as sediment, leaving lighter debris suspended above it.

REDUCED TO A PURER CLUSTER

After a seven-minute whirl in the centrifuge, pellets of thymus nuclei cluster at the bottom of the test tubes. These clusters will be re-suspended in fluid and further purified by centrifuging them through layers of liquid with differing densities. Then, after radioactive amino acids are added as tracers, the now nearly pure nuclear suspension will be incubated.

SEALED OFF FOR MEASUREMENT

Dr. Vincent Allfrey (left) and a graduate student "turn off" the now radioactive nuclei after removing them from the incubator (above). The student pours an acid into the nuclear solution. With the addition of the acid, the protein manufacture is halted and no further amino acids are absorbed by the nuclei. A scintillation counter measures the uptake of the amino acids by the nuclei.

VIGOROUS RIDE TO SYNTHESIS

Protein synthesis takes place during the rough ride in the machine above, a shaking incubator. The flasks in the incubator contain nuclear suspension plus amino acids bearing radioactive tracers. Jarring the contents and keeping them at a constant temperature of 99° F. assists the process. Following incubation, the nuclei are studied by scintillation counter or a microscope.

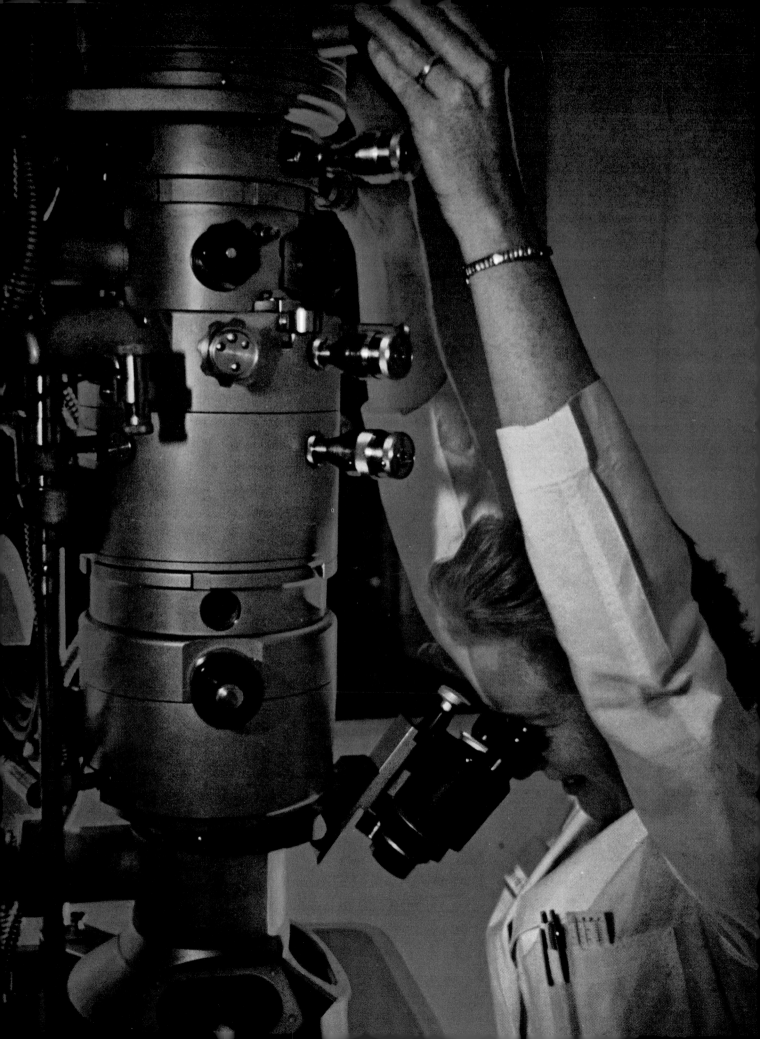

From Seeing to Understanding

The fine art of isolating the nucleus is only a preliminary skill in the long process of understanding just what goes on within that nucleus. When at last pure nuclei have been obtained, and when these have been labeled with radioactive amino acids, and when, further, the nuclei have been sliced and prepared for viewing—then it is that electron-microscope study can begin.

Such careful studies have already done much to clarify one of the greatest problems in genetics: what is the mechanism within the nucleus that selects only a part of the genetic information stored there? How does a cell containing all of the numerous and complex instructions of the original fertilized cell learn to select only part of its heritage and thus become specialized so that it will perform specific functions? Until recently this remained a mystery.

Some of the first steps toward answering this vital question have been taken by the professional team headed by Dr. Mirsky. This group's research has recently focused on a particular class of proteins within the nucleus known as the histones.

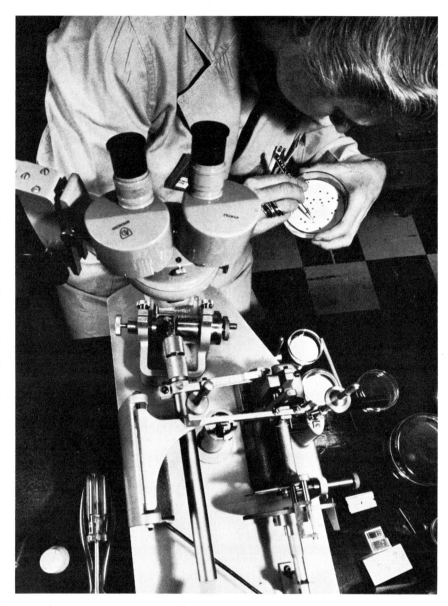

PLUCKING A GRID OF SPECIMENS
With a pair of tweezers, Dr. Littau plucks up one of the tiny copper grids on which lie the sections of radioactive thymus nuclei, sliced to four hundred thousandths of an inch. The sections will be covered with a photographic emulsion, allowed to lie in complete darkness for about a month or longer, developed and then observed through the electron microscope (opposite).

REACHING FOR A BETTER VIEW
Adjusting the column of an electron microscope, Dr. Virginia Littau sharpens her view of thymus nuclei. In the darkened room the only glow is from the red and green signal lights and the fluorescent screen, shining through the porthole. On the screen, the nuclei's image—enlarged about 30,000 times—appears, disclosing a clear radioactive record of protein manufacture.

TRACKING PATHS OF SYNTHESIS
The bulk of the nucleus within a whole thymus cell is revealed in the electron micrograph at right. An autoradiograph (far right) is a kind of photographic record produced by amino acids containing radioactive tracers. Useful in studying the process of protein manufacture in the nucleus, the autoradiograph here gives a clue to the location of the ingested amino acids.

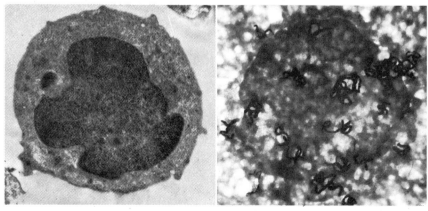

PHOTOMICROGRAPH OF WHOLE THYMUS CELL   AUTORADIOGRAPH OF THYMUS-CELL NUCLEUS

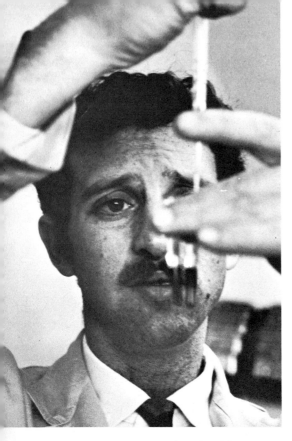

A Young Man and an Old Mystery

Dr. Eric Davidson, a recent graduate of The Rockefeller Institute now working on problems of genetics in Dr. Mirsky's lab, was born in 1937 and had finished his graduate work by 1963. This enthusiastic scientist is representative of the younger explorers who have felt the fascination of the newly opened and barely charted domain of the nucleus.

Dr. Davidson approaches his project—the study of differentiation of millions of variously specialized cells from a single fertilized egg cell—through the eggs of the *Xenopus* toad. This toad's eggs are useful for this purpose because they grow and mature before they are fertilized. Within these bulging eggs, called oocytes, a special form of chromosome is found. Comparatively large and hence more visible, they are referred to as "lampbrush" chromosomes. Dr. Davidson focuses on them to discover how they are able to eventually shift their commands from the order to duplicate, which all cells must give at first, to the more subtle command which initiates specialization. It is the genetic-message-carrying RNA produced by these chromosomes that bears the varying commands, and it is this RNA that Dr. Davidson must observe and try to unravel.

A COMPARISON FOR CONTROL

Dr. Eric Davidson compares blood samples taken from two radioactive toads. These samples will be used as a control to help determine how much radioactive tracer has entered the eggs of the toads and how much has passed off into the animals' bodies through the bloodstream.

A TOAD WITH REMARKABLE EGGS

The *Xenopus* toad, used by Dr. Davidson in his study of cell differentiation, is one of the few kinds of animal that lays unfertilized yet highly developed eggs. Bred in large quantities by toad "farms" for use in pregnancy tests, *Xenopus* is available year-round for experimental work.

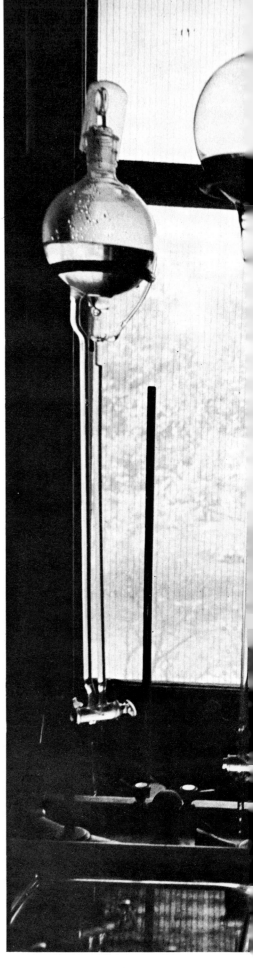

A SHOT TO START PRODUCTION
Gripping a slippery toad, Dr. Davidson injects it with a shot of hormones that will induce egg formation. In its natural habitat the toad ovulates without such help but in captivity it refuses to cooperate. Each batch will produce several hundred eggs suitable for this study.

SPRINTING AFTER A SPECIMEN
A loose toad means a spry search through the crowded laboratory. Such chases provide Dr. Davidson with an occasional interruption in a long day of research. He usually begins work shortly after nine, goes on until at least seven at night and often continues into the next day.

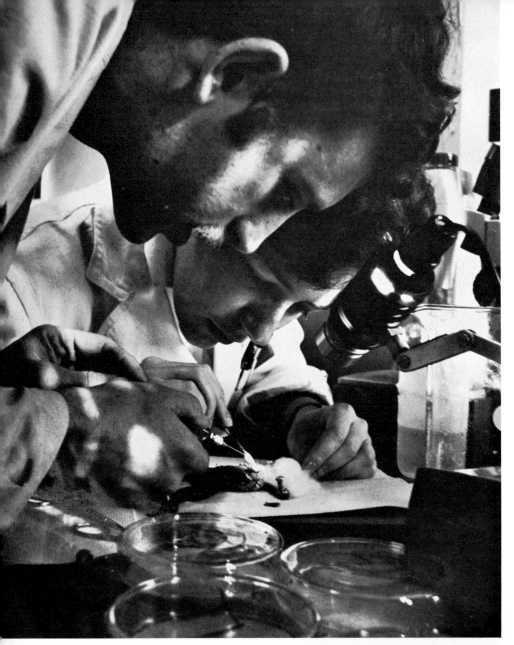

A Question Aimed at Mankind

The work which Dr. Davidson has begun at The Rockefeller Institute will continue as such work does, through investigation to new findings and from those findings on to new investigation. Yet as understanding deepens so too does the concern of the scientist for the use that will be made of his discoveries. Thus, above the specific problems of research loom problems of more general significance.

One of these is the question of controlled heredity. It is a question Dr. Mirsky has directly faced and eloquently stated: "For thousands of years man has been manipulating the inherited characteristics of domestic animals and plants by selective breeding. Such selective breeding of mankind has frequently been proposed but it is repugnant to most people. Control of heredity at the molecular level is as novel as the control of atomic energy was a few years ago and, like the control of atomic energy, raises problems that are too important to be left to scientists alone."

BACKING OFF TO LOOK FORWARD
In the picture opposite, Drs. Mirsky *(right)* and Davidson take time out from their work to talk informally. Such talks are a relaxed part of intensive research. They help to relate single experiments to Dr. Mirsky's project as a whole, and questions raised from another point of view may often suggest new ways of looking at problems that have grown too familiar.

DISSECTING TO INVESTIGATE
Dr. Davidson, aided by a laboratory assistant, dissects a toad for its supply of ripe eggs. Such handiwork, like the isolation of nuclei in protein-synthesis research, is a time-consuming but essential part of scientific investigation. To the public, discovery may seem sudden and brilliant; for the scientist, each discovery has slowly grown from months of routine work.

TAKING THE PICK OF THE CROP
After the eggs have been taken from the toad, Dr. Davidson separates them, selecting only those eggs that have sufficiently matured to contain the sought-for lampbrush chromosomes. It is with those enlarged chromosomes that he will best be able to study the variable and enigmatic behavior of message-carrying RNA, one of the genetic factors which control heredity.

7

The
Message
Carriers

THROUGHOUT THE ANIMAL KINGDOM there is an intimate relationship between nerve and muscle, between brain and brawn. As an animal increases in size, its nervous system must grow in complexity; if this accommodation to bigness is not made, the organism may become so unwieldy and inefficient that it fails to meet the challenge of its environment. The price of this failure is extinction, and it has been paid by many species in the past; the dinosaur is an example of an animal that simply became too big for its nervous system. The nerve cell is thus a critical factor in the constant development of more complex life forms.

Bigness in any organization calls for effective communication between its parts. In the multicelled organisms, the nervous system is the primary communications network. The first such systems took shape some half a billion years ago, to connect remote parts of the larger organisms, and to speed and coordinate their muscular movements.

At that time, one of the most advanced species on earth was the ancestor of today's sea anemone, a flowerlike creature which clung to rocks and lived on what the tide happened to bring within range of its tentacles. Its primitive nervous system was geared to simple and unvarying reactions. If the creature was touched it would collapse, pulling in its tentacles and contracting into a tight ball.

More sophisticated nervous systems appeared later with the development of mobile and more aggressive species of aquatic animals. Streamlined, free-swimming creatures darted through the waters, hunting and being hunted, chasing and escaping. These primitive vertebrates—jawless, fishlike creatures known as ostracoderms—are now totally extinct, but the bony armor in which they were encased left many fossil records. The ostracoderms possessed the precursor of the animal brain; it took the form of three irregular swellings in the hollow nerve cord which served as their nervous system. It has taken 400 million years for modern man's brain to develop from these rudimentary control centers.

The brain is the site of the mental processes concerned with learning, reasoning, dreaming, imagination and the planning capabilities generally associated with the higher species, particularly with man. This capacity for thought depends upon the unique structure of nerve tissue and the workings of many millions of nerve cells.

The very complexity of the nervous organization which serves the mental processes introduces an example of a phenomenon common to all cellular biology—a complete system can be infinitely more than the sum of its parts. For although the nervous system as a whole is the source of all thought, the individual nerve cell appears to engage in nothing which would pass as mental activity. Investigators find little more than a cell which in many basic ways resembles all other cells.

Nerve cells possess the same mechanisms that are found in other cells

A NERVE-TINGLING PERFORMANCE
Viennese vaudevillian Francis Brunn demonstrates the superb control and coordination that made him one of the world's most talented jugglers. Throughout his body, an intricate network of nerve cells is carrying information to his brain and transmitting orders back to his muscles in the form of millions of electrical impulses, without winding up in a hopeless snarl.

for synthesizing proteins and energy-rich ATP, and they are equipped with conventional cellular structures such as membranes, nuclei, ribosomes and mitochondria. In several other respects they are less conventional: nerve cells, like muscle cells, do not reproduce—the ones we are born with must serve us all our lives. Nerve cells also resemble muscle cells in being electrical units which discharge, or fire, in response to an appropriate stimulus.

The study of nerve cells also reveals that they use some common cell attributes in unusual ways. Like all cells, nerve cells are centers of electrical activity. (Even plant cells are miniature generators, and sensitive instruments show that simply poking a root produces tiny currents.) What distinguishes nerve cells is that much of their electrical activity is in the form of pulsed signals which flow throughout the body.

Nerve pulses at 200 mph

During the course of evolution, nerve cells have become effective signaling units, the components of extensive message-relaying networks. The nerve cells' structure reflects this function. A representative cell may have a main body shaped something like a turnip or a bulb, out of which sprout the dendrites—fine, many-branched fibers forming a kind of root system. These dendrites are pickup devices, elements which receive signals from other nerve cells.

Sprouting from the main body of the nerve cell like a tap root is a single thicker fiber, the axon, which may extend from a few thousandths of an inch to more than three feet (as in the case of fibers running from toes to spinal cord). The axon is a transmitting device; it passes signals on to other nerve cells or muscles. All nerve signals are electrical pulses similar to those produced by opening and closing a switch or working a telegraph key. They may travel through fibers at speeds of as high as 200 miles an hour.

Nerve fibers, like muscle fibers, often contain hundreds of fine filaments. Unlike muscle filaments, which are packed into cablelike fibrils, the nerve filaments are usually individual strands surrounded by fluid cytoplasm. In some cases these filaments run the full length of the nerve cell, from the receiving fibers at one end through the main cell body and on to the tip of the transmitting fiber at the other end. Nerve fibers also contain a unique structure not found in other types of cells—hollow, protein tubules so small that they become visible only under the high magnifications of the electron microscope. It is thought that the tubules may provide channels for transporting compounds necessary to the signaling system to the nerve-fiber endings. The function of the filaments is still undetermined.

The receiving and transmitting fibers of a nerve cell do not make phys-

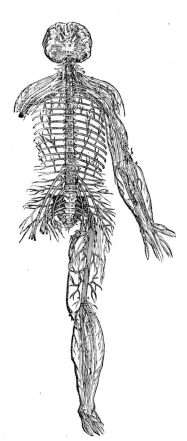

AN EARLY BUNDLE OF NERVES
Vesalius, the 16th Century Flemish anatomist, explored the human body by dissection; his work in anatomy led to an experimental basis for later cellular theories.
Mapping the complexity of human nerves *(above)*, Vesalius proved that they are not tubes as had been assumed but flexible fibers. He also linked nerves and organs by proving that certain organs malfunction when nerves serving them are severed.

ical contact with the fibers of a neighboring cell. There are gaps of about a millionth of an inch at every junction. These gaps are bridged by the same sort of process involved in the stimulation of muscle. The ends of a nerve cell's transmitting fiber release small quantities of neurohumors, chemicals which stimulate the receiving fibers of other nerve cells.

The release of neurohumors may pose special transportation problems for nerve cells. It is likely that the neurohumors are manufactured in the main body of the nerve cell. If this is true, biologists would like to know how they are carried from the main body of the cell to the tip of a transmitting fiber, which may be a yard long. One possible answer to this question is that rings of contraction, which have been observed running down the surface of the cylindrical fiber, squeeze the material along somewhat in the manner of a snake swallowing a mouse.

Studies with the electron microscope indicate that the main body of the nerve cell may package neurohumors before sending them along the transmitting fiber. The packaging material is thought to be membrane fragments from the cell's cytoplasm and the packages to be the tiny, oval-shaped bodies which have been observed in high concentrations at the tips of the transmitting fibers. Investigators have succeeded in separating quantities of these bodies from nerve tissue and have found that they contain acetylcholine—the neurohumor that stimulates nerve action.

The yes or no vote

The stimulation of a nerve cell to fire and release excitatory neurohumors at the junction of its transmitting fiber and another cell is but a part of the communication process carried on by the nervous system. Nerve cells also employ inhibitory signals which tend to prevent a cell from firing. These signals travel along transmitting fibers that release inhibiting neurohumors—compounds which counteract the effect of the stimulating neurohumors which are being released at the same time.

The over-all effect of these contradictory stimuli—the excitatory and the inhibitory neurohumors—is that the nerve cell exists in what biologists call "a state of poised instability"; it can, at any moment, fire or remain quiescent. The determination of the course the cell will take depends upon the net effect of all the signals which reach it in an interval of a thousandth of a second or less.

This conduct of a nerve cell in a "to-fire-or-not-to-fire" situation evidently depends upon a kind of chemical vote. A nerve cell, according to one estimate, receives signals from up to 25,000 other nerve cells—which means that the cell may be affected by 25,000 squirts of either "yes" or "no" neurohumors. As a general rule, the majority wins. If the yeses predominate, the cell will fire through its transmitting fiber. Otherwise it will remain quiescent.

MODERN AND MEDIEVAL IDEAS OF THE HUMAN BRAIN

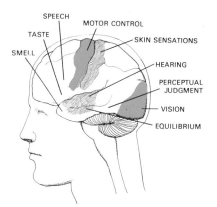

INCORRECT THEN, INCOMPLETE NOW

The complex association of nerve cells called the brain has puzzled and intrigued scientists for centuries. It is now known to govern nearly every phase of life; sensory and muscle centers have been pinpointed, and processes like "perceptual judgment" have been vaguely outlined *(above)*. But today's scientists are not as bold as 16th Century savant Georg Reisch, who distinguished between such functions as "imagination" and "fantasy" *(below)*.

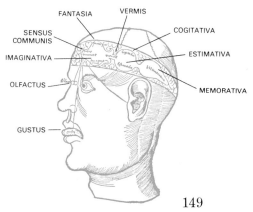

This description of the operations that take place in the single nerve cell suggests the incredible extent and complexity of the chemical and electronic events constantly under way in the 10 billion signaling cells of the human brain and nervous system. Each of the nerve cells within this vast, labyrinthine network fires at a minimum rate of once a second, which means that the nervous system hums with the passage of 36 trillion impulses an hour.

Though the brain and the nervous system comprise a restless, busy community of cells, a notable feature of the nerve network is the high degree of organization it manifests in carrying on its work. This organization, in fact, has been both the cause and the result of the brain's remarkable evolution—for the nerve cells themselves seem to have changed little over the past hundred million years or so, the period during which warm-blooded creatures developed from ratlike shrews to the higher apes and man.

Wiring the brain for sound

In general, the rank of a species on the evolutionary ladder is directly related to the number of nerve cells in its brain and the complexity of the patterns in which the cells are arranged. Information concerning these patterns is now being gathered through a new technique for tapping the biological communications lines. Investigators have developed microelectrodes, tiny fluid-filled glass probes with tips less than one hundred-thousandth of an inch in diameter; inserted into the body, these electrodes pick up signals carried by individual cells and reveal some of the processes that take place in the nerve centers.

The researchers have found, for example, that certain nerve fibers running from the arm send signals to the brain, relaying detailed information about the arm's position to the appropriate brain centers. If the arm makes a 90° angle at the elbow, the cells fire at a characteristic rate—say, 50 times a second. Then as the arm is flexed, bringing the hand toward the shoulder, the firing rate changes; for every angle of flexion there is a characteristic firing rate—a specific number of electrical pulses flashed each second. When the process is reversed and the arm is extended, increasing the elbow angle, the nerve cells register changes in position.

The manner in which this precisely coded set of signals is transmitted—along nerve fibers in the arm, into the great cable of the spinal cord and on to the brain—has been demonstrated in experiments conducted with monkeys at the Johns Hopkins School of Medicine. The signals relating to the elbow angle, carried by flexion and extension nerve cells, are of course only a fraction of the total of the communications involved in even the simplest action—such as reaching for a glass of water. For as one flow of pulse signals indicates the step-by-step position of the arm, other torrents of signals are streaming into the brain from the other muscles involved in such a movement. At the same time, barrages of signals pass in the reverse direction, from brain to muscles, conveying commands for muscle action to turn the shoulder, shift body weight on the feet, and adjust finger, hand and wrist muscles —while still other signals order the eyes to follow the entire sequence of movements and adjustments.

This same two-way network of communications is involved in every bodily movement. Merely standing upright demands a constant interchange of information between muscles and nervous system; more complicated activities involve more complex signaling sequences.

The coordination of muscular action is chiefly the responsibility of a part of the brain known as the cerebellum. Other brain centers serve as communications headquarters for other types of information. The faintest of audible sounds, such as a whispering rustle of leaves, causes fibers in the auditory nerve running from the ear to the brain to fire at a rate of 10 to 15 pulses a second. The rate increases with the intensity of the sound, with a rate of some 300 to 400 pulses a second representing extremely loud sounds. The auditory nerve conducts these signals to a specific section of the brain's outer bark, or cortex. Other regions of the cortex are reserved for messages conveying information concerned with other sensory events.

What a frog sees

Researchers are also gaining insights into the manner in which creatures with brains analyze the world around them. An important study of frogs by Jerome Lettvin, Humberto Maturano, Warren McCulloch and Walter Pitts of the Massachusetts Institute of Technology has turned up a reaction pattern which also applies to the higher species.

In this experiment a frog is placed in front of a screen, with its vision restricted to images that appear on the screen. A microelectrode is inserted into the frog's optic nerve to pick up signals originating in a single fiber. The researchers have found that the fiber remains electrically active even when there is nothing for the frog to watch. It fires with a steady rhythm, audible as a soft, muttering sound in a loudspeaker connected to the electrode. This sound continues unchanged as many different kinds of objects appear in the frog's field of vision. Moving a realistic color photograph of grass and flowers across the visual field, for example, does not change the fiber's muttering. The sight of squares, rectangles and triangles is also without effect. The nerve in the eye of the frog and its associated receptors obviously do not respond to such stimuli.

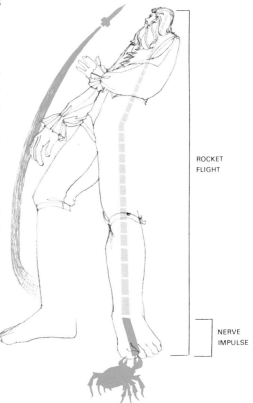

ROCKET FLIGHT

NERVE IMPULSE

SLOW BUT EVENTUALLY PAINFUL
It was once thought that nerve impulses, the signals passed from one nerve cell to the next, were the swiftest phenomena in nature. But compared to modern technology, nerve cells are downright sluggish. This drawing compares a nerve impulse with the speed of a rocket. If a crab nipped a 50-mile-high giant and a rocket were launched at the same instant, the pain would only be at his ankle when the rocket whooshed by his head.

151

There are other objects, however, which will produce a marked response from the fiber. When a small circular object is moved into the field of vision, or any small object with a positively curved front end, the fiber goes into action. The muttering on the loudspeaker promptly changes to a loud put-put sound. Plainly, this particular nerve and its receptor cells are designed to react to one type of stimulus only, an object having a curved front. Furthermore, it will react only when the object is moving, a fact of special significance as far as the survival of the frog is concerned.

The world of the frog includes many small objects with curved front ends and many objects that move. The probability is that objects possessing all three of these qualities are insects—and nature has recognized this probability in designing the frog's nervous system. A nerve cell that responds exclusively to these qualities thus serves as a bug detector. The cell can be identified under the microscope by its appearance, its network of receiving fibers being arranged in a characteristic pattern that somewhat resembles a fence.

When is a bug not a bug?

Experiments show that the frog's eye contains many such cells. Their presence accounts for a peculiar fact which naturalists have known for some time. A frog will starve to death in a cage containing plenty of freshly killed insects. Objectively speaking, from the standpoint of creatures with more advanced nervous systems, the food is there, ready to be eaten. From the standpoint of the frog, however, an object which does not move is not an insect. So the frog is a slave of its nervous anatomy—though a highly efficient slave, it should be added. The frog has survived for some 200 million years. Man has yet to prove that he can do as well.

In addition to its bug-detector cells, the frog's eye also includes four other types of nerve cells that help to find food and contribute to its survival. There is an "edge" detector, which responds only to the borders of black and gray areas; it registers the boundaries of trees, lily pads and other features of the frog's environment. An "event" detector responds to varying distributions of light and shade and to movement of any sort, thus keeping the frog aware of any changes in its surroundings. A third type of cell, a "dimming" detector, fires only when the general level of illumination decreases. This cell would discharge, for instance, if a bird of prey approached and cast a shadow. The frog senses the nature of its immediate surroundings through still another optic nerve cell, a color detector, which responds to a watery shade of blue.

There are about half a million nerve cells that contribute individual fibers to the optic nerve cable of a frog. Of this total, about 485,000 of

152

the cells are bug and event detectors; most of the remaining 15,000 or so are edge or dimming detectors. This allocation suggests that the evolutionary process has resulted in a sort of order of priorities in the survival factors of a frog's existence; eating is apparently the creature's most pressing concern.

Research into the mechanism of a frog's visual processes can have practical as well as theoretical implications. The bug-detector cell is a natural device which electronic experts would like to duplicate in man-made instruments. The unique feature of the bug-detector cell, in the eyes of these experts, is that it does not respond to insects as individual objects, but to what might be called the "concept of insectness." To phrase this another way, the bug-detector cell does not react to the number of an insect's legs, its coloring, the shape of its wings or any of the other features which characterize types of insects—it reacts only to the curved front end, a common feature of almost all insects.

An instrument which operated on this sort of "concept recognition" principle would have many practical applications. For one thing, it might be a most valuable addition to the nation's air defenses. The image an approaching airplane forms on a large radar screen varies with the plane's direction and altitude. The plane may be flying straight into the radar beam or moving in at an angle or negotiating some sort of maneuver. In each case a differently shaped image would appear on the screen; the possibilities run into the hundreds. Air defense experts would like to have a device that recognized approaching aircraft automatically. The problem is to design an electronic scanning eye which would react to the features common to all such images—which, in short, would respond to the abstract notion of "planeness."

Reality is what you see

Investigations involving the principles upon which nerve cells work can have even broader implications. Among the important features of all ocular systems are their limitations—what they do *not* do. The frog's eyes, for instance, do not distinguish colors other than watery blue, or many forms in the frog's environment, or wing shapes or certain other features of insects. The result of this discrimination built into the frog's eye is that it does not see all of the real world. Reality is corrupted before visual signals reach the frog's brain. Like the frog, man sees only what he is equipped by nature to see. Man, of course, is not as restricted as the frog; his version of reality is many times richer. It would be presumptuous, however, to say that man's reality is *the* reality. There must be as many realities as there are species. Creatures with brains and sense organs more advanced than man's would undoubtedly be aware of a broader spectrum of the environment.

It follows, too, that reality must also vary subtly for different individuals, depending upon their sensory equipment. Every man lives amidst a mosaic of impressions which is peculiarly his own—a world that is interpreted through his individual network of highly specialized nerve cells. One of the major goals of current research is to discover how such cells work and how they differ from one another.

The variations in sensory interpretations which exist among the species underscore the fact that limitations and fixed patterns are built into all nervous systems in the form of inflexible, genetically determined structures of cells. Such fixed structures are not enough, however, to provide for the survival of higher organisms. Progress and survival demand nervous systems which can be shaped or modified by experience, which can learn and remember.

The basic nature of learning and memory is another unsolved problem of biology. It is known that as organisms mature, the fibers extending from their nerve cells grow, become more highly branched and develop denser networks. Growth of this sort and the formation of new cell-to-cell contacts may be involved in acquiring new skills. Changes of another sort, however, must take place to account for the content of "factual" memory, for the capacity of the brain's miniature storehouses.

The brain can hold an enormous amount of information. This information is stored by a largely unknown but undoubtedly complex process. Things remembered, like all sensory information, stream into the nervous system in the form of signals which represent intensities, colors and sounds. Each signal is an electrical pulse which lasts for only a few thousandths of a second. In the formation of memory traces, these fleeting pulses are somehow "frozen" and transformed into enduring records.

The bridge of memory

The search for an explanation of memory has involved many speculations. One theory suggests that memory may be the result of structural changes in neurons, or nerve cells, caused by the repeated passage of specific nerve impulses. It is thought that these changes may take place at the synapse, or gap, which the impulse must bridge on its way from one cell to another. The result would be a closed loop of nerve cells, with each loop representing a unit of memory. This loop-forming process might be likened to the formation of channels which occurs when rivulets of water continue to flow over sand or soft ground.

Chemical explanations of memory have also been suggested. One theory speculates that memory may be the result of changes in the nerve-cell proteins. Experimental work indicates that heightened activity in nerve cells increases their complement of RNA, which is vital to the synthesis of proteins in the cells. If there is a valid connection between

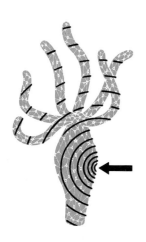

THE NEED FOR CENTRAL NERVES
A central nervous system is vital to higher forms of life. The hydra (above) has no such system; its nerves, primitive specialized cells, are diffused evenly throughout its body in a thin net. A mild stimulus (arrow) causes only a slight contraction and even a sharp jab does not particularly disturb it. Sensation travels in its body like ripples expanding in a pond. A frog, on the other hand, needs a more advanced nervous system to cope with his environment. A sensation both touches off a reflex action, causing him to leap, and sends a message to his brain, enabling him to make an intelligent decision about additional responses.

repeated or continuous message activity (representing the repetition so often necessary to the memory-forming process) and RNA, it may be found that nerve-cell proteins act as memory traces.

The possibility that RNA and protein synthesis may be involved in the memory-forming process is also suggested by recent experiments on the flatworm, a cross-eyed little creature which is about half an inch long and which has a brain about the size of the period at the end of this sentence. Despite its primitiveness, the flatworm has an amazingly persistent memory. For instance, the little worm can be conditioned to contract when a light is flashed. If the creature is then cut in half, the head end grows a new tail and the tail end grows a new head. Each of the two new flatworms remembers what the original flatworm had learned: each will contract when a light is flashed.

The forgetful worm

There is, however, an effective way of reversing this process, at least in part. If the tail-end worm is placed in a dilute solution of an enzyme which destroys RNA, the creature forgets what it has learned. The memory slate is wiped clean. This suggests that RNA and the proteins it synthesizes may in some way be connected with the storage of information—even though the enzyme for some reason seems powerless to exert the same influence on the other (or head-end) worm.

Though the theory suggesting proteins as memory traces is still conjecture, some investigators are convinced that a relationship exists between memory and the heredity apparatus at the molecular level. DNA, RNA and proteins may play a role in our remembrance of things past as they do in evolution and the development of the embryo.

Related to this question is the additional one of explaining recall—the retrieval of information once it is stored. This is one of the great cultural problems in today's society. As more and more books and journals are published, the difficulty in locating specific material increases inordinately. Nature's system of information retrieval is one we might well copy—if we knew how it worked. If someone asks, "Do you know Robert Brown?" your answer, usually correct, comes within a few seconds. During that period your mind has "thumbed through" your extensive memory records of names of friends, acquaintances, public figures and fictional characters, and produced a relevant answer. Science does not know how this is done.

It is obvious that our memory files are organized in such a manner as to enable us to deal with abstractions and to bring order into our experience. We recognize a lump of sugar, a modern skyscraper, a book and a matchbox as examples of rectangular solids; and the setting sun, apples, stoplights and boiled lobsters as examples of red objects. We classify people and plots and theories in many different ways, creating an elaborate cross-indexing system for our memory traces. The mechanics of this cross-indexing present a series of problems which remain to be solved.

Imagination is another aspect of cerebral activity which will undoubtedly challenge investigators for many years. What happens when two diverse concepts are brought together—when a poet compares a man to an island, or a scientist compares the atom to a solar system? Can such ingenious notions result from a simple biological mechanism like the joining of memory-trace proteins to form a new molecular complex? Again, biologists do not know—though combinations of some sort must take place in the brain when we construct analogies, similes, metaphors. Similar combinations presumably occur when mentally disturbed persons construct the delusions of their private worlds.

All of these unsolved problems stem from one general area of inquiry in brain research. Information retrieval, cross-indexing, abstractions and imagination are simply labels which refer to some of the brain's activities; they do not describe what goes on in the nervous tissue as we think. The next great step in the understanding of man's mind will be to account for these mental processes in terms of the behavior of living groups of cells.

The Body's Expert Signal Corps

Nowhere are cells more highly specialized than in the body's signal corps. The nerve cells—or neurons—are communications specialists that transmit information from one part of the body to another. Moreover, by responding to stimuli from both outside and within (opposite), they keep the body informed of what is going on. Through them, everything seen, heard, smelled, tasted and touched is scrutinized and identified. Neurons are the body's transmitters, switches, cables and receivers—and each has its own built-in electric power generators. Each neuron is designed to do a single, special job and no other. They are hooked together in coordinated teams which form a labyrinthine maze of communications circuits that extends to the farthest outposts of the body. Most remarkable of all is their capacity to combine by the billions in that organ called the brain, the awesomely versatile and puzzling site of thought, memory and creativity.

SENTRIES FOR SENSATION

Some of the specialized neuron outposts reporting different sensations are illustrated opposite. One kind of nerve ending records a light touch, another, heavy pressure. Still another type registers heat and pain. There may be 10,000 such sentries per square inch of skin. The complex of nerve and muscle cells in the thumb aids coordination by reporting on muscular contraction.

Nerve-Cell Tools and Techniques

The individual neuron is an ingenious device that sends and receives electric signals. To accomplish this, it has two kinds of highly specialized structures: dendrites *(first panel, below)*, antennae which receive signals; and a single axon *(far right)*, a filament which acts as a self-powered transmission cable. The power originates in a chemical exchange between the axon and its surroundings, which sets up a minute voltage difference. When a dendrite or the cell body is stimulated by an incoming signal from another cell or by an original cause such as a pinprick or a loud noise, this voltage is perturbed, causing a wave of fluctuations to travel down the axon and, as described below, stimulate the cell next in the chain.

The neurons that thus flash messages around the body are of three kinds. Sensory neurons report on the outside world and on internal muscular status. Interconnecting cells act as middlemen and, in the brain, sort out messages and issue orders. Finally, motor neurons *(right)* conduct action commands out to the muscles.

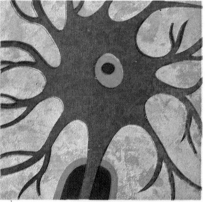

HOW A SIGNAL IS SENT

STARTING with the branching, tentacle-like dendrites, where the stimulus is received, these panels show in views of increasing magnification the beginning and end of a signal's journey through the anatomy of a neuron. The dendrites conduct the stimulus to the cell body *(red)* and to the axon, with its membrane *(green-blue)* and protective sheath *(dark blue)*, where it initiates electric impulses.

TRAVELING in waves along the axon, the impulses come to the axon's end, which branches out in tiny filaments. These filaments, which are not covered by the axon's sheath, terminate in many bulbous feet, shown here in near-contact with a dendrite of another neuron. They may also make connections with muscle or gland cells, and different types of neurons have different-shaped endings.

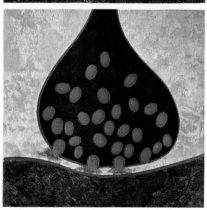

ARRIVING at a synapse, which is a junction of two neurons, the signal has to jump a slight gap. The way it makes the leap is shown at left. The pulse's arrival at the foot releases packets of a chemical messenger, which cross the gap and stimulate the neighboring dendrite to start the cycle again. Even in cells with long axons, the complete process takes no more than a fraction of a second.

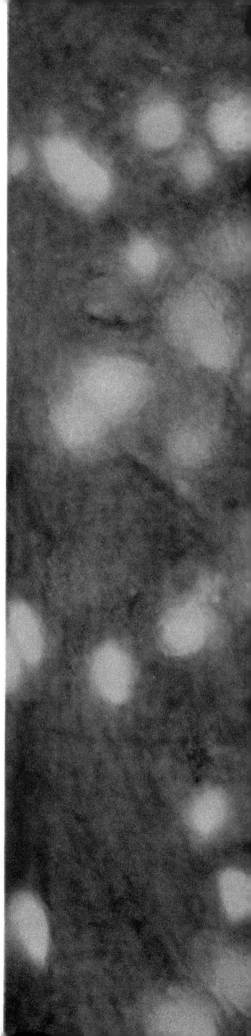

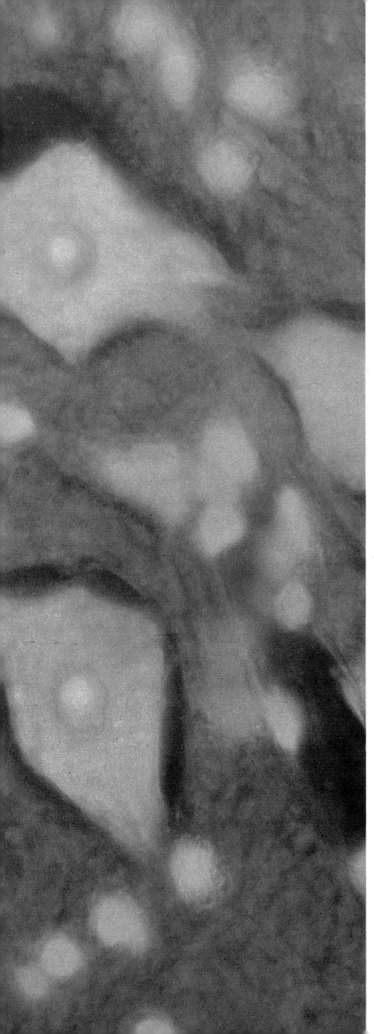

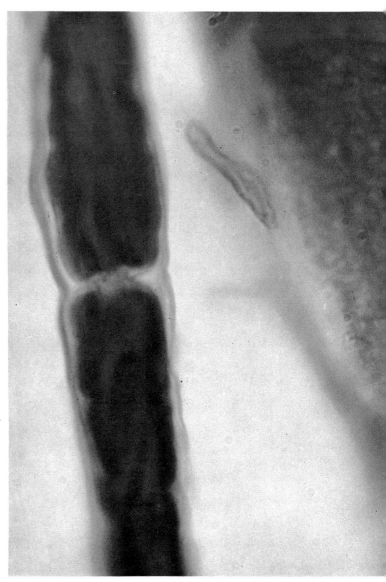

AN INSULATED POWER LINE
Part of an axon is seen above magnified about 2,000 times. The material sheathing the axon is called myelin, and the gaps where its segments meet are known as nodes of Ranvier, after the French scientist who discovered them. They are relay stations which boost the signal as it travels. Some axons, like those joining the spinal cord to distant muscles, are three feet long.

COGS IN THE CHAIN OF COMMAND
This photomicrograph of a section of the spinal cord shows, dyed orange, several motor neurons—the type that carry orders to muscles and glands. In two of them the cell bodies and nuclei are clearly visible, as well as the dendrites and axons. The whitish bodies are nuclei of small cells which in the spinal cord and the brain bind neurons together into nerve tissue.

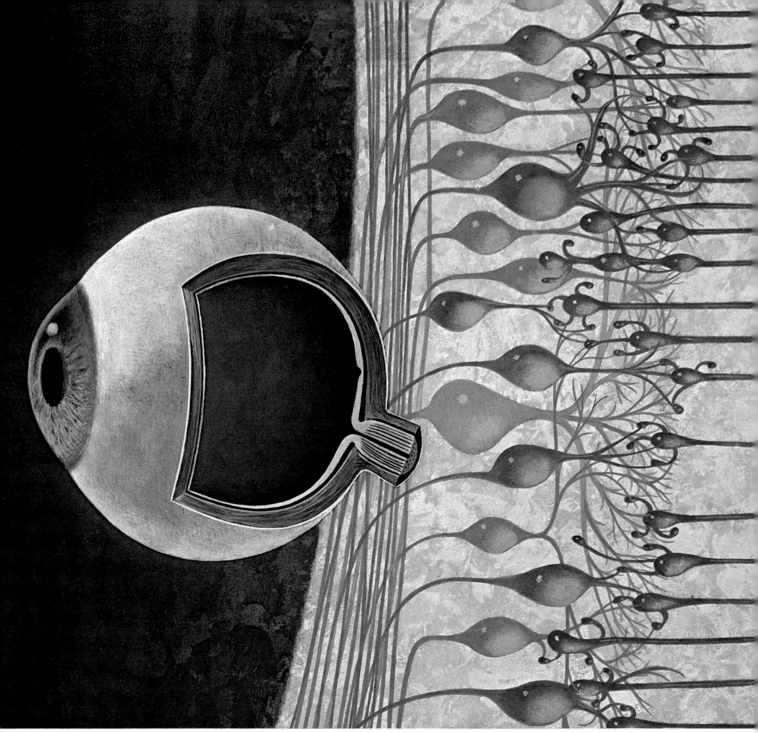

EYEBALL   OPTIC NERVE AXONS   OPTIC NEURONS

Complex Circuits for Seeing

The nerve cell is a self-contained unit, but it works effectively as part of a team. All over the body, ganged up by the millions, battalions of neurons work together, each individual cell contributing its special talent toward the common goal. These pages show the intricate joint effort made by neurons to give man his precious sense of sight.

Within the one-inch spheres of man's eyeballs are more than 100 million neurons, all working to keep him visually informed. They are stacked up in three layers in the retina, the "film" at the back of the eyeball, where they intercept the light-waves focused on them by the lens in the front part of the eye. Their job, simply, is to convert the light-waves into electric signals and send them along to the brain, where they will be interpreted. How the several different kinds of sight nerve cells team up to accomplish this magic is illustrated in these two cross-section views of the neuron-seeded retina.

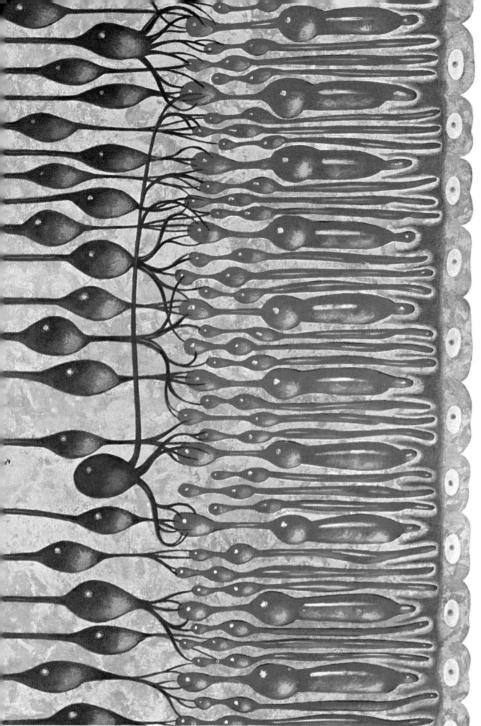

BIPOLAR CELLS   RODS AND CONES   PIGMENT CELLS

A NETWORK OF NEURONS

THE FIRST STEPS IN SEEING occur in the nerve cells of the retina, whose relative position in the eye is seen in the cutaway drawing of the eyeball at far left. The eye's lens is built to focus light on the retina *(gray lining),* much as a camera lens focuses light on film. (The exact focal point of the lens, the fovea, is shown by a notch in the retina.)

The enlarged cross section of the retina shows three distinct groups of neurons. Light entering the retina (from the left) proceeds through two cellular layers to the third layer. Here, at the very back of the retina, the receptor cells receive the light and convert it into electric impulses. There are two kinds of receptors: the thick-bodied cones report on colors and work best in bright light; the more numerous rods are sensitive to dim light and are concentrated at the retina's periphery. (Because of this rod distribution, we see things better in darkness by looking just to one side of them.)

The electric signals from the rods and cones are returned to the front of the retina by the next bank of neurons, the bipolar cells, which are go-betweens leading to the third bank, the optic nerve cells. The long axons of the optic neurons form the front layer of the retina, and they converge in one bundle as the optic nerve. This nerve leaves the eye (as seen in the cutaway drawing) and takes the signals to the brain, where they will be combined and interpreted, and then perceived as visual images.

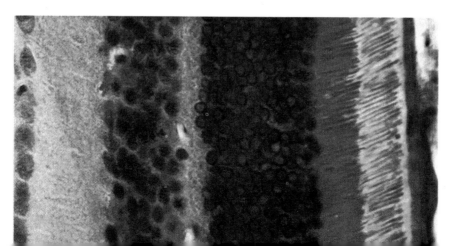

A CROSS SECTION OF SIGHT

This photomicrograph of a dyed section of retina corresponds to the drawing above. At right is the layer of pigmented cells which serves as the "skin" of the retina. (These cells also transmit from the bloodstream the vitamin A needed by the receptors—especially the rods, which is why night vision improves with vitamin A intake.) Then come the light-receiving ends of the rods *(light crimson)* and the cones *(dark crimson)* followed by the granular layer made by their nuclei. The bipolar cells' nuclei make purple blobs *(third band from left)* and the optic neurons show up in a crimson layer at far left.

Normal humans see a lion in technicolor

Seeing Things in Different Ways

The eye, for all its complex wizardry, is not a faultless instrument. Often the lens is distorted and cannot focus properly and the result is nearsightedness. The nerve cells malfunction too, and one of the results may be color blindness.

Humans normally see the whole range of colors, from violet at one end of the visible spectrum to red at the other. Many physiologists now think there is a different kind of receptor mechanism for each of the three primary colors of light. If any of these mechanisms is defective or lacking, the various shades of color which they should be reporting will not be "seen" by the brain. Thus, for some people the full-colored lion above becomes a dull pinkish lion *(above right)*.

But what is a defect in humans is a normal condition for most of the world's creatures, which lack the well-developed color receptors of man. They see the world differently, sometimes with limited or fragmentary color perception or, more usually, with no color at all. Some idea of how different animals' variously constructed eyes see the world around them is suggested by the photographs at right and those on the opposite page.

FOUR LOOKS AT A LION

A TWO-HUED VIEW

Yellow-blue blindness, in which objects are seen in reds and greens only *(left),* is one form of human color blindness. Far more common is red-green blindness, in which these two colors cannot be distinguished. About 8 per cent of men are color blind, only 1/2 per cent of women.

AN EDGE OF LIGHT

The frog's retina contains special neurons to distinguish edges between light and dark areas *(right)*. Other neurons respond to a sudden dimming of the general illumination. Frogs feed on insects and their eyes are very sensitive to motion, while stationary objects are only dimly seen.

A COLORLESS WORLD

Dogs, horses, cattle, deer and, in fact, most mammals, see no colors at all *(left);* everything they look at is perceived in shades of gray. Most birds and probably some fishes, on the other hand, do see some colors. Only the apes and higher monkeys share man's full color vision.

A FRAGMENTED EYE

Insects do not have retinal rods and cones, but have large compound eyes with hundreds of separate transparent "windows." The insect's view of life *(right)* is thus segmented and diffused. But some insects can see color in the short-wavelength ultraviolet range not visible to humans.

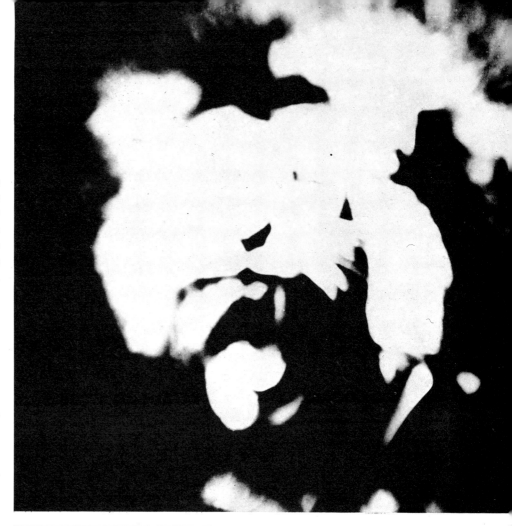

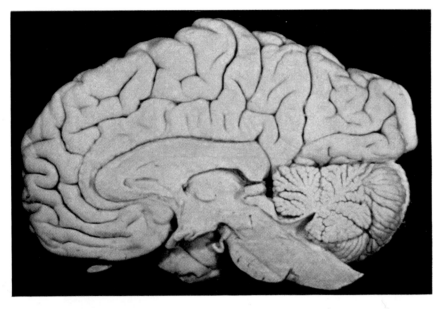

THE CONVOLUTIONS OF A BRAIN
The right half of the human brain is shown above in longitudinal section. At the top and curling around the left, or fore, end, is the cerebral cortex, where speech and vision are centered. Under the cortex at right is the cerebellum, the center of unconscious physical coordinations.

A Live, Compact Computing Machine

In the spongy, three-pound lump pictured at left are massed some nine tenths of the body's 10 billion nerve cells. It is the brain, the most compact computer known. Within its convoluted folds is an untidy, microscopic jungle of tangled dendrites and axons *(opposite)* which crisscross one another in a vastly complicated switchboard of interconnected circuits—a single neuron may be in direct communication with as many as 270,000 of its neighbors.

In this way, billions of single neurons can be hooked into an almost unlimited number of variations and combinations. The same principle underlies big electronic computers, in which many thousands of tiny electric on-off switches are linked by a tangle of wires in an enormous number of possible combinations. When a question is fed to the machine, some of these associations get activated and the pattern of the switches' ons and offs produces an answer. Similarly, when the brain gets signals from the eye, complex patterns of neurons are stimulated—and the result is an answer which is our perception of the reality reported by the eye. At the same time, the brain may send out an order for responsive action. A chain of command for executing such an order is illustrated opposite and on pages 166 and 167.

Brains and computers are also alike in that they both use electricity—but with a considerable difference in consumption. A large computer might operate on 70,000 watts; the brain, making its own, requires about as much power as a 10-watt bulb.

THE SWITCHBOARD OF A "BRAIN"
Computer wiring, like the multicolored network in the small adding machine below, serves to interconnect many individual electric units, just as neurons' dendrites and axons form multiple contacts. The sequence in which the wires are hooked up determines what the machine does.

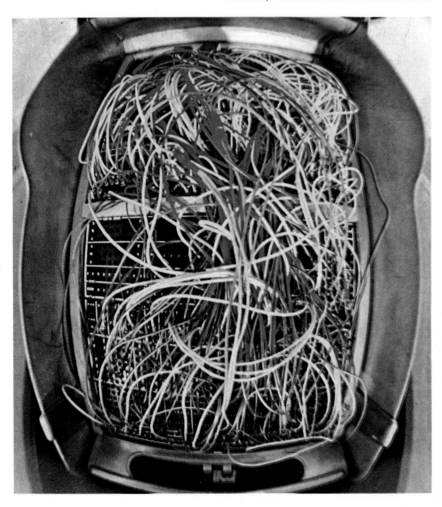

THE NEURONS INSIDE THE BRAIN
Brain cells typical of the cerebral cortex are shown stained brown in the photomicrograph opposite. Called pyramidal cells, they are triangular, with dendrites coming from each corner and an axon from one side. Though numbering in the billions, these and other neurons occupy only one twelfth of the cortical volume, the rest being nonnervous connective tissue *(yellow)*.

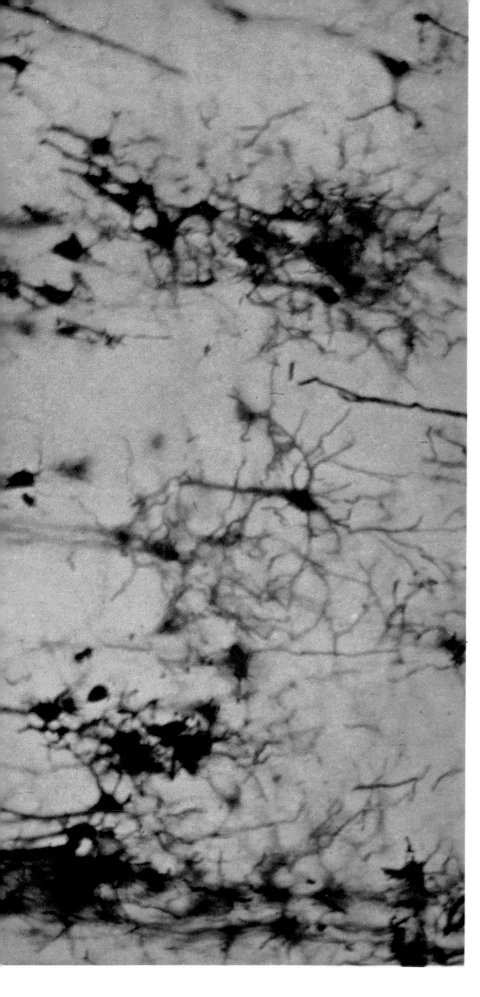

ORDERS FOR ACTION

THE PATH OF AN ORDER from the brain for muscular action is followed in this schematic diagram. From a neuron *(red)* in the cortex a signal leaves the brain, crosses to the other side of the spinal cord (each side of the brain controls the opposite side of the body) and stimulates a motor neuron in the spinal column. The neuron's axon, encased in its sheath, leads to the muscle and makes contact with its fibers, which then react to the signal by contracting.

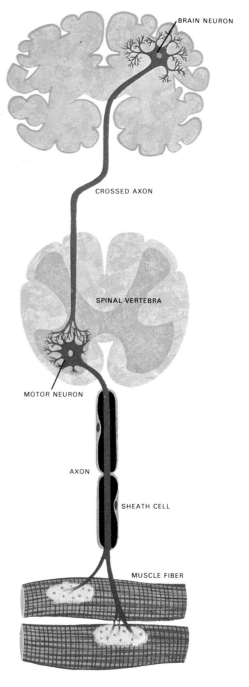

BRAIN NEURON

CROSSED AXON

SPINAL VERTEBRA

MOTOR NEURON

AXON

SHEATH CELL

MUSCLE FIBER

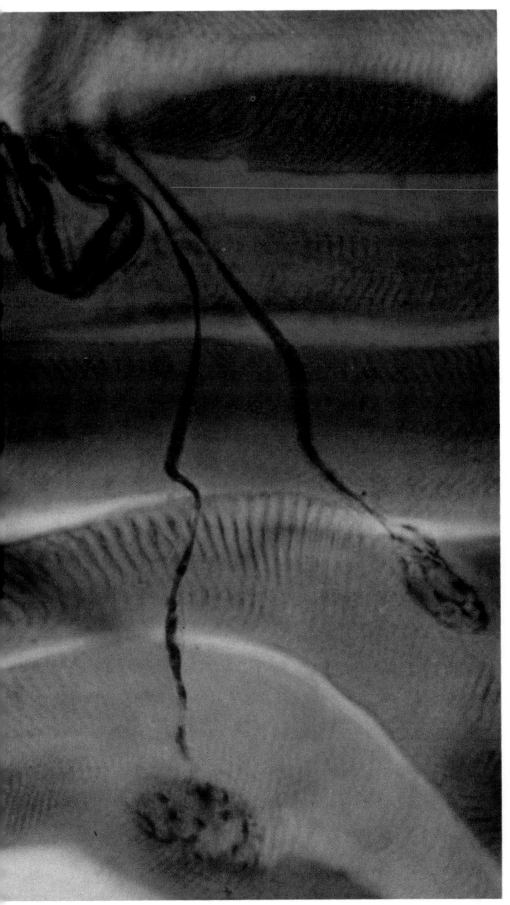

Turning a Message into Action

Besides being portable, the brain has another vital advantage over its mechanical cousin the computer: the ease with which it learns. Once a computer has been programmed, or preset with given patterns of operation, it can do only what it was built to do. The brain, however, is constantly reprogramming itself and coming up with new answers. A young child may, at first, be unafraid of a lion, but his brain soon hooks up a "program" for crying and running away. Later, the brain develops the capacity for directing a plan of action, such as aiming and throwing a spear (*opposite*).

That act looks simple; actually it is a prodigiously complicated exercise in coordination. Before the spear can be thrown, the eyes have had to make their reports; the brain has had to receive, digest and interpret the messages; orders have had to be sent to every part of the body. In the throwing arm alone there are some 40 major muscles at work lifting the spear, and each one has hundreds of nerve connections like those shown in the picture at left. There the final order for action is delivered—the end of the line for the flashing sequence of neuron signals which transmutes the messages from the eye into the action of the arm.

GETTING THE SIGNAL
Running horizontally across the picture at left are five fibers of a striated muscle. Coming down from the top are two branching axons, bringing action signals from the brain. The areas where muscle and nerve connect are known as motor end plates. The electric signal from the axon starts a similar signal that travels from the end plate over the muscle fiber, causing it to contract.

EXECUTING THE ORDER
A ceremonially dressed Warega warrior from the Republic of the Congo brandishes a spear. Throwing the weapon is the culmination of a coordinated effort of nerve and muscle, but the nervous system's telegraphic operation will not stop there. The eyes will report on the success of the effort, while the brain is already at work ordering the body's next course of action.

8

The Cell
in Sickness
and in Health

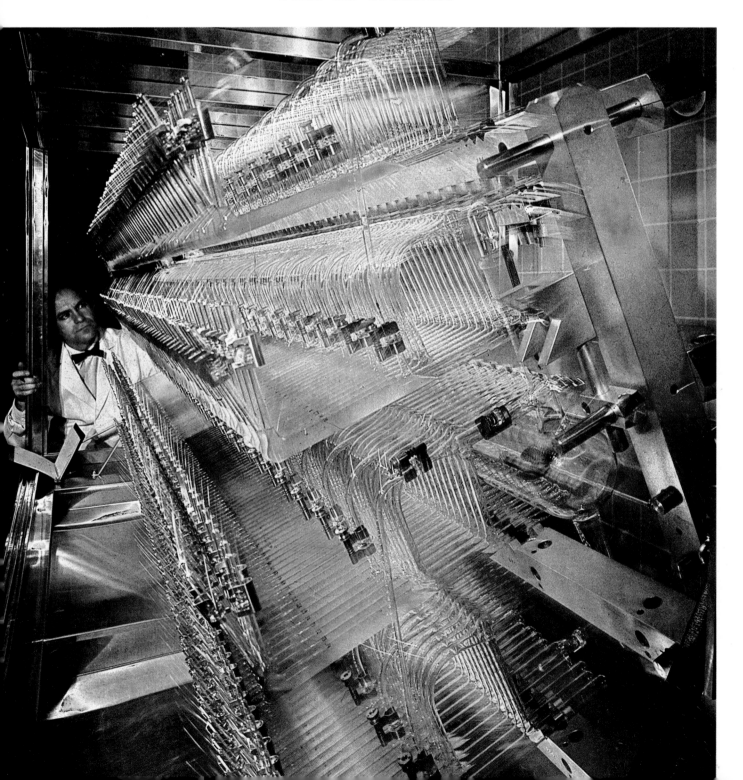

LIVING IS A RACE FOR SURVIVAL, a ceaseless struggle to exist. All cells and systems of cells are engaged in a never-ending effort to obtain energy and convert it to their own special purposes. Every biological act of the living organism, from synthesizing ATP and proteins to producing pulses of electricity, is directed to one predominant goal: whatever happens, the organism must try to keep itself alive.

To stay alive, every organism must preserve itself in the face of external forces which threaten its existence—and which finally do destroy it when it ceases to work energetically enough on its own behalf. This ultimate disaster threatens the organism in many forms: poisons may accumulate in the environment, temperatures may vary beyond tolerable limits, food supplies may fail, competing organisms may move in and occupy its living space.

As part of its defense against these forces, the organism walls itself off from alien elements in the world. The skin of the body is such a wall, forming a natural border between the individual and the environment. No barrier, however, can be completely effective. Large communities are always vulnerable to sneak attacks and the human body, a vast community of cells, is no exception. Foreign substances are always slipping through the body's outer defenses and attacking its internal systems. Such attacks can be particularly troublesome when the foreign agents work their way into the bloodstream. In such cases, the entire organism may be endangered.

Fortunately, there is a second line of defense which stands ready to repel any invaders which breach the body's protective barriers. Manning this line is a certain type of white blood cell called the lymphoid cell. These defenders swim through the blood and the lymph fluids, ready for action whenever trouble occurs. They respond aggressively to invaders, producing a different weapon or countermeasure for each type of intruder—a kind of magic bullet designed to hit a specific target.

This matching of defense to attack is not a simple matter, for man is vulnerable to many breeds of germs and viruses. Each breed is clearly and definitely distinguished from other breeds by specific chemical compounds—either substances it carries within itself or toxins it passes into the host's bloodstream. These natural identification tags, molecules with characteristic structures, are known as antigens. They are generally compounds of proteins and sugars.

When antigens get into the bloodstream, the body is alerted to the presence of invaders. Though there is still much to be learned about the mechanism of the response to foreign substances, it is known that each antigen stimulates the lymphoid cells to manufacture proteins on a large scale and to dump them into the bloodstream. It is these proteins that lead the body's attack on invaders.

A VIRUS UNDERGOING ANALYSIS
The rainbow of pipes and tubes opposite is the protein separator of the University of California's Virus Laboratory in Berkeley. Complex protein mixtures derived from viruses are fed into the machine, where they flow from tube to tube and break down into their basic components. When the resultant chemicals are analyzed, they will reveal the virus' structure.

How does this system work? Suppose the body is attacked by typhoid germs for the first time. Since the body's natural defenses have never encountered these particular germs before and are unprepared for them, there will be a period during which the germs will multiply with relatively little hindrance.

Evidences of steps taken to combat the infection are not immediately apparent, for it takes some time (usually from four to 10 days) for the body to prepare its defenses. During this period, there is activity inside the lymphoid cells. Some of these cells begin to manufacture large supplies of protein molecules, which form a match with the contours of typhoid-germ antigens. These made-to-order molecules belong to a class of substances called antibodies. These substances pour into the bloodstream, attach themselves to the typhoid germs and cause a chemical change in the germs, which makes them vulnerable to the next step.

This step is accomplished by a crew of wandering scavenger cells called the phagocytes. The phagocytes attack specific types of germs which have been tagged by the antigen-antibody interaction and eliminate the invaders by swallowing them whole. In most cases, the combined offensive by the antibodies and the phagocytes continues until the infection subsides—or until the body's defenses prove inadequate and death results.

The body's defense cadre

One consequence of the body's reaction to any infection is that there is a permanent change in the biochemistry of the organism. The nature of this change becomes evident when the body is exposed to an infection for the second time. On this occasion the body will probably be better prepared to defend itself, for there may be numbers of appropriate antibodies still circulating in the bloodstream as a result of the previous infection. Furthermore, the defenses are more rapidly organized and the antibody-producing cells respond to the threat with such massive quantities of antibodies that the invading germs are quickly overwhelmed. The biochemical structure of the body has been modified so that there is a built-in cadre of defense units always ready to go into action against a specific invader.

This is true whether the first exposure to a disease is the result of a naturally occurring infection or of an infection deliberately induced by injections of a vaccine containing killed germs. The body does not differentiate between the live germs of a true infection and the killed germs of the vaccine: in either case the antibody system goes into action against the invading infection. Thus a vaccine sets up a defense system before the disease itself can strike.

The formation of antibody proteins takes place whenever foreign sub-

A PREVENTIVE MEDICINE MAN
This 19th Century cartoon satirizes some of the devices that were supposed to protect against cholera. The heavily clothed man carries an incense-burning lantern to purify the air; his face is covered by a mask, and he carries bundles of strange and wonderful palliative plants. All these failing, he still has the pouch around his neck, which is sometimes effective: it is filled with herbs that smell so bad that disease carriers avoid him.

stances—germs, viruses or other infecting matter—attack the body. The body's capacity to adapt itself to the number and variety of these threats is impressive. During the course of a lifetime the average person may be exposed to as many as 100,000 different antigens—yet his body will develop antibodies to identify and cope with each invader.

The body's antigen-antibody reaction can also produce side effects which sometimes result in acute physical discomfort. The general term for this condition is allergy—defined as an unusual sensitivity to substances which are generally considered harmless in themselves. Poison ivy toxin is a good example of this type of agent. On a first exposure to the toxin, the body forms antibodies to counteract the foreign substance. After a second exposure, some people react in a hypersensitive way and the antigen-antibody reaction produces (for some reason still unexplained) a side effect in the form of an uncomfortable rash. In some cases, allergies are also caused by pollens, foods, animal fur and drugs.

When an organism successfully defends itself against an attack by an alien substance, it often gains an immunity to that particular invader.

Research on the mechanisms of immunity—the manner in which the body conquers infection—has become one of the most active fields in biology. It has attracted the interest of leading biologists at centers throughout the world: Peter Medawar of Oxford University, Macfarlane Burnet of the Royal Melbourne Hospital in Australia, and a group of scientists at The Rockefeller Institute, among others. Their investigations promise to yield advances in a number of medical areas. For one thing, researchers are seeking improved ways of fighting viruses, the smallest and simplest of the reproducing agents that attack cells. Viruses are so small that they approach molecular dimensions. Some 2,000 average-sized human cells placed side by side would extend about an inch; yet a single one of these cells could hold more than 60 million polio viruses. Research into viruses has assumed an increased significance and urgency now that an increasing number of medical scientists regard some forms of cancer as a virus-induced disease.

"The ultimate parasites"

Viruses have been called "the ultimate parasites," not only because they are the smallest agents that prey on cells but also because they are among the fiercest. They are designed for direct attacks on the genetic machinery which is essential for building the material of the cell. A harmful virus represents infection stripped down to the essentials; it consists of nothing but a core of hereditary material, DNA or RNA, enclosed in a protein shell.

A virus attacks a cell in the most direct manner possible. As it penetrates the cell, the virus discards its protein shell. The DNA or RNA

A CAUTIOUS DOCTOR
Looking like a man-bird hybrid, this 17th Century doctor was on the right track in protecting himself against the London plague. His clothes were leather, his eyes protected with glass and his beak loaded with fumigants. Though medical science had not yet discovered the microorganic cause of disease, such safeguards served as barriers against bacteria. In addition, most medical men refused to touch their patients.

A PLAGUE IN HIMSELF
This 19th Century drawing depicts a typical quack—a charlatan who hawked phony cure-alls to a credulous public. This one is extolling the curative powers of a snake. (Since snakes are immune to their own venom, "logic" led quacks to proclaim that snake-flesh drugs would make human beings immune to disease.) Among their other panaceas, quacks prescribed unicorn horn, powdered pearls, musk, Egyptian mummy dust and crocodile dung.

171

core of the virus then makes its way into the cell's cytoplasm. The subsequent action is a form of war between two groups of hereditary material. If the virus material wins, as much as 80 per cent of the infected cell's DNA may be broken down and resynthesized into viral DNA. Thus, instead of producing its own hereditary material and proteins, the infected cell's nucleus is producing virus substances. After 20 minutes or so, the cell may burst and release hundreds of new viruses. The body responds to viruses, as to germs, by making antibodies—the stimulating antigens in this case being the proteins of the virus shells.

The cow versus smallpox

The first vaccine ever developed was used to combat smallpox, a disease resulting from infection by a virus. More than 150 years ago, when the existence of viruses was unknown, the English physician Edward Jenner began thinking about a bit of contemporary folklore. Gloucestershire farmers believed that if a person became infected with cowpox, a relatively minor disease, his chances of contracting smallpox were considerably reduced. Unlike his medical colleagues, Jenner took this notion seriously enough to put it to the test. His vaccine containing live cowpox viruses proved notably successful in immunizing subjects against the more virulent smallpox. Much later, in the light of more extensive knowledge, investigators were able to prepare vaccines against other virus diseases such as yellow fever, polio and measles.

Future research will undoubtedly feature attempts to develop vaccines against certain diseases in which the viruses involved fail to breed true. A particular strain of the influenza virus, for instance, may produce a proportion of changed or mutated offspring with shells made of slightly different proteins. In this case, the vaccine which protects against the parent strain will probably do little good against the mutants. The essential problem to be solved in this situation is to stimulate the formation of antibodies which will recognize and attack an invader which has changed its identifying characteristics; a protection must be found against a masked attacker. An effective way of stimulating the production of all-purpose antibodies might solve many problems involving immunity. Indeed, recent studies have revealed a hitherto unsuspected kind of natural defense which may lead to new treatments. Investigators have discovered an antivirus protein called "interferon" within the body. This compound is produced by many kinds of cells. Interferon counteracts the effects of many viruses rather than just one.

Although the major objective in fighting germ and virus diseases is to create or enhance immunity, in treating other diseases this may not always be a desirable step. There is, in fact, an important and growing field of medicine in which successful treatment depends primarily on

MICROSCOPIC MUTINY AND MURDER

A virus can invade, enslave and destroy a cell with frightening efficiency. Like a tiny tadpole, its head full of DNA or RNA, the virus drifts until it hooks onto a cell. It bores into the cell and, like a hypodermic needle, injects its nucleic acid. The cell helplessly relinquishes its machinery to the invader, which reproduces at breakneck speed. In about half an hour the dead cell ruptures and releases a flood of new parasites.

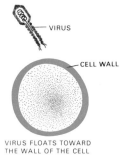

VIRUS FLOATS TOWARD THE WALL OF THE CELL

THE VIRUS ATTACHES ITSELF TO THE CELL

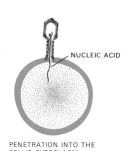

PENETRATION INTO THE CELL'S CYTOPLASM

VIRUSES BEING PRODUCED IN THE HOST CELL

VIRUSES RELEASED TO DESTROY MORE VICTIMS

inhibiting certain natural immune reactions. A system of antibody manufacture that fights all foreign agents may sometimes work against the best interests of the human organism.

This is certainly the case when it comes to transplanting tissues and organs. For some time, surgeons have been studying techniques for replacing damaged parts of the body with healthy parts. They have made considerable progress; indeed, a list of the operations that might be possible from a strictly surgical standpoint is a long one. What surgeons can actually accomplish for patients, however, is limited by the automatic efficiency of the body's antibody mechanisms.

Skin grafts are subject to this limitation. If the skin is obtained from the patient's own body, healing sets in promptly. Blood vessels grow into the replaced tissue as it begins to merge with the edges of surrounding tissue. The graft "takes" within a matter of weeks and persists for life. But the grafted tissue meets with a different reception if it comes from someone other than the patient. Although healing seems to proceed normally at first, blood vessels in the area soon break down and the graft is generally rejected within 10 to 20 days.

The body rejects foreign tissue in the same way that it opposes invading microbes—by producing antibodies which react specifically against the unique protein antigens of the other person's skin. In so reacting, it is obeying a universal law of exclusion, a law which holds for all antibody-producing species. This law holds for all attempted grafts, of whole organs as well as skin.

The only normal exception in this universal rejection of foreign tissue occurs in the case of identical twins. An individual can accept tissue from his identical twin because both have the same genes and their skins contain the same proteins; the body treats the tissue from an identical twin as native rather than alien. In all other cases, genetic differences are too great for successful grafts and preparatory countermeasures are called for. These countermeasures are aimed at eliminating the body's defense mechanisms temporarily.

Attacking the antibodies

One technique for the grafting of foreign tissues involves the use of intense irradiation and special drugs which kill many of the patient's antibody-producing cells. However, this is a drastic treatment: since it suppresses the patient's antibody-producing processes, it leaves him extremely vulnerable to all sorts of infections. The patient must live in a completely sterile environment for weeks or months following the treatment, and even with these precautions there is generally little reason to hope that the graft will take permanently.

The irradiation-drug-treatment procedure has been used in connection

DWELLERS IN THE REALM OF THE LIVING DEAD

VIRUS

PYRITE CRYSTAL

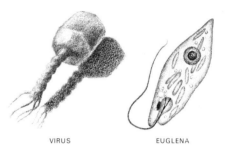

VIRUS

EUGLENA

NEITHER FISH NOR FOWL

Until the discovery of the virus, scientists felt that even if life was difficult to define they could at least distinguish between animate and inanimate matter. But the virus cannot accurately be described as either. Some are shaped very much like pyrite or other mineral crystals; others resemble living organisms such as the euglena. The virus has no means of locomotion, it possesses no source of power and it cannot grow. On the other hand, a virus contains vital DNA or RNA; like living matter, it can reproduce but not until it has commandeered a cell. It can reduce a healthy, productive cell to a mere nursery that fosters a new generation of viruses.

with attempted organ transplants on a number of occasions when it represented the only chance of saving the patient's life. Using these methods, the first successful kidney transplant from one fraternal twin to another was accomplished in Boston's Peter Bent Brigham Hospital in 1959. The significance of this operation lies in the fact that fraternal twins, being the product of the union of separate egg and sperm cells, are not genetically identical and the grafted tissue would therefore cause an antibody response. Four years after the operation the recipient twin was still alive and happy.

In 1963 the University of Mississippi Hospital reported an apparently successful lung transplant after the use of antibody-inhibiting drugs. Although the patient died 18 days later of an unrelated kidney disease, the subsequent autopsy showed little evidence of graft rejection. Though such successes are heartening, the fact is that most attempted organ transplants are failures.

Blitzing the body's defenses

More sophisticated techniques for tissue transplantation may be expected in the future. One new approach is foreshadowed by a series of experiments at the University of Minnesota Medical School, where a group of workers achieved a notable breakthrough, working with laboratory animals. This procedure relies upon a blitz technique which makes use of the fact that the body can cope more effectively with small-scale infections than with major attacks. All-out invasions of foreign agents may actually cause an immunological paralysis, shattering the body's defenses so completely that antibodies are not produced. The sheer mass of antigens seems to swamp immunization mechanisms. The consequences may be tragic, of course, when the invaders are germs or viruses. People who have never been exposed to slight infections of measles in childhood—and who therefore lack any measure of resistance —may die when subjected to a severe attack in later life.

When the invader is a grafted tissue, however, immunological paralysis would be desirable. The individual would then produce few if any antibodies against the tissue and the graft would take. The Minnesota group accomplished this by injecting mice with large and repeated doses of killed cells obtained from mice whose skin was to be used for grafts. Apparently, the concentrations of antigen molecules in the dead cells had a paralyzing effect on antibody producers in the mice that were to receive the grafts. After such conditioning, mice accepted grafts from donor mice which were closely related to them.

Such experimentation may ultimately teach the medical profession how to circumvent nature's molecular defenses. Using killed donor cells is one possible method. Investigators are also trying to isolate certain

MEDIEVAL NOSE GRAFTS

Gaspare Tagliacozzi, a 16th Century anatomist of Bologna, practiced the sophisticated techniques of rebuilding missing or deformed noses. He grafted a strip of flesh from the patient's own arm to the nose *(below)*. Flesh donors could not be used because the patient's body rejected the genetically different cells. In one such case, it was reported, the graft lasted about a year; then the "ingrafted nose grew cold, putrefied, and within a few days dropt off."

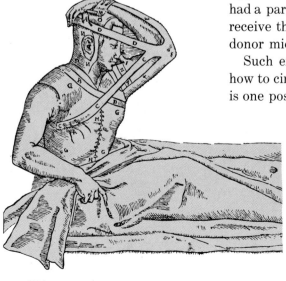

purified antigens from the donor cells—the specific proteins which in normal concentrations stimulate the production of antibodies against grafts and in massive concentrations prevent such reactions. If they succeed, large doses of appropriate antigens administered beforehand may prepare patients to accept new skin or new organs.

The cellular processes which result in antigen recognition and antibody production are also involved in establishing a collateral recognition system—one which enables the body's cells to recognize their own kind. This self-recognition system starts to function within two or three weeks after birth, when a child starts the large-scale manufacture of its own antibodies. (During the embryological stage the infant is protected by the mother's antibodies.)

While scientists do not yet know how the body distinguishes its own cells from foreign cells, it has been suggested that self-recognition may be another example of immunological paralysis, with the antibody-producing mechanisms being overwhelmed by the chemical products of the native cells. There is so much of "self," in other words, that it takes over the organism. Another suggestion is that the cells of an organism may have what one investigator has called "self-markers," chemical structures which identify them.

A case of mistaken identity

Whatever the system used, it is known that these self-recognition procedures sometimes fail and that, in consequence, the body turns on itself. In such cases the body may actually destroy its own cells, mistaking them for aliens and turning out antibodies that operate against them. Certain blood, kidney, thyroid and heart diseases have been traced to such reactions.

The medical gains from research on immunity are obvious, whether they involve fighting and preventing infections, transplanting tissue or repairing the body's defective recognition systems. Such developments, however, are not the only reason this field is attracting investigators. There is a growing feeling among biologists that immunological studies may soon provide significant insights into the factors which make each organism a distinct individual. It is impossible to foresee what will come of such continuing basic studies, involving as they do the investigation of transmitting molecules, protein synthesis and the organization of the body's devices for the long-term storage of information. Scientists can only speculate about future trends.

The continuing study of the cell's role in protecting the body against infection is following the familiar pattern of checking assumption against fact. The basic feature of immunity research, as with the study of muscle fiber or nerve cells, of the cell's working parts and of the genetic code,

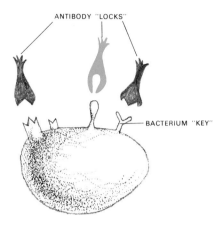

ANTIBODY "LOCKS"

BACTERIUM "KEY"

THE "LOCK-AND-KEY" THEORY

In 1885, Paul Ehrlich, a German bacteriologist, proposed the first theory of immunity to disease. He postulated the existence in the bloodstream of antibodies, protein molecules manufactured by various cells. Floating free, these antibody "locks" seek out the specific bacterial "keys," or antigens, which they fit. Then they neutralize them.

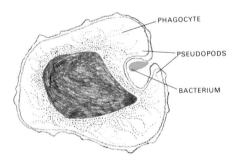

PHAGOCYTE

PSEUDOPODS

BACTERIUM

GLUTTONOUS LITTLE WARRIORS

A phagocyte (above) also performs a vital disease-fighting service: with its pseudopods it engulfs hostile bacteria and viruses. And it "eats" worn-out cells and engulfs chunks of inanimate matter, such as inhaled carbon. There are two types of phagocytes: white blood cells, and stationary phagocytes located in the linings of various organs.

is that it still must be classified as work-in-progress. As is the case with all biological investigations at the cellular level, where the molecule fades into the still-invisible atom and strange events change the very form of energy, scientists of many disciplines are working from a thin base of known fact into an area of assumptions-to-be-tested. The outer boundary of this arena, where trial and error struggle, is the shadowland of outright conjecture.

The pioneering nature of current biological research, the sense of ever-greater discoveries to be found in the next experiment or in the latest microphotograph, is what makes cytology, the study of the cell, one of the most exciting fields of modern science. As research accelerates, it involves experts in many areas. Only by an intensive group effort can we begin to approach a basic understanding of the cell, a speck of living matter organized so exquisitely that it challenges the ingenuity of physicists, chemists, mathematicians and electronics engineers as well as biologists. Every year investigators come up against problems of increasing complexity.

We may have to wait a long time before some contemporary problems are solved, although discoveries have come at a breathtaking pace during the past decade or so. In any case, the ultimate rewards will be great. For within the cell man will find new knowledge about life—and about the shaping of his own future.

Medicine's Journey from Faith to Fact

In the last century the dazzling progress of scientific medicine has dispelled the demonic apparitions that dominated man's ideas of disease for centuries. During most of recorded history, medical theory and practice had been bound to a belief in magic, religion (*opposite*) or philosophy. Since spirits of the dead, not living cells, were often held accountable for everything from pox to the plague, it followed that ritual and prayer, not prophylaxis, were considered the universal cures. How else could mortal men combat the cunning of devils or respond to the wrath of God? Not until a hundred years ago, when Louis Pasteur demonstrated that living organisms could cause sickness, did popular superstition begin to yield to an enlightened attitude toward the microscopic world where affliction begins. Thus the record of man's attitude toward infectious ailments commences with ancient fears and evolves to today's assault on the tyranny of disease.

CHRIST CURING A LEPER
A 12th Century mosaic in a Sicilian cathedral depicts a Biblical reference to Christ casting out devils which afflict the worshipers with leprosy. Blaming sickness on malignant demons was a common diagnosis until the last century, when the microscope first identified the cellular world of disease organisms. Leprosy's real cause, a rod-shaped bacterium, was discovered in 1873.

A Sickness unto Death

"Doubtless the visitation itself is a stroke from Heaven . . ." wrote Daniel Defoe of the plague of 1665, ". . . a messenger of His vengeance. . . ." In assigning the cause of plague to divine retribution, Defoe reflected a tradition dating back to the Old Testament, which records, in I Samuel, that "the hand of the Lord was against the city" during an outbreak of plague.

Indeed, to men who little understood their true causes, the periodic plagues which reaped a huge harvest of human life must have seemed a monstrous punishment for even more monstrous sins. Fifty years after the pestilence broke out in the Egyptian port of Pelusium in 542 A.D., for example, it spread through Europe and Asia, and took 100 million lives.

Although it was not until 1894 that a one-celled organism, the bacillus *Pasteurella pestis*, was found to cause both forms of plague (bubonic and pneumonic), some medieval scientists had sensed a relationship between the disease and the endemic filth in which the bacillus thrives. When the Black Death roamed Europe in the 14th Century, one physician, Balavignus, warned his fellow Jews in the ghetto near Strasbourg to burn their refuse and observe sanitary practices. They did, and the rats, which carry the common fleas that transmit the bubonic plague, deserted the Jewish quarter. The result: the ghetto suffered only 5 per cent of the losses incurred by the rest of the community in the epidemic.

AN ANCIENT TORMENT
A German woodcut of the 15th Century illustrates the death of the Biblical prophet Eli and the plethora of mice (now thought to be rats) that preceded an outbreak of plague. From the earliest days, an abundance of dead rats was frequently noted during epidemics. But until recent times the creatures were considered only as victims of the disease rather than its carriers.

A GHOSTLY RIDER
In *The Triumph of Death,* a fresco attributed to an unknown 15th Century artist, the figure of Death and his skeletal steed form an ironic triumphal arch over the bodies of dying potentates. The painter no doubt witnessed a plague epidemic, for he has detailed the democracy of the disease, which has struck or is about to strike all members of the social order.

Allaying Fears and Beating Pox

By the end of the 18th Century the misconceptions that ruled the popular mind were dealt a series of deadly blows by the emerging forces of scientific medicine. Most innovations, however, met massive resistance. In Europe, the idea that inoculations could produce immunity to certain diseases caused a furor; "since smallpox was a punishment from God, no man has a right to interfere," as one historian has put it. In England, medical caricatures like the one at left, which expressed the public's anxiety, enjoyed a great vogue. Ironically, the greatest medical triumph of the age was stimulated by an old wives' tale. Dr. Edward Jenner noted that in his native Gloucestershire it was a common belief that dairymaids who had contracted cowpox did not come down with the far more fatal smallpox. In 1796 Jenner took some fluid from the arm of a local milkmaid who was suffering from cowpox and inoculated a young boy with it. Jenner believed the lad was now immune to smallpox; when the boy was inoculated with live smallpox virus, he failed to develop the disease.

Despite initial ridicule—he was almost drummed out of his medical society—Jenner's contribution virtually eliminated epidemics of what the 19th Century historian Thomas Macaulay has called "the most terrible of all the ministers of death." Equally important, the success of his vaccine ultimately overcame the widespread opposition to inoculations and proved that scientific principles based on experimental evidence were able to replace traditional hit-or-miss treatments.

AN OUTBREAK OF COWS
Popular resistance to the new smallpox vaccine is reflected in this satirical painting, titled *The Cow Pock—or—the Wonderful Effects of the New Inoculation!* Dr. Jenner is seen inoculating his patients with "vaccine pock hot from ye cow" while little cows burst from various parts of their bodies. Before Jenner's vaccine, smallpox killed 30 per cent of all English babies.

ANTON VAN LEEUWENHOEK

AN EARLY MICROSCOPE

The paddlelike instrument below is one of Anton van Leeuwenhoek's many homemade microscopes. Specimens were mounted on the pinpoint *(below)* and adjusted by the thumbscrew and the round knob above it. Opposite the pinpoint, between two metal plates, is the lens. Also shown are sketches of teeth bacteria reproduced from a Leeuwenhoek letter.

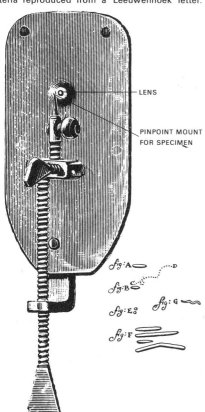

LENS

PINPOINT MOUNT FOR SPECIMEN

A FANCY INSTRUMENT

The microscope above, with its reflecting mirror and movable barrel, was an advanced instrument in the 18th Century. Now in London's Wellcome Historical Medical Museum, it was once used by the Italian naturalist Lazzaro Spallanzani, noted for his experiments on blood circulation and fertilization. He also did research to rebut the theory of spontaneous generation.

First Views of a World upon a Pin

Toward the end of the 17th Century early scientists were provided with a powerful new weapon—the microscope—in their quest for the causes of disease.

The first man to study the cell, Anton van Leeuwenhoek, the Dutch naturalist, armed himself with homemade instruments. Among many other discoveries, he systematically examined the blood's red corpuscles and the structure of muscles.

In England, Robert Hooke, a contemporary of Leeuwenhoek's, described the cellular nature of plant tissue and first called their basic unit "cells."

But despite these observations, it was not until the mid-19th Century that researchers proved that some of these microorganisms actually produced disease.

The important links in this chain of cause and effect were the studies revealing that rod-shaped bacilli were responsible for anthrax, a cattle disease. The German, Robert Koch, knew that large numbers of these rods were always present in the blood of diseased animals. In 1876 he contaminated healthy blood serum with a single drop of infected blood from an anthrax victim. Then, after the culture had grown, a drop from it was transferred to another quantity of healthy serum. After eight successive transfers the concentration was still virulent enough to infect a healthy animal. This conclusive demonstration led to discoveries of the bacterial nature of many other diseases (tuberculosis, typhoid fever, plague, tetanus) now controlled by modern medicine.

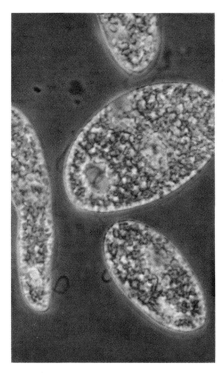

A PRIMITIVE ANIMAL
Euglena gracilis, a one-celled animal, is in the same category as the amoeba and paramecium. A whiplike appendage (not seen here because of its rapid motion) pulls the organism along.

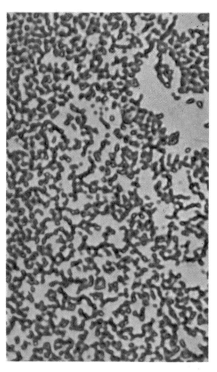

A DRIFTER IN DUST
Staphylococcus aureus organisms are spherical bacteria that are found alone, in pairs and in masses. Most of the boils that have beset humans from the time of Job are caused by them.

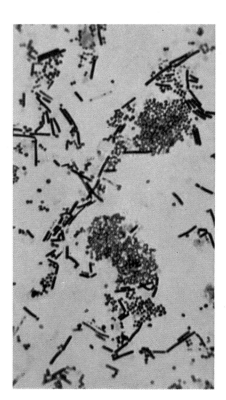

THE COMMONEST BACTERIA
Rodlike bacilli and round cocci are shown in microscopic colonies. The rod-shaped forms (from the Greek *bakterion,* a rod) gave the whole group of organisms its name, *Bacteria.*

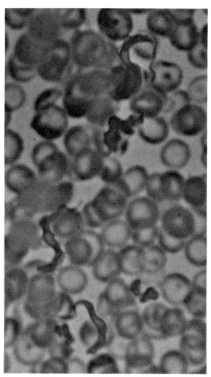

AGENTS OF SLEEPING SICKNESS
Trypanosoma gambiense is a protozoan parasite transmitted by the bites of the tsetse fly. A thousandth of an inch long, they are shown in blood, in which part of their life cycle occurs.

The War on Surgical Pests

Before the origins of infectious diseases had been located among invisible microorganisms, unsanitary hospital conditions led to a high rate of death from postoperative infections. Even in the mid-19th Century, when more scrupulous cleanliness was practiced, the English surgeon Joseph Lister observed that 45 per cent of his amputees were dying from tetanus, septicemia and hospital gangrene. Noting that closed wounds did not form pus while open ones exposed to the air did, he concluded that pus formation was due to contact with something in the air. Later, hearing of Pasteur's proof of the microorganic cause of putrefaction, Lister began using carbolic acid to destroy germs on the site of open wounds. These antiseptic measures eliminated every single case of postoperative infection in Lister's ward.

A crude 16th Century practice is depicted in this Flemish painting of the surgical removal of a forehead cyst as treatment for insanity.

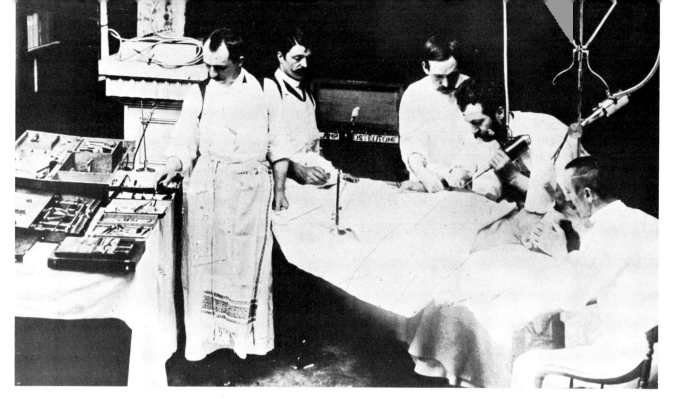

AN ABSENCE OF NURSES

A photograph of a bone operation in New York taken in 1870 shows that nurses were not yet available to assist in surgery. In 1873 Bellevue Hospital established the first nursing school laid down along the lines suggested by Florence Nightingale. Today, a function of the operating-room nurse is to keep working conditions aseptically clean so that infections do not develop.

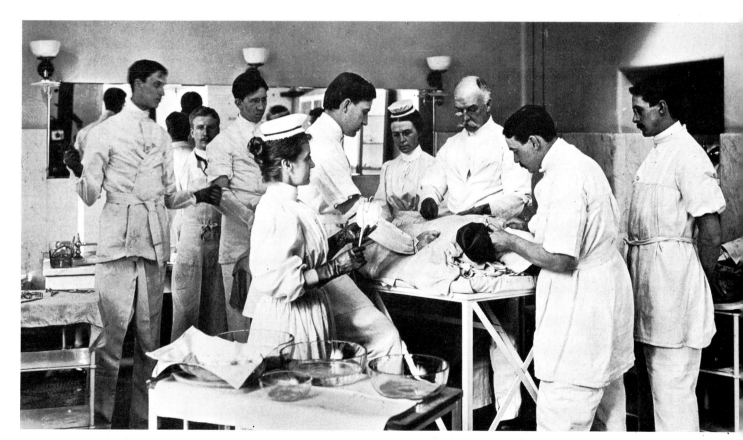

A SURFEIT OF ASSISTANTS

Operations like this appendectomy performed in 1900 called for many more assistants than are found in a modern operating room. Today, members of a surgical team are highly special-ized and equipment is more elaborate. Anes-thesia, too, is safer. Although still highly volatile, anesthetics are used with superior equipment, virtually eliminating the danger of explosion.

Knocking Out Germs before They Breed

The turn of the century saw an interest in preventive medicine grow apace with the newly effective antiseptic precautions in hospitals. Methods ranged from the simple expedient of wearing gauze masks during influenza epidemics *(below)* to highly organized efforts at mass smallpox vaccinations *(right)*—a practice which no longer unleashed the superstitious fury that attended similar events in Jenner's time.

A remarkably effective preventive technique was to attack germs at their source. For example, following U.S. Army Major Walter Reed's proof in 1901 that yellow fever is transmitted to man by the mosquito *Aëdes aegypti*, these mosquitoes' breeding grounds in Havana were destroyed and the disease was wiped out.

SMITING SMALLPOX
Dutch women are vaccinated against smallpox around 1900 *(above)*. Although the disease has ceased to be endemic in most countries of the world, travelers have periodically reintroduced it into "clean" areas. In 1947 some five million New Yorkers were vaccinated within 20 days after a smallpox scare. Today, the U.S. demands that all incoming travelers must be vaccinated.

SIGNALING A VIRUS TO STOP
The mask worn by this New York policeman directing traffic at the height of the 1918 influenza epidemic offered little protection from the disease, for the tiny viruses that cause it could easily filter through. The 1918 scourge ranks with the Black Death as one of the most destructive holocausts ever to sweep the earth: in a few months it took some 20 million lives.

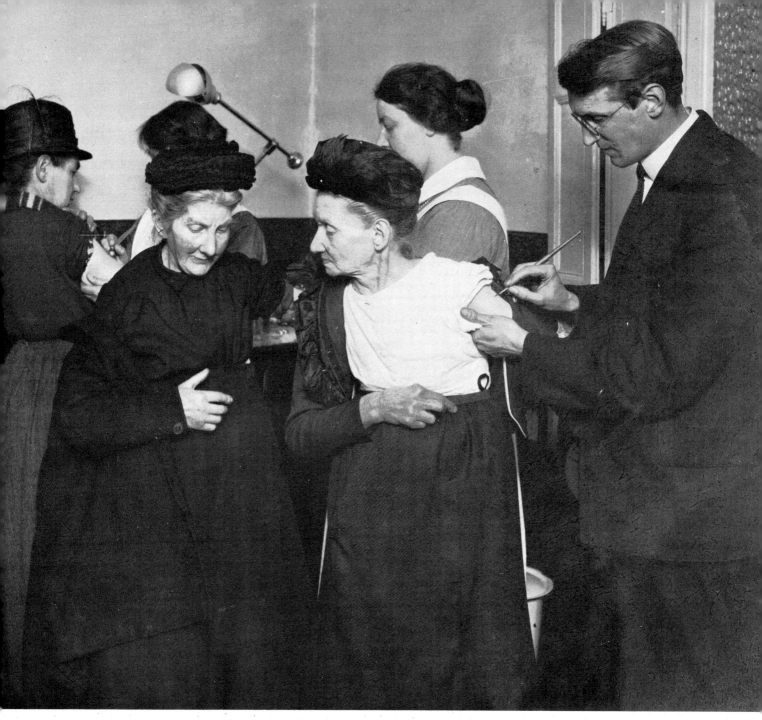

MOSQUITO MARAUDERS

Workers in Brazil *(left)* clear a swamp in a campaign against yellow fever launched in 1903 and financed by The Rockefeller Foundation. Victims of the disease were screened against further mosquito bites; homes and factories were fumigated; cisterns and water containers where the insects like to breed were covered. As in Cuba, the efforts curtailed the disease.

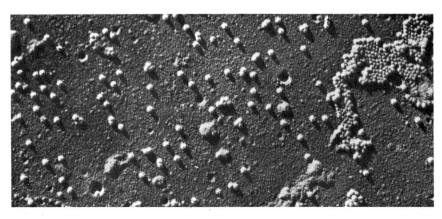

In 1953, for the first time an electron microscope magnified polio virus 77,000-fold.

On the Trail of a Tiny Tyrant

The changing role of medical researchers in Western society—from eccentric to popular hero—is in many ways reflected in the history of poliomyelitis research which reached a dramatic climax with the acclaim lavished on Dr. Jonas Salk for the introduction of an effective vaccine in 1955.

But before Salk, researchers in half a dozen countries had paved the way for polio prevention. By the first decade of the 20th Century, it was known that it was infectious, was transmitted by personal contact and did not always result in paralysis.

However, the cause of polio had been thought to be bacteria. Then in 1909 Dr. Simon Flexner, an American pathologist, finally isolated the agent responsible: a virus so small it could pass through the finest filters known. But the virus had not yet been found in the bloodstream of its victims. It was assumed it grew only in nerve cells. And a vaccine made from infected nerve tissue produced side effects sometimes as crippling as the disease itself.

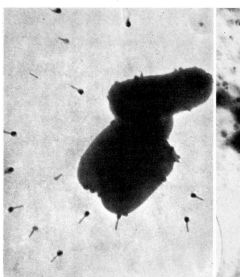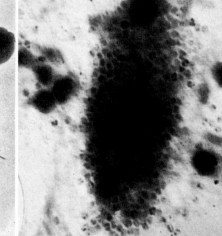

GANGING UP ON A CELL

A contingent of tadpole-shaped viruses converges on three living cells to break them to bits *(above, left)*. The photograph at right shows viruses multiplying rapidly inside the cell. Soon they will rupture the host cell. Taken with an electron microscope, these photos have caught viruses attacking a living cell from the outside and from within. Virologists do not know how viruses kill a cell or how they are multiplied within the cell. Once science learns the answers, cures may be found not only for polio but also for colds, influenza and other baffling ailments.

188

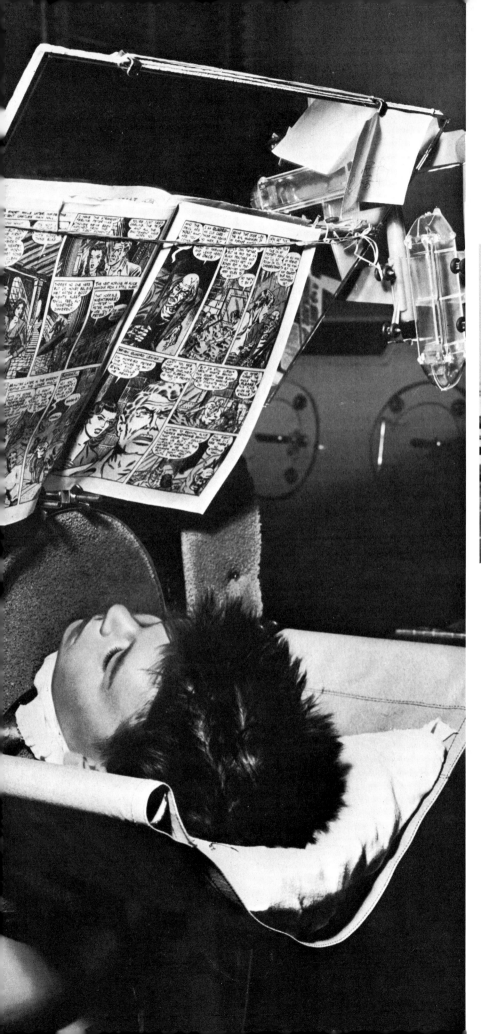

A BOYHOOD IN BRACES

A four-year-old polio victim *(above)* helps collect funds for a new county hospital in his native High Point, North Carolina, during a polio epidemic in 1948. North Carolina was particularly hard hit. In Greensboro, a makeshift Army hospital had twice as many patients as beds.

LIFE IN AN IRON LUNG

Before the introduction of polio vaccines, this young iron-lung patient was one of 36,000 U.S. victims of paralytic polio in the year 1952. A decade later, after nationwide inoculations with both Salk vaccine and the live vaccines, polio incidence was reduced by 99 per cent.

A PIONEER RESEARCHER
Dr. Jonas Salk *(above)* and his associates at the University of Pittsburgh made up a vaccine from viruses killed by formaldehyde. It sets up a protective antibody barrier in the bloodstream.

DOCTOR WITH A DARING IDEA
Dr. Albert Sabin of Cincinnati developed the first live-virus polio vaccine to be put into regular use. Licensed in the U.S. in 1962, it generates immunity in both the blood and intestinal tract.

ASSEMBLED FOR SPRAYS
Toting babies and parking under parasols to escape the tropical sun, natives of the Congo wait their turn for a vaccination by mouth spray during an anti-polio drive among 250,000 Congolese in 1958 *(right)*. In this first mass trial of live vaccine, the immunization team utilized the live-virus vaccine developed by Dr. Hilary Koprowski of The Wistar Institute, Philadelphia.

Immunity for Millions

Forty years after Flexner's findings, a team of American scientists was able, for the first time, to grow polio viruses in non-nerve tissue. Other researchers had shown that there were three distinct types of polio viruses which produced identical symptoms and aftereffects. These viruses proliferate in the lower intestinal tract and the throat, causing symptoms so mild they are often overlooked. Occasionally, however, they enter the bloodstream and eventually attach themselves to nerve cells, resulting in dreaded paralytic polio. These discoveries provided the theoretical basis for the vaccines. For they proved that the disease's path allows for the production of antibodies that intercept the viruses before they reach the vital nervous system, where they do their damage.

Thus, beginning with the discovery that some cells support life while others—like the bacteria discussed on these pages—threaten to destroy it, medical investigators have developed unprecedented new weapons to combat lethal afflictions. The success of this cell research holds a promise of even greater triumphs in the unending struggle against disabling disease.

DRIVE-IN SHOTS
Motorists in Glendale, California, receive anti-polio shots while sitting in their cars *(right)*. Some 2,250 vaccinations were dispensed in a single two-and-one-half-hour session. Within seven years after the vaccines were put into use, 98 million Americans had received one shot or more of the multiple-shot Salk vaccine and millions more were taking the oral vaccines.

The Vocabulary of Cellular Biology

MANY NEW TERMS have been coined by scientists to describe the working parts and processes recently revealed within the cell by new experimental techniques and modern research equipment. The glossary of cellular nomenclature on this and the following pages includes some of these new terms.

ACTIN One of the two protein constituents of muscle fibrils responsible for muscular contraction; the protein of which the thin filament is composed. (See also **MYOSIN.**)

ANGSTROM A measuring unit equal to one two-hundred-fifty-millionth of an inch.

ANTIBODY A protein, produced by an animal cell, that acts to neutralize an invading foreign agent, or antigen.

AMINO ACIDS A group of organic substances that are the building blocks of the large protein molecules.

ANTIGEN A foreign substance that stimulates the formation of antibodies when introduced into the bloodstream.

ATP An abbreviation for adenosine triphosphate, a compound which serves as a carrier of energy for cells.

AXON The fiber that carries message impulses from the nerve cell to other cells.

BACTERIA Microorganisms usually classified as plants. Some bacteria are helpful to man; others cause disease.

BASE-PAIR A rung of the DNA spiral ladder composed of two nitrogenous bases chemically linked; the base structures are such that adenine will fit precisely only with thymine and guanine only with cytosine.

BILE CANALICULUS A groove on the surface of the liver cell which acts as a collecting system for bile made by the cell.

CARBON CYCLE The life cycle as it relates to carbon compounds. By photosynthesis, plants take carbon from carbon dioxide in the air and use it to form carbohydrates. Animals then use the carbohydrates as food; in this process carbon is returned to the air in the form of carbon dioxide.

CATALYST A substance which speeds up or slows down a chemical change but which is not itself changed or used up in the reaction.

CELL MEMBRANE A thin film that encloses the cell. It consists of a layer of fat molecules sandwiched between two layers of protein molecules.

CENTRIOLE A small body which plays a part in cell division. It is found near the nucleus of a cell.

CHLOROPHYLL The green pigment which extracts energy from sunlight during photosynthesis in plants.

CHLOROPLAST A globular body, found in plant cells, in which photosynthesis takes place.

CHROMATIN A threadlike network within the nucleus of a cell. The chromatin contains the cell's hereditary material, and at the time of mitosis condenses into chromosomes.

CHROMOSOMES Long threads containing DNA found within the nucleus of a cell. Chromosomes contain the cell's hereditary material.

CILIUM A hairlike appendage on the surface of a cell, it is a shorter variant of the flagellum. It aids in cellular locomotion and creates currents in surrounding fluids.

CLEAVAGE The stage of an embryo's development immediately following fertilization when rapid cell division takes place, but little or no growth of the entire organism.

CYTOPLASM The viscous material surrounding the nucleus of a cell.

DENDRITES Fibers which carry message impulses toward the nerve cell from other cells and sensory areas of the body.

DNA An abbreviation for deoxyribonucleic acid, a substance within the chromosomes of a cell. It carries the genetic information necessary for the replication of the cell and directs the building of proteins.

ELECTRON One of the elementary particles which make up an atom. Electrons surround the nucleus of an atom at various energy levels and have a negative charge.

ELECTRON-TRANSPORT CHAIN A series of biochemical reactions in which excited electrons are passed along a chain of acceptor molecules. This results in a release of energy, which is used for life processes within the cell.

EMBRYO A young organism prior to birth or hatching.

ENZYME An organic catalyst, usually a protein, which controls a cell's chemical reactions.

EPITHELIUM A membranous tissue that covers exposed surfaces and lines the hollow organs of the animal body. Examples: skin, the linings of the digestive and respiratory tracts.

ER An abbreviation for endoplasmic reticulum, a system of hollow sheets found in the cytoplasm. ER may function as a transport system within the cell.

FIBRIL A bundle of filaments in a striated muscle cell.

FILAMENTS Threadlike structures found in nerve and muscle cells. In striated muscles, the filaments provide the mechanism for muscle contraction.

FLAGELLUM A whiplike appendage of a cell. It can function either as an organ of locomotion or as a device for moving the fluid surrounding the cell.

GENE A unit of hereditary material which is related to a particular characteristic, such as blond hair. It is thought that genes are sections of the DNA molecules.

GLUCOSE A form of sugar, glucose is the end product of the photosynthetic process. Glucose contains stored energy derived by the plant from sunlight.

GLYCOGEN (Animal Starch) A nutrient stored in various types of animal cells.

GLYCOLYSIS A process in animal and plant cells which is the first step in recovering the energy that was stored in glucose during photosynthesis.

GOLGI COMPLEX A cellular structure consisting of several flat hollow disks "stacked" one on top of the other. The Golgi complex acts as a packaging center for proteins to be secreted from the cell.

GRANA Drum-shaped cylindrical bodies within the chloroplasts. Grana contain the light-trapping chlorophyll molecules.

HEME That portion of hemoglobin which contains iron. It unites with oxygen in the lungs, then carries the oxygen to the body's tissues.

KREBS CYCLE The final process in breaking down glucose in plant and animal cells. The end product is carbon dioxide.

LYMPHOID CELL A type of blood cell, including lymphocytes and plasma cells. It is currently thought that both may produce antibodies.

LYSOSOME A structure in the cell containing digestive enzymes that break down large molecules.

METABOLISM The process by which a living cell uses food material to build up living matter or break down material within the cell into simpler substances.

MICROBODIES Structures found in the cytoplasm of some cells and currently believed to contain various enzymes.

MICRON A unit of measure equal to one twenty-five-thousandth of an inch, or one millionth of a meter.

MICROSURGERY Surgical procedures on the cellular level; a light microscope and miniaturized instruments are used.

MICROVILLI Fingerlike projections on the surface of the cell membrane which serve to increase the surface area and therefore increase the cell's ability to absorb materials from the environment.

MITOCHONDRIA The cellular "powerhouses" which provide the cell with most of its usable energy.

MOLECULE The smallest unit of a substance that can exist in a free state and still retain the properties of the mass of the substance. Molecules are made up of atoms.

"MORTISE AND TENON" JOINT A woodworking term used by biologists to describe one of the many attachment mechanisms which hold cells to one another.

MUSCLE Specialized cells organized into contractile and expansible tissues that govern all movement—interior and exterior—in the body. Muscles are of three kinds: (1) skeletal muscles are responsible for all voluntary or deliberate movement; (2) smooth muscles are responsible for involuntary movement; (3) cardiac muscle, resembling both skeletal and smooth varieties, is responsible for the involuntary movement of the heart.

MYOSIN One of the two protein constituents of muscle fibrils responsible for muscular contraction; the protein found in the thick filaments. (See also **ACTIN**.)

NEUROHUMOR A chemical substance which apparently effects the passage of nerve impulses from one cell to another at the synapse.

NUCLEOLUS A structure, found in the nucleus of the cell and associated with the chromosomes, which contains most of the RNA in the nucleus.

NUCLEOTIDE The basic unit of DNA and RNA, consisting of a base attached to a sugar-phosphate unit.

NUCLEUS The structure, usually near the center of the cell, which contains the chromosomes holding the hereditary material. The nucleus controls many cell activities.

ORGANIC An adjective used to describe any substance containing carbon; formerly, anything living or derived from living organisms.

PHAGOCYTE A scavenger cell which engulfs foreign matter invading the body.

PHOTOSYNTHESIS The process by which green plants use the energy of sunlight to turn carbon dioxide and water into food substances.

PROTEIN A naturally occurring substance which is made up of amino acids that contain carbon, hydrogen, oxygen, nitrogen and sometimes sulphur. Present in many forms in all living matter, proteins direct and speed the life processes, form structural materials and provide energy for cellular processes.

PROTOPLASM The general term for the material of which all cells of plants and animals are formed. It is usually a jelly-like substance, grayish in appearance. Protoplasm is formed of varying amounts of water, proteins, fats, carbohydrates and traces of other matter.

RESPIRATION The release of energy, carbon dioxide and water as oxygen is consumed; the opposite of photosynthesis.

RIBOSOMES Structures within the cell where the protein compounds found in all living matter are manufactured.

RNA The abbreviation for ribonucleic acid. A nucleic acid similar to DNA, but with somewhat different components.

SOMITES Masses of middle-layer cells in an embryo which, in later stages of development, give rise to the vertebrae, part of the skin and certain trunk muscles.

SYNAPSE The junction where a nerve impulse must cross from one nerve cell to another; actually a gap which can be as narrow as a millionth of an inch.

TOXIN A poisonous product arising from a plant or animal cell.

VIRUS A disease-causing agent (smaller than any cell) made of a core of DNA or RNA and a shell which is usually protein. Viruses can reproduce only in living cells.

THE CONSTRUCTION OF A CELL

The illustration below (and the one on page 17) is a cross section of a model of a liver cell, magnified about 10,000 times. The labeled components are defined in the preceding glossary. Though this is a highly specialized cell, each of its parts except the bile canaliculus is found in most other cells.

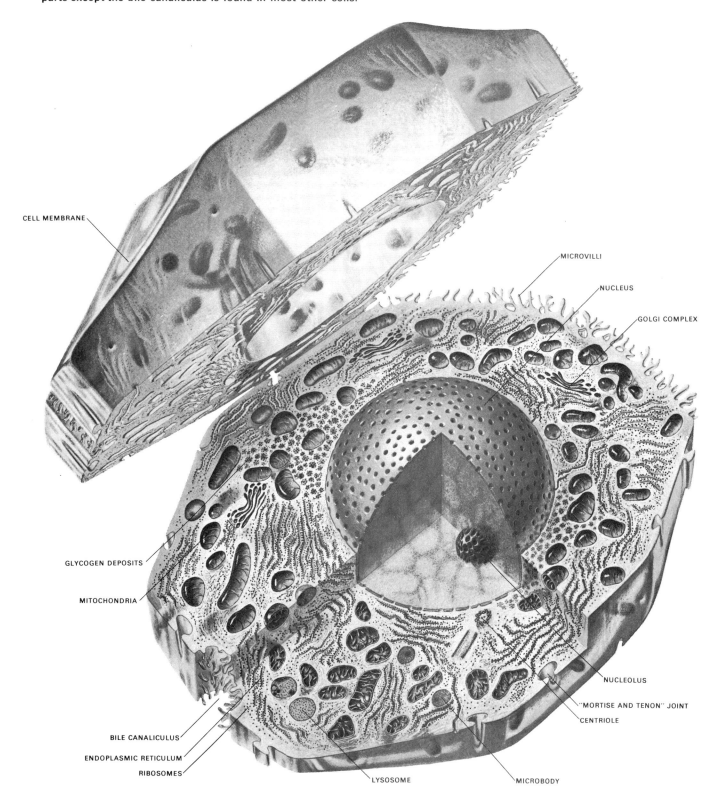

CELL MEMBRANE

MICROVILLI

NUCLEUS

GOLGI COMPLEX

GLYCOGEN DEPOSITS

MITOCHONDRIA

NUCLEOLUS

"MORTISE AND TENON" JOINT

CENTRIOLE

BILE CANALICULUS

ENDOPLASMIC RETICULUM

RIBOSOMES

LYSOSOME

MICROBODY

BIBLIOGRAPHY

General

*Blum, H. F., *Time's Arrow and Evolution*. Princeton University Press, 1951.

Bonner, John Tyler, *The Ideas of Biology*. Harper and Bros., 1962.

Darling, Lois and Louis, *The Science of Life*. World, 1961.

†Hoffman, Joseph G., *The Life and Death of Cells*. Doubleday, 1957.

†Mercer, E. H., *Cells: Their Structure and Function*. Doubleday, 1962.

Stanley, Wendell M. and Evans G. Valens, *Viruses and the Nature of Life*. E. P. Dutton, 1961.

Cell Biology

*Asimov, Isaac, *The Chemicals of Life*. Abelard, 1954.

Buchsbaum, Ralph, *Animals without Backbones*. University of Chicago Press, 1948.

†Galambos, Robert, *Nerves and Muscles*. Doubleday, 1962.

†Galston, Arthur W., *The Life of the Green Plant*. Prentice-Hall, 1961.

†Gerard, R. W., *Unresting Cells*. Harper and Bros., 1961.

†Johnson, Willis H. and William C. Steere, eds., *This Is Life: Essays in Modern Biology*. Holt, Rinehart and Winston, 1962.

†Loewy, Ariel G. and Philip Siekevitz, *Cell Structure and Function*. Holt, Rinehart and Winston, 1963.

†Swanson, Carl P., *The Cell*. Prentice-Hall, 1960.

†Waddington, C. H., *How Animals Develop*. Harper and Bros., 1962.

Wyburn, G. M., *The Nervous System*. Academic Press, 1960.

Cell Biophysics

Asimov, Isaac, *Life and Energy*. Doubleday, 1962.

*Schrodinger, Erwin, *What Is Life?* Cambridge University Press, 1963.

Origin of Cellular Life

*Adler, Irving, *How Life Began*. New American Library, 1957.

†Editors of *Scientific American*, *The Physics and Chemistry of Life*. Simon and Schuster, 1956.

*Ehrensvärd, Gösta, *Life: Origin and Development*. Phoenix, 1961.

†Gamow, George, *Biography of the Earth*. Viking, 1959.

†Oparin, A. I., *Origin of Life*. Dover, 1953.

†Rush, J. H., *The Dawn of Life*. New American Library, 1962.

Evolution and Heredity

*Asimov, Isaac, *The Genetic Code*. Orion, 1963.

*Asimov, Isaac, *The Wellsprings of Life*. Abelard, 1960.

†Bonner, David M., *Heredity*. Prentice-Hall, 1961.

†Carrington, Richard, *A Guide to Earth History*. Mentor, 1956.

Frisch, Karl von, *Man and the Living World*. Harcourt, Brace and World, 1963.

†Moore, John, *Heredity and Development*. Oxford University Press, 1963.

Cells and Disease

*de Kruif, Paul, *Microbe Hunters*. Harcourt, Brace, 1932.

Dubos, René, *The Unseen World*. Rockefeller Institute Press, 1962.

†Gale, A. H., *Epidemic Diseases*. Penguin, 1959.

Taylor, Gordon Rattray, *The Science of Life. A Picture History of Biology*. McGraw-Hill, 1963.

Williams, Greer, *Virus Hunters*. Alfred A. Knopf, 1959.

*Also available in paperback edition.

†Only available in paperback edition.

ACKNOWLEDGMENTS

The editors of this book are especially indebted to Dr. Teru Hayashi, Professor of Zoology, Graduate Faculties, Columbia University, Dr. David C. Luck, Research Associate, The Rockefeller Institute, and Dr. Lee D. Peachey, Associate Professor of Zoology, Columbia University, who served as general consultants. The Rockefeller Institute and Woods Hole Oceanographic Institution were also especially helpful in the preparation of the book, as well as the following persons: Dr. Robert D. Allen, Professor of Biology, Princeton University; Dr. Vincent G. Allfrey, Associate Professor, The Rockefeller Institute; Dr. Elso S. Barghoorn, Professor of Botany, Harvard University; Albert H. Blum, Advertising Manager, Bausch and Lomb, Inc., Rochester, New York; Anthony Cerami, Graduate Fellow in Biochemistry, The Rockefeller Institute; Dr. Britton Chance, Professor of Medical Physics, University of Pennsylvania Medical School; Dr. George Claus, New York University Medical Center; Dr. Eric Davidson, Research Associate, The Rockefeller Institute; Dr. Gerald Edelman, Associate Dean of Graduate Students, The Rockefeller Institute; Dr. Heinz F. Eichenwald, Professor of Pediatrics, Cornell University Medical College; Institute of Animal Physiology, Cambridge University, England; Professor Aharon Katchalsky-Katzir, Chairman of the Department of Polymer Research, Weizmann Institute of Science, Rehovoth, Israel; Dr. Hilary Koprowski, Director, Dr. Rupert E. Billingham and Dr. Stanley A. Plotkin, The Wistar Institute, Philadelphia; Dr. Virginia Littau, Research Associate, The Rockefeller Institute; Mrs. Adele Mathyssee, The Burndy Library, Norwalk, Connecticut; Dr. Alfred E. Mirsky, Professor, The Rockefeller Institute; Dr. Norman D. Newell, Curator of Fossil Invertebrates, American Museum of Natural History; Dr. Charles Noback, Professor of Anatomy, College of Physicians and Surgeons, Columbia University; Dr. William Rubey, Professor of Geology and Geophysics, Institute of Geophysics, University of California at Los Angeles; Dr. Ruth Sager, Department of Zoology, Columbia University; Lewis M. Stark and Assistant Librarians, Rare Book Department, Miss Elizabeth B. Roth and Wilson A. Duprey, Print Department of the New York Public Library; Dr. William Stein, Professor, The Rockefeller Institute; Dr. Roman Vishniac; and Mrs. Alice D. Weaver and Librarians of the Rare Book Department at the New York Academy of Medicine.

INDEX

Numerals in italics indicate a photograph or painting of the subject mentioned.

A

Acantharia, *19*
Acceptor molecules, in electron-transport chains, *35,* 36-37, 39, 40
Acetylcholine, 149
Acrasin, 106, 110
Actin, 128-129, 130
Actomyosin, 129
Adaptation, 89-90
Adenine, 60-61, *70*
Adenosine triphosphate. *See* ATP
ADP (adenosine diphosphate), 46, 47
Aging: cellular, 107-108, 124; of organism, 107-108
Albinism, *76-77*
Algae, 18, *19, 112-113;* in carbon cycle experiment, *43;* fossils, 89; habitats, 112; number of species, 112; pigment of, and capture of sunlight, *diagram* 39; sizes, 112; as space food, *diagram* 41
Allergies, 171
Allfrey, Vincent, *138*
Amino acids, 84; in Krebs cycle, 48; laboratory creation of, *80,* 83-84, *diagram* 85; laboratory linking into polymers, 86, 97; number of, 73; possible synthesis in early earth atmosphere, 84-85; protein synthesis from, 72, *73;* research into protein synthesis from, *diagram* 136-137, *138-141*
Amoeba, 9, 20, 110; food ingestion, *24-25;* life cycle, 24; locomotion, *24,* 28, *104,* 123; protective shell, 30
Amoeboid movement, 28, 130
Anatomy: 14th Century, *124;* 16th Century, *125, 148*
Anesthesia, 185
Angstrom, unit of measurement, *11,* 13
Animal cells, *17, 18-19;* energy transformations in, 34, 38-40, 41, 42, *diagram* 48, 49; flexibility of shape, 19, *24-25;* food storage in, 41; Krebs cycle, 39-42, *diagram* 48. *See also* Animals
Animalcules, 82
Animals: emergence and evolution, 90; *vs.* plants, 19, 30, 49; protective cover, 30; respiration, 42, *diagram* 48, 49; role in carbon cycle, 33, 42, *43,* 49. *See also* Animal cells; Multicelled organisms; Single-celled animals
Anthrax, 183
Antibodies: all-purpose, 172; defined, 170; failure of self-recognition system, and immunological paralysis, 175; function of, 170, *175;* inhibiting treatments, 173-175; manufacture of, 170, 171, 172; rejection of surgical transplants by, 172
Antigens: defenses against, 169-171, 172, *175;* defined, 169; diversity of, 171; in surgical transplants, 173
Antithamnion plumula, 112-113
Aristotle, 81, 86
Atmosphere, earth: early composition of, 83, 90; increase in carbon dioxide, as step toward life, 88; increase in oxygen, and emergence of animals, 89-90; possible synthesis of organic compounds in, 84-85, 92; post-deluge composition of, 85
ATP (adenosine triphosphate), *49,* 50, 86; coupling problem, 128; energy release, 37, 50, 128; function of, 21, 37, 47; production in animal cells, *diagram* 38, 39-40, *diagram* 48, 127; production in muscles, 127-128; production in plant cells, 37, 39-40, *diagram* 46-47; role in muscle contraction, 128-129; structure of, *37*
Autoradiograph, *141*
Avery, Oswald T., 59-60
Axons, 148, *158-159, 165, 166*

B

Babylonian myth of origin of earth, *82*
Bacilli, *183*
Bacillus Pasteurella pestis, 178
Bacteria, 88-89, *183;* defense mechanism against, *175;* and disease, 176, 183; origin of name, 183; size of, 18
Bacteriology, beginnings of, 183
Balavignus, 178
Bark, *19,* 30
Beadle, George, 59
Bellevue Hospital, New York, *185*
Biochemistry, 13, 58
Birth defects, 58. *See also* Hereditary diseases
Blood cells, *107;* life-span, 107; lymphoid, function of, 169-170; phagocytes, 170, *175;* red, shape and function of, 9; white, 169, *175*
Blood plasma, salinity of, 89
Blood vessel cells, development of, 102
Body temperature, maintaining, 131
Bohr, Niels, 62
Bone cells, *107;* development of, *diagram* 102
Bone tissue, human, regenerative power, 118
Botulism, effect on nerve-muscle junctions, 127
Brain: complex organization of, 150; control of muscle action, 130, 150-151, *diagram* 165, *166-167;* electric power consumption of, 164; evolution of, 147, 150; human, *164-165;* information storage and recall, 154-156; seats of various functions, *149,* 151, *164;* sensory interpretation, 151-154, 161, 164, *diagram* 165, *166-167;* 16th Century concept of, *149;* thought processes, 147, 156
Brain cells, 164, *165;* development of, 103
Bread mold, genetic research with, 59
Breeding, selective, 54, 144
Brunn, Francis, *146*
Buffon, Georges Louis Leclerc de, 82
Burnet, Macfarlane, 171

C

Calcium, 21
Cancer cells, 16; migration of, 106
Cancer research, *8,* 42, 106, 171
Carbon compounds. *See* Organic compounds
Carbon cycle, 42, 49, 85; experiments, 33, *36, 43;* initial establishment of, 89-90; in rocket ship, *diagram* 41. *See also* Photosynthesis; Respiration
Carbon dioxide: in photosynthesis, 33, 36, 37, 38, 42, 44, *45, diagram* 47, 90; pre-life appearance in atmosphere, 85, 88; waste product of animal cells, 39, 42, *diagram* 48, 49, 90
Cardiac muscle tissue, 125, *129*
Carnegie Institution, Cold Spring Harbor, 60
Carrier molecules: in chloroplasts, 37; in mitochondria, 48. *See also* Electron-transport system
Cartilage cells, development of, 102, 103
Cartilage tissue, regenerative power, 118
Cell division, 20; by meiosis, 56, *diagram* 56-57; by mitosis, *diagram* 54-55, 55-56, *66-67*
Cell fossils, early, *88,* 89
Cell-like fossils, from meteorites, *88*
Cells: basic categories, *18-19;* basic structure, 10, 13-14, *17;* discovery of, 9, 12; origin of term, 10, 18; precursor of, 88; shapes, 9, 19; sizes, 9-10, 18-19
Cellulose, 30
Cerebellum, 130, 151, *164*
Chance, Britton, 40, 42
Chase, Martha, 60
Chemical basis of cell differentiation, 102, 103-104
Chemical energy: conversion into muscle action, 128-129, 131; production in plant cells from sunlight, 36-38, 47; release in glycolysis and Krebs cycle, 38-39, *diagram* 48, 49; storage in ATP, 21, 37, 49, 50
Chemical reactions in cells: in photosynthesis, 37-38, *diagram* 46-47; in respiration and Krebs cycle, 39-40, 41, 42, *diagram* 48, 49. *See also* Muscle fiber, chemical activity of; Nerve cells, chemical activity of
Chemical reactions of carbon compounds, antecedent to life, 84-85, 86, 87-88, 92, 97, 98
Chemical ties between like cells, 106
Chemicals as cause of mutation, 75
Chick embryo, *103*
Chicken, naked-neck (mutation), *75*
Chlorophyll, 11, *diagram* 34, *35,* 44; composition of, 34; early precursor, 87; emergence of, 89, 112; function of, 34-35, 46, 47
Chloroplasts, 11, *44;* electron-transport system of, 35-36, 39; photosynthesis process in, 34-37, 39; structure of, *diagrams* 34, 36, 40
Cholera, old superstitions in fighting of, *cartoon* 170
Chromatids, 66
Chromatin material, *20,* 55-56
Chromosomes, *8,* 56; carriers of heredity, 56-57; chemical analysis, 59; DNA molecule in, 61; lampbrush, 142, 144; number of, in various species, 57; reduction in meiosis, 56, *diagram* 56-57; replication in mitosis, *diagram* 54-55, 55-56, *66-67;* structure of, 57, *diagram* 58
Cilia, *29,* 123, 130
Cleavage stage, embryonic, 101
Cnidoblast cells, *115*
Cocaine, effect on nerve-muscle junctions, 127
Cocci, *183*
Colonies of single-celled organisms, 11-12, 18, *19, 100, 109-113*
Color blindness, human, *162*
Color vision, 153, 161, *162-163*
Colored light, use by plants, *diagram* 39, *44-45*
Communication: within cells, 20, 22; in multicelled organisms, 147 (*see also* Nervous system)
Communities of cells. *See* Multicelled organisms; Tissue
Congenital defects, 58. *See also* Hereditary diseases
Connective tissue: in brain, *165;* cell, *107;* human, regenerative power, 118
Control system of cell, 20
Cortex, 151, *164-165*
Cosmic radiation, and genetic mutation, 58, *75*
Coupling problem in cell research, 128
Crick, Francis H. C., 61, *64,* 68
Curare, effect on nerve-muscle junctions, 127
Cytology, present standing of, 176
Cytoplasm, 10, 11, 13-15, *17,* 20, 21, 22
Cytosine, 60-61, *70*

D

Dark Ages, concept of origin of life, 81-82
Dark reactions, 34, 37-38
Davidson, Eric, *142-145*
Dead cells, disposal of, *175*
Death of cells, 16, 107
Defense mechanisms: external (*see* Protective devices); against infectious diseases, 169-172, *175;* rejection of foreign tissue, a problem in transplants, 172-175
Defoe, Daniel, 178
Dendrites, 148, *158-159, 165*
Deoxyribonucleic acid. *See* DNA
Deoxyribose, 60
Descartes, René, 82
Diatoms, 18, *19*
Dictyostelium discoideum, 110-111
Differentiation. *See* Specialization
Digestive enzymes, 15
Dinosaur, extinction of, 147
Diseases: cancer, 16, 106, 171; hereditary, 62, *75;* infectious, 169-172, *175,* 176, *177-179,* 183, *186-189,* 190; muscular, 130-131; old misconceptions, *170-171,* 176, 178, 181, *184;* resulting from immunological paralysis, 175. *See also* Transplants
DNA (deoxyribonucleic acid), *52, diagram* 58, 62, 66, 132; arrangement of hereditary material in, 61, 68, 70; chemical composition of, 60-61, 68; discovery of, 59-60, 64; identified as hereditary material, 60; laboratory synthesis of, 75, 76; lengths of strands of, 61; mutation of, 61, *74,* 75, 89; production of RNA from, *72;* replication of, 62, *66, 70-71;* structure of, *diagram* 60, 61, *63,* 64, 68, *69,* 70; Wilkins' partial model, *64*
Dominant genes, 57

E

Ear, human inner, example of specialization, 103
Earth: age of, 90; ancient myths of origin of, *82-83;* early history of, 83, 85-86, 94; fraction of sunlight received by, 33; origin of, 90; theory on beginnings of life on, 87-89, 97, 98. *See also* Atmosphere
Ectoderm, 114, *115*
Egg cell, 101; ostrich, size, 9-10, 19
Ehrensvärd, Gösta, 87
Ehrlich, Paul, 175
Electric circuitry. *See* Electron-transport systems
Electrical energy: conversion from chemical energy, in Krebs cycle, 39-40, *diagram* 48; conversion from sunlight, in photosynthesis, 34-36, *35,* 47; conversion into chemical energy, in photosynthesis, 36-38, 47
Electricity, role in synthesis of organic compounds. *See* Lightning; Miller experiment
Electron micrograph, *141*
Electron microscope, 12-13, 136, *diagram* 137, *140,* 141; limitation of, 14; magnification, 132, 137
Electron-transport systems: basic importance, 40-41; in chloroplasts, 35-36, 39, 40, *diagram* 46-47; in mitochondria, 39-40, 41, *diagram* 48; strength of currents, 41
Electronic reactions, in cells: in Krebs cycle, 39-40, *diagram* 48; in photosynthesis, 34-37, 39, *diagram* 46-47. *See also* Muscle fiber, electrical activity of; Nerve cells, electrical activity of
Electronic systems, man-made, compared to nature, 36, 40, 164, 166
Elodea, 45; cell, *44*
Embryology: defined, 101; and research on aging, 107
Embryonic development: cleavage stage, 101; differentiation of cells, 102-104, 120; human, 102, *103,* 104, *120-121;* organ assembly, 103, *120;* retraces evolution, *103;* synchronization, 103, 104, 120; tissue building, 104-106, 120; tissue layers, 102
Endoderm, 114, *115*
Endoplasmic flow, *104*
Endoplasmic reticulum. *See* ER
Energy, muscle: efficiency of transformations, 131; feedback control of, 124; normal production of, 127; oxygen-free emergency production of, 127-128; reserve, 123, 130; transfer from ATP to fibrils (coupling problem), 128-129
"Energy currency" of cell, 37
Energy storage, in ATP, 21, 37, 49, 50
Energy transformations, 46
Energy transformations by animal cells, 34, 39-40, 41, 42, *diagram* 48, 49; efficiency, *diagram* 40
Energy transformations by plant cells: conversion of electrical into chemical energy, 36-38, 47; conversion of sunlight into electrical energy, 34-36, *35,* 47; efficiency, 38
Enzymes: ATP-triggering, 37, 39, 50; control by genes, 58-59, 102, 104; general function of, 14, *15,* 38; in glycolysis, 39, 48; isolation of, 58; in Krebs cycle, 48; pre-life, 87
Epidermis, 102
Epithelial cell, 30, *106;* life-span, 107
ER (endoplasmic reticulum), 13, 14, 15; function of, 13, 22; structure of, *22*
Euglena, *26, 28-29; gracilis,* 10-12, *183*
Euglenoid movement, *28-29*
Evolution, 12; through adaptation, 89-90; basis of, 89; beginnings of, 86; chemical, 88; controlled, 76, 144 (*see also* Selective breeding); degree of, related to size and complexity of brain, 150; emergence of element of competition for survival, 88; by mutation, 76, *77,* 89; of nervous system and brain, 147, 148, 150; primary steps in, 89-90; retraced in embryonic development, *103;* and specialization, 105, 108, *109-117*
Extinction, 89, 147
Eye, 162; compound, of insects, 163; frog's, 151-153; hawk's, *152;* human, *160-161. See also* Vision

F

Fallout and genetic mutation, 58, 75
Fat-storage cells, 101
Fat-storage tissue, regenerative power, 118
Fats: in Krebs cycle, 41, 48; reserves in animals, 41

Faust, Goethe, 87
Fermentation in cells, 128
Fetus, human, *103,* 120
Flagella, 29, 123, 130
Flatworm, memory experiments with, 155
Flexner, Simon, 188, 190
Florida State University, 86
Food. *See* Protein synthesis; Sugar
Food ingestion, 11, 15; amoeba, *24-25;* hydra, *114-115*
Food storage, 14, 23; in animal cells, 41; in plant cells, 38, 48
Foraminifers, *30-31*
Fossils: cell-like, from meteorites; *88;* of early cells, *88,* 89
Frog, *18;* cell response to electrical stimulus, 26; embryonic development, 101-102; length of DNA strand, *61;* nervous system of, *154;* study of optic nerves of, 151-153

G

Garfinkel, David, 42
Garland, Judy, and daughter Liza, *67*
Genes: chemical nature of, 58, 59-60; control of enzymes by, 58-59, 102, 104; dominant *vs.* recessive, 57; location of, 57, *diagram* 58; makeup and determination of character of, 61, 70; role in specialization of cells, 102, 104; units of inheritance, 57-58, 102
Genetic diseases, 62, *75*
Genetic mutation. *See* Mutation
Genetics, 57, 58, 132; research at Rockefeller Institute, 132, 141, *142-145*
Germs, 169-171, 172; antiseptic measures, 184; preventive measures, *186-187*
Glands, nerve-stimulation of, 158, 159
Globigerina, *31*
Glucose: composition of, 37; manufacture of, 37-38; break-up in animal cells, 38-39, 127. *See also* Sugar
Glycolysis, 39, 42, 127-128
Goethe, Johann Wolfgang von, 87
Goldfish mutations, *78-79*
Golgi, Camillo, 14, 23
Golgi complexes, 14; in aging cells, 108; function of, 14, 23; structure of, 14, *23*
Grafts. *See* Transplants
Grana, chlorophyll, *diagrams* 34, 36
Greeks: Aphrodite myth, *89;* myth of origin of universe, *83;* theories on origin of life, 81
Green, David, 40
Griffith, Frederick, 59-60
Guanine, 60-61, *70*

H

Harvey, William, 82
Hawk, sense of sight, *152*
Hayashi, Teru, 129
Healing of wounds, 106-107, 118; capacity reduced with age, 107-108
Heart muscle, 125, *129;* maximum pumping capacity, 127; nonregenerative, 118
Heart surgery, 131
Heat: as cause of mutation, 75; effect on amino acids, 86, 97
Helmont, Johann Baptista van, 33, 44
Heme, 87
Hemoglobin, 65, 75; normal *vs.* mutated cells, *75*
Hereditary diseases, 62, *75*
Heredity, 53-62; ancient misconceptions, 53-54; carriers of, 20, 56-58, *diagram* 58, 102; complexity, 57-58; controlled, 76, 144; DNA as hereditary material, 60, 61-62, 66, 68, 70; dominant *vs.* recessive traits, 57; Mendel's laws, 54-55, 56-57; special talents, 67. *See also* Genetics; Mutation
Hershey, Alfred, 60
Histones, 141
Homunculus, 82, *87*
Hooke, Robert, 9, 18, 183; his microscope, *12,* 13
Human Body, On the Fabric of the, Vesalius, *125*
Humus Theory, 33
Hydra, 112, 114; anatomy, *114;* cell layers, *115;* food ingestion, *114-115;* grafts, *105, 116-117;* nervous system, *154;* regenerative faculty of, 105, 117
Hydra viridis, 113
Hydrogen, as substance in plants' food manufacture, 37, *diagram* 46-47

I

Identical twins, 58; surgical transplants among, 173
Imagination, brain process, 156
Immunity, against infectious diseases, 171-172
Immunity research, 172-175
Immunological paralysis, 174-175
Infectious diseases, *177-179,* 183; old misconceptions, *170-171,* 176, 178, 181; bodily defense, 169-170, 172, *175;* germ-induced, 169-170, 172; immunity to, 171, 172; vaccination, 170, 172, 181, 186, *187,* 188, *190-191;* various preventive measures, *184-187;* virus-induced, 171-172, *188-189,* 190
Influenza epidemic of 1918, *186*
Influenza virus, 172
Inoculation. *See* Vaccination
Interferon, antivirus protein, 172
Intestinal tissue, mouse, *18*
Iris, *19*
Iron lung, *188-189*
Irritability (response to stimuli), 26

J

Janssen, Hans and Zacharias, 12
Jenner, Edward, 172, *180-181*
Johns Hopkins School of Medicine, 150

K

Kangaroo, albino, *76-77*
Kendrew, John, 64, *65*
Kidney transplants, 174
Koch, Robert, 183
Koprowski, Hilary, 190
Krebs cycle, 39-42, *diagram* 48; end products of, 39, 40, 48; in muscle cells, 127

L

Lampbrush chromosomes, 142, 144
Landau, Lev Davidovich, 65
Layers, embryonic tissue, 102-103
Learning capacity. *See* Memory
Leeuwenhoek, Antony van, 82, *182,* 183; microscope of, *182*
Leprosy, *177*
Lettvin, Jerome, 151
Life: criterion of, 88; dating of origin of, 89; dependence on sunlight, 33, 44, 46, 90; earliest forms of, 88-89; existence beyond earth, 88; history of theories on origin of, 81-83, *86-87;* laboratory creation of basic components of, *80,* 83-84, *diagram* 85, 86, 97; laboratory-produced pseudo-cell, *88;* present theory on conditions leading to, 83-87, 92, 94, 97; present theory on origin of, 87-89, 97, 98
Life expectancy of man, 108
Life-span of cells, 107-108; examples, 107
Light. *See* Colored light; Sunlight
Light microscope, 12, 13, *133;* development of, *12-13, 182,* 183; magnification, 13
Lightning, 92-93; possible role in creation of life, 83-84, 92 (*see also* Miller experiment)
Lister, Joseph, 184
Littau, Virginia, *140-141*
Liver cell, 195; life-span, 107; of rat, *17*
Locomotion of multicelled organisms, 123, 132. *See also* Muscle action
Locomotion of single-celled organisms, 28, *29,* 123, 130, 132; amoeboid, *24,* 28, *104;* by cilia, *29;* euglenoid, *28-29*
Luminescence, *50-51*
Lung, human: oxygen supply capacity, 127; tissue, *52;* transplant, 174
Lymphoid cell, 169-170

M

Macallam, A.B., 89
Macaulay, Thomas, 181
McCarthy, Maclyn, 59-60
McCulloch, Warren, 151
MacLaine, Shirley, and daughter Stephanie, *66*
MacLeod, Colin, 59-60
Magnesium, 21
Man: aging, 107-108, 124; embryonic development, 102, *103,* 104, *120-121;* energy needs, and electron flow in mitochondria, 41; fat reserves, 41; heredity, 57-58, 66-67; internal defense systems, 169-175; length of DNA strands, *61,* 68; life expectancy, 108; limited regenerative power, 118, 124; number of cells in body, 15; number of chromosomes, 57; reserve strength, 123, 130; starvation, 41; sugar and starch reserves, 41; vision, 153-154, *160-162. See also* Brain; Disease; Muscle action; Nervous system, human; Transplants; Vaccination
Man-made machines and instruments: efficiency comparisons with nature, 38, 40, 131; electronic systems compared to nature, 36, 40, 164, 166; frog's eye as model for electronic detection device, 153; muscles as model for, 131-132, *diagram* 131
Massachusetts Institute of Technology, 151
Matsui, Yoshiichi, *78-79*
Maturano, Humberto, 151
Measles, 174; vaccine, 172
Medawar, Peter, 171
Medical research: cancer, *8,* 42, 106, 171; hereditary diseases, 62, 75; immunity research, 172-175; muscular diseases, 130-131; vaccines, 172, 188, *190;* virus research, *168,* 171, 172, *188, 190*
Medicine, history of, *178-191;* anatomy, *124, 125, 148;* antiseptic measures, 184; bacteriology, 183; infectious diseases in past centuries, *177-179;* old misconceptions, *170-171,* 176, 178, 181, *184;* preventive medicine, *186-187;* surgery, *184-185;* transplants of tissue and organs, *119,* 173-175, *174;* vaccination, 172, *180-181,* 186, *187,* 188, *190-191*
Meiosis, 56, *diagram* 56-57
Membrane, outer, 10, 13, 15, *17,* 24, 30
Memory-forming process, 154-155; recall, 155-156
Mendel, Gregor Johann, 54-55, 56-57
Mental disturbances, 156
Mental processes, 147, 154-156
Mesoglea, *115*
Meteorites, cell-like fossils from, *88*
Microbes, 9, *183. See also* Bacteria; Germs; Viruses
Micron, unit of measurement, *10,* 13
Microorganisms. *See* Bacteria; Germs; Single-celled animals, organisms, plants; Viruses; etc.
Microscopes. *See* Electron microscope; Light microscope
Microspikes, 105
Microsurgery, 101, *117*
Middle Ages, concept of origin of life, 81-82, *87*
Miescher, Friedrich, 64
Miller, Stanley L., 83-84, 85
Miller experiment, *80,* 83-84, *diagram* 85
Minnelli, Liza, *67*
Minnelli, Vincente, 67
Mirsky, Alfred E., 134, 141, 142, 144, *145*
Mitochondria, 14, 15; abundance in muscle cells, 127; in aging cells, 108; efficiency of, *diagram* 40; electron-transport system of, 39-40, 41, *diagram* 48; function of, 13, 21, 39-40, *diagram* 48; membranes of, *21, diagram* 38, 40; rate of electron flow in, 41; role in use of fat reserves, 41; structure of, 14, *21, diagrams* 38, 39
Mitosis, *diagram* 54-55, 55-56, 66-67
Molecular biology, 62, 65
Monkey, in carbon cycle experiment, *43*
Moth, black peppered, 76, *77*
Motion, 104-105; endoplasmic flow, *104. See also* Locomotion
Motor end plate, *166*
Motor nerves, *158-159;* stimulation of muscle by, 124, 126-127, 150-151, *diagram* 165, *166*
Mouse, intestinal tissue, *18*
Movement. *See* Locomotion; Motion
Multicelled organisms, 9-10, 19; cell specialization, 102-104 (*see also* Specialization); communication in, 147 (*see also* Nervous system); embryonic development, 101-106; external protection, 30, 169; immobility of most cells in, 28, 105, 106; locomotion of, 123, 132 (*see also* Muscle action); tissue building, 104-106. *See also* Animals; Man; Plants
Muscle action, 123-124, *diagram* 127; control and equilibrium, 129-130; emergency procedure, 127-128; feedback control of energy expenditure, 124; heat production, 131; mechanics of, 125-127, 128-129; and nervous system, 129-130, 150-151, *diagram* 165, *166-167;* psychology of, 130; reserve energy, 123, 130; speed of, 126, 129; voluntary *vs.* involuntary, 125
Muscle anatomy: early studies, *124, 125;* opposing muscles, *130*
Muscle cells, 50, 101, *106;* development of, 102, 124; fusion of, into fiber, 124; nonreproductive, 124. *See also* Muscle fiber
Muscle fiber, 123, *126;* chemical activity of, 126-128; contraction of, 123-124, 125-126, *diagram* 127, 129-130; electrical activity of, 126-127; energy requirements of, 127; fibrils, 125, *126, diagram* 127; filaments, 125, *126, diagram* 127, 128-129; formation of, 124; junctions with nerves, 126-127, 158, *diagram* 165, *166;* production of ATP, 127-128; relationship of size of, to level of activity, 124-125; response to motor-nerve stimulus, 124, 126-127, *diagram* 165, *166;* resting potential, 126; shape and size, 124; smooth, 125, *129,* 130; striated, 125, *129,* 130, *166;* structure of, 125, *129;* transfer of energy from ATP to fibrils, 128-129
Muscle machine, synthetic, 131-132, *diagram* 131
Muscle tissue, *126;* aging, 124; composition of, 123; efficiency of, 131; limited regenerative power, 118; structure of, 123-124, *129;* types of, 125, *129. See also* Muscle fiber
Muscle transplants, 131
Muscular diseases, 127, 130-131
Muscular dystrophy, 131
Mutation, genetic, 58, *75-79;* causes of, 58, 75; explanation of, 61, *74,* 75; role in evolution, 76, *77,* 89
Myasthenia gravis, 127
Myelin, *159*
Myoglobin, *65*
Myosin, 128-129, 130

N

Needham, John Turberville, 82
Nematocysts, *115*
Nerve cells, *106,* 147-156, *158-159;* basic kinds, 158; chemical activity of, 149, 158; development of, 102-103; electrical activity of, 148, 158; excitatory *vs.* inhibitory signals, 149; junctions of, 148-149, *158,* 164; length of, 101, 159; life-span of, 107; manufacture and transmission of neurohumors, 149; nonreproductive, 107, 148; sensory detection and reaction, 151-153, 156, *157, 160-163,* 164, *diagram* 165, *166;* specialization of, for various tasks, 152-153, *157,* 158, 160; speed of electrical pulses, 148, *diagram* 150, 158; "state of poised instability," 149; structure and shape, 9, 148, *158. See also* Nerve fibers
Nerve fibers, 148-149; axons, 148, *158-159, 165, 166;* dendrites, 148, *158-159, 165;* filaments, 148, *158;* growth of, 154; tubules, 148
Nerve-muscle junctions, 126-127, 158, *diagram* 165, *166*
Nerve tissue: brain, *164-165;* retina, *161;* spinal cord, 158-159
Nervous system, 147-156; basic parts of, 158; central, need of higher organisms for, *154;* evolution of, 147, 148; functioning of, 148-151, *158, diagram* 165, 166; microelectrode studies of, 150-152; sensory perception and interpretation, 151-154, 156, *157, 160-163,* 164, *diagram* 165, *166-167;* size related to size of organism, 147. *See also* Brain; Nerve cells; Nerve fibers
Nervous system, human: central, nonregenerative, 118; hand, *157;* and muscle action, 129-130, 150-151, *diagram* 165, *166-167;* number of cells, 150, 164; peripheral, regenerative power, 118; 16th Century anatomical view, *148*
Neurohumors, 126-127, 149; manufacture and transmission of, 149; stimulating *vs.* inhibiting, 149
Neurons. *See* Nerve cells
Newton, Sir Isaac, 82, 86
Nightingale, Florence, 185
Norse myth of origin of earth, *82*
Nose grafts, 16th Century, *174*
Nucleic acids, 59-60, 132. *See also* DNA; RNA
Nucleolus, *20*
Nucleotides, *diagram* 58, 60-61; in production of RNA, *72;* in replication of DNA, *70*
Nucleus, 10, 11, 15, *17, 20,* 53; in cell division, 20, 55-56, 66-67; current research, 132, *134-144;* function of, 20, 22; isolation for research, 134, *diagram* 136, *138;* protein synthesis in, current research, *diagram* 136-137, *138-141;* radioactive tracers in, *137;* structure of, *20*

O

Oceans: origin of, 85, 94, *95;* pre-life organic compounds in, 85-87, 94
One-celled organisms. *See* Single-celled organisms
Onion-tip cell, reproduction of, *66-67*
Oocytes, 142; genetic research with, *142-144*
Optic nerve cells, *160-161*
Organelles, 16
Organic (carbon) compounds: laboratory synthesis of, *80,* 83-84, *diagram* 85, 86, 97; possible synthesis in early earth atmosphere, 84-85, 92; progressing synthesis in early oceans and lakes, 86, 87-88, 94, 97, 98; self-replication of, as beginning of life, 88
Organic matter, annual production, 44
Organs, 18-19, 108; activation by

muscles, 125; assembly in embryo, 103, *120;* primitive, *114;* transplants of, 173-175
Ostracoderm, 147
Ostrich egg, 9-10, 19
Ovum, fertilized, 56, 101
Oxygen: in plant respiration, 42, 49; use by animal cells, 39, 40, 42, 44, *diagram* 48, 49, 90; waste product of plant cells, 37, 38, 40, 42, 44, *45, diagram* 46-47, 89-90
Oxygen-carbon dioxide cycle. *See* Carbon cycle
Oxygen supply, human, 127

P

Paracelsus, 82
Paramecium, 9, *27,* 29, 123
Pasteur, Louis, 82-83, 128, 176, 184
Pea, Mendel's experiments with, 54-55, 56-57
Pepsin, 15
Perutz, Max, *64*
Peter Bent Brigham Hospital, Boston, 174
Phage, genetic research with, 60
Phagocytes, 170, *175*
Phosphates: in ATP, 37, 46, 47; in DNA, 60-61, 68, 70; laboratory linking of amino acids with, 86
Photon: defined, 34; transformation to electric energy, 34, *35*
Photosynthesis, 33-38, 42, *diagram* 46-47; beginnings of, 89; with colored light, *diagram* 39, *44-45;* dark reactions, 34, 37-38; efficiency of process, 38; from electrical to chemical energy, 36-38, 47; end product, 37, 42, 44, 45, 47; reversal by Krebs cycle, 39, 49; sparking sequence, 34-37; from sunlight to electrical energy, 34-36, *35,* 47; waste product, 38, 40, 42, 44, *45,* 46, 47
Pine bark cells, *19*
Pitts, Walter, 151
Plague, *178-179,* 183; 17th Century protection against, *171*
Plankton, *19*
Plant cells, *19, 44;* endoplasmic flow, *104;* energy transformations in, 34-38, 42, *diagram* 46-47; food manufacture in, 37-38, 42, 44, *45, diagram* 46-47; food storage in, 38, 48; rigidity of shape, 19
Plants: *vs.* animals, 19, 30, 49; capture of sunlight by, *diagrams* 34, 47; capture of sunlight under water, *diagram* 39; fraction of sunlight used by, 33; growth, basis of, 33, 44; photosynthesis process, 33-38, 42, *diagram* 46-47; protective cell layers, 30; respiration, 42, 49; role in carbon cycle, 33, 42, *43,* 49. *See also* Plant cells; Single-celled plants
Pleuropneumonia microbe, 9
Poison ivy, allergic reaction to, 171
Poliomyelitis: vaccinations, 189, *190-191;* vaccines, 172, 188-190; victims, *188-189;* viruses, 171, *188,* 190
Polymers, laboratory synthesis of, 84, 86
Power plant of cells, *21. See also* Energy transformations
Priestley, Joseph, carbon cycle experiment, *36*
Protective devices, 26, 169; multicelled organisms, 30; single-celled animals, *27, 30-31. See also* Defense mechanisms
Protein separator, *168*
Protein synthesis, 22, 72, *73;* location of, 13-14, *22;* nuclear, current research, *diagram* 136-137, *138-141;* possible connection with memory-forming process, 154-155; reduced in aging cells, 108
Proteins, 13-14; action of ATP on, for energy production, 128-129; diversity, 72; enzymes, 14, 38; nuclear, 20; pre-

life, 87; research, 64, *65;* role in body defenses, 169-170, 172; storage of, 23. *See also* Enzymes; Protein synthesis
Protoplasm, defined, 16
Protozoans, *183;* in plankton, *19*
Pseudopods, 24, *31*
Ptyalin, 15
Puchet, 82
Pyruvate, 39, 48
Pyruvic acid, 48

Q

Quantasomes, *diagrams* 34
Quantum, defined, 34

R

Radiation, and genetic mutation, 58, 75
Radioactive tracing of cell activities, 13; identification of DNA, 60; nucleus research, 134, *137, 139, 141, 142*
Railroad worms, *50-51*
Rains, primeval, 85, *94-95*
Ranvier, nodes of, *159*
Rat liver cell, *17*
Rattlesnake, sense of heat, *152*
Redi, Francesco, 82; experiment, *86*
Reed, Walter, 186
Regenerative faculty: of hydras, 105, 117; limitations in higher organisms, 105, 118, 124, 148. *See also* Healing
Reisch, Georg, 149
Reproduction, 55-56; ancient misconceptions, 53; criterion of life, 88; hydra, 114; reduced rate in aging cells, 107-108; replication of DNA, 62, 64, *66, 70-71;* sexual, 56; slime mold, *109, 111. See also* Cell division; Heredity
Respiration, 42, *diagram* 48, *49;* waste products, 42, 48, 49. *See also* Krebs cycle
Respiratory assembly, in mitochondrion, *diagrams* 38, 48
Response: to external stimuli, *26-27;* internal, to foreign substances, 169-175
Retina, *diagram* 160; tissue, *161*
Rhizopod, number of chromosomes, 57
Ribonucleic acid. *See* RNA
Ribosomes, 13-14, 15, *22,* 72; function of, 13, 22
RNA, *52;* function of, 72, *73;* laboratory synthesis of, 75, 76; messenger-RNA, 72, *73;* possible connection with memory-forming process, 154-155; production of, *72;* research, 134, *142-144;* transfer-RNA, 72, *73*
Rockefeller Institute, The, New York, 59, 132, *134-145, 171*
Rosenhof, A. J. Rösel von, 105

S

Sabin, Albert, *190*
Salinity of sea and blood plasma, Macallam's theory, 89
Salk, Jonas, 188, *190*
Schleiden, Matthias, 9
Schwann, Theodor, 9
Scintillation counter, 136, *diagram* 137, 139
"Sea Moss," *112-113*
Selective breeding, 54, 144
Sensory neurons, 158
Sensory perception and interpretation, 151-154, 156, *157,* 164, *diagram* 165, *166-167. See also* Vision
Septicemia, 184
Sex cells, in meiosis, 56, *diagram* 56-57
Shapes of cells, 9, 19; flexibility, in animal cells, 19, *24-25;* rigidity, in plant cells, 19
Shivering, function of, 131

Sickle-cell anemia, 62, *75*
Sight, sense of. *See* Eye; Vision
Single-celled animals, *19;* food ingestion, *24-25;* locomotion, 24, *28-29;* protective shells, *30-31;* response to stimuli, *26-27*
Single-celled organisms, 9, 19; colonies, 11-12, 18, *19,* *100, 109-113;* euglena as example of, 10-12
Single-celled plants, *19;* emergence of, 89; response to stimuli, *26*
Sizes of cells, 9-10, 18-19
Skeletal (striated) muscle tissue, 125, *129*
Skin, 30; color, determination of, 58; grafts, *119,* 173
Skin cells, development of, 102
Sleeping sickness, 183
Slime mold, 106, *109-111*
Smallpox vaccination, 172, 186, *187;* initial public resistance to, *180-181*
Snake bites, quack prescriptions for, *cartoon* 171
Solar radiation. *See* Sunlight
Solar system, origin of, 90
Somites, 103-104
Space travel, food and oxygen supply, *diagram* 41
Spallanzani, Lazzaro, 182
Sparking sequence in photosynthesis, 34-37
Specialization, 101-106, 108, 120; chemical mechanism, 102, 103-104; current research, *142-144;* evolution of, 108, *109-117;* examples (bone; inner ear), *diagram* 102, 103; primitive forms of, *100, 109-117;* process, 102-104; timing, 103, 104; tissue-building, 104-106, 120
Sperm cell, 101; locomotion, 123; in meiosis, 56
Spinal cord nerve tissue, *158-159*
Spontaneous generation, theory of, 81-83, 84, *86,* 182
Stalks of cells, 9, 30
Stanford University, 59
Staphylococcus aureus, 183
Starch reserves in animals, 41
Starvation, 41
Steinbeck, John, *65*
Stimulus, 26. *See also* Response
Structure of cells, basic, 10, 13-14, 16, *17*
Strychnine, effect on nerve-muscle junctions, 127
Sugar(s): caloric energy content of, 48; in DNA, 60-61, 68, 70; as food for animal cells, 38-39, 42, 44, *diagram* 48, 49; production in plants, 37-38, 42, 44, *45, diagram* 46-47; reserves in animals, 41. *See also* Glucose
Sunlight: capture by plant cells, *diagrams* 34, 46-47; capture by water plants, *diagram* 39; dependence of life on, 33, 42, 44, 90; fraction received by earth, 33; fraction used by plants, 33; role in creation of life, 84-85, 90, 92
Surgery: antiseptic measures, 184; history of, *184-185. See also* Transplants
Synapse, *158*

T

Tagliacozzi, Gaspare, 174
Tatum, Edward L., 59
Tetanus, 183, 184
Thymine, 60-61, 70
Thymus gland of calf, use for nucleus research, *135-141*
Time, biological sense of, 11-12
Tissue, 9, 18-19, 101, 108; building of, 104-106, 120; chemical bonding, 106; composition of, 123; embryonic layers, 102; grafts and transplants of, *118,* 173-175; healing process, 106-107; immobility of cells in, 105, 106; process

of specialization, 102-104; regeneration of, 105, 117, 118
Toxins, 169. *See also* Antigens
TPN, 47
TPNH$_2$, production of, 37, *diagram* 47
Transistors, comparison with grana in chloroplasts, 36
Transplants, 173-175; kidney, 174; lung, 174; muscle, 131; rejection by antibodies, and antibody-inhibiting treatments, 173-175; 16th Century nose graft, *174;* skin, *119,* 173
Transport system within cell, 13, *22*
Trapping center, in chloroplast, 35
Trichocysts, *27*
Tritium, as radioactive tracer, 137
Trypanozoma gambiense, 183
Tuberculosis, 183
Twins: identical, 58; surgical transplants among, 173-174
Typhoid fever, 170, 183

U

Ultraviolet light, synthesis of organic compounds with, 84, 92
Units of measurement, *10-11,* 13
University of California, Virus Laboratory of, *168*
University of Minnesota Medical School, 174
University of Mississippi Hospital, 174
University of Pennsylvania, 40, 42, 103
University of Pittsburgh, 190
University of Wisconsin, 40

V

Vaccination, history of, 172, *180-181,* 186, *187,* 188, *190-191*
Vaccines, working of, 170, 172
Viruses, 169, 171; defense mechanism against, 172, *175;* makeup and size of, 171; method of attack of, 171, *172,* 188; mutant, problem of defense against, 172; research, *168,* 171, 172, *188, 190;* shapes of, *173*
Vision: color, 153, 161, *162-163;* of euglena, 11; of frog, 151-153, *163;* of hawk, *152;* human, 153-154, *160-162;* human color blindness, *162;* limited reality of, 153-154, *162-163*
Vital-force theory, 82-83
Volvox, 100

W

Water: as substance in plants' food manufacture, 33, 36, 37, 38, 40, 42, 44, *diagram* 46-47; waste product of animal cells, 39, 40, 42, 48, 49
Water plants, pigment of, and capture of sunlight, *diagram* 39
Watson, James D., 61, *64, 65,* 68
Wilkins, Maurice H. F., 61, *64*
Wounds, healing, 106-107, 118; capacity reduced with age, 107-108
Wright, Sewall, 58, 59

X

Xenopus toad, *142;* genetic research with, *142-144*
X-rays, and genetic mutation, 58, 59, 75

Y

Yeast, fermentation, 128
Yellow fever: destruction of carrier mosquito, 186, *187;* vaccine, 172

PICTURE CREDITS

The sources for the illustrations appear below. Pictures are separated left to right by commas, top to bottom by dashes.

CHAPTER 1: 10, 11—Drawings by Otto van Eersel. 12—Courtesy Science Museum, London—drawings by George V. Kelvin. 13—Drawings by George V. Kelvin. 15—Drawings by Fred Hausman. 17—Drawing by Jack J. Kunz. 18—Martha Holmes —John J. Lee, American Museum of Natural History—Steve Wilson from Alpha Photo Associates Inc. 19—Wards Natural Science Establishment, Dr. Roman Vishniac, Walter Dawn—left Eric Lindgren, Photo Researchers Inc.; right Kosti Ruohomaa from Black Star. 20, 21—Martha Holmes—drawings by Jack J. Kunz. 22, 23—Martha Holmes—drawings by Jack J. Kunz. 24, 25—Dr. Robert Allen except top left Martha Holmes. 26—Sol Mednick except top left Martha Holmes. 27—Eric V. Grave. 28—Sol Mednick except top left Martha Holmes. 29—Walter Dawn, drawing by Otto van Eersel—Sol Mednick. 30—Martha Holmes—Carl Strüwe from Monkmeyer Press Photos. 31—Courtesy American Museum of Natural History.

CHAPTER 2: 32—George Silk. 34—Drawings by Lowell Hess. 35, 36—Drawings by Otto van Eersel. 37—Drawing by Charles Gottlieb. 38—Drawings by Lowell Hess. 39—Drawing by Richard Boland. 40—Drawings by Fred Hausman. 41—Drawing by Otto van Eersel. 43—Ralph Morse. 44, 45—Wards Natural Science Establishment, J. R. Eyerman, Sol Mednick. 46, 47, 48—Drawings by Blake Hampton. 49—Sol Mednick—Elgin Ciampi. 50, 51—Fritz Goro.

CHAPTER 3: 52—Fritz Goro. 54 through 57—Drawings by Fred Hausman. 58—Drawing by Otto van Eersel. 60—Drawing by Richard Boland. 61—Drawing by Otto van Eersel. 63—Courtesy National Archives. 64, 65—Ian Yeomans from Sunday *Times*, Loomis Dean—European. 66—PIP Photos—Allan Grant. 67—PIP Photos—Bill Kobrin from Globe Photos. 68—Peter Stackpole. 69 through 74—Fritz Goro. 75—Edmund B. Gerard—Dr. G. Lockard Conley, Johns Hopkins Hospital. 76, 77—Larry Burrows, Dr. H. B. D. Kettlewell (2)—drawing by Otto van Eersel. 78, 79—John Launois from Black Star.

CHAPTER 4: 80—Arthur Rickerby. 82, 83—Drawings by Fritz Kredel. 85—Drawing by Anthony Saris. 86—Drawings by Otto van Eersel. 87—Bettmann Archive. 88—Drawings by Charles Gottlieb. 89—Bettmann Archive—drawing by Richard Boland. 91 through 99—Gordon Parks.

CHAPTER 5: 100—Dr. Robert Allen. 102—Drawing by Otto van Eersel. 103—Drawings by Lowell Hess. 104—Drawings by Otto van Eersel. 105—Herb Orth from *Historiae Polyporum*, Rosel von Rosenhof, courtesy Dr. Roman Vishniac. 106, 107—Drawings by Charles Gottlieb. 109, 110, 111—Dr. Roman Vishniac. 112, 113—Douglas Wilson, Hermann Eisenbeiss from Photo Researchers Inc. 114, 115—Roy Hyrkin models by Louis Di Valentin—drawings by Donald Crowley. 116, 117—Sol Mednick. 118—Dr. Andrew E. Rudnai. 119—James Whitmore. 120—Dr. L. B. Shettles—Professor E. Ludwig, Chester Reather; courtesy Dr. Chester Heuser, Carnegie Institution of Washington. 121—Courtesy Carnegie Institution of Washington and *The First Nine Months of Life*, by Geraldine Flanagan; Simon and Schuster, 1962.

CHAPTER 6: 122—Paul Schutzer. 124—Courtesy Bodleian Library, Oxford. 125—New York Public Library. 126, 127—Drawings by Otto van Eersel. 129—Drawings by Otto van Eersel. 130—Drawings by Richard Boland. 131—Drawings by Otto van Eersel. 133, 135—Arthur Rickerby. 136, 137—Drawings by Ronald Becker. 138, 140—Arthur Rickerby. 141—Arthur Rickerby—Dr. Virginia Littau, The Rockefeller Institute (2). 142 through 145—Arthur Rickerby.

CHAPTER 7: 146—Ralph Morse. 148—Vesalius Fabrica from New York Public Library. 149—Drawings by Charles Mikolaycak—from *A Short History of Anatomy and Psychology*, by Charles Singer, Dover Publications Inc., New York. 150—Drawing by Charles Mikolaycak. 151, 152, 154—Drawing by Otto van Eersel. 157—Drawing by Birney Lettich. 158, 159—Drawings by Joseph Lambandero. 160, 161 —Drawing by Joseph Lambandero—Dr. Ned Fedder. 162—Robin Bradshaw, Robin Bradshaw and Norman Snyder (2). 163—Robin Bradshaw and Norman Snyder, drawings by Otto van Eersel. 164—Clay Adams Inc., New York City—Erich Hartmann from Magnum Photos. 165—Drawing by Joseph Lambandero. 167—Eliot Elisofon.

CHAPTER 8: 168—N. R. Farbman. 171—Radio Times Hulton Picture Library—Culver Pictures Inc. 172, 173—Drawings by Otto van Eersel. 174—Bettmann Archive. 175—Drawings by Charles Mikolaycak. 177—Emmett Bright. 178, 179—Henry Groskinsky, Emmett Bright. 180, 181—Courtesy of the Trustees, British Museum. 182—Courtesy the *Rijksmuseum*, Amsterdam—Bettmann Archive, drawing by Rudolf Freund, courtesy Wellcome Historical Medical Museum. 183—Walter Dawn except bottom left Eric V. Grave. 184—Eddy van der Veen; courtesy *Musée de Périgueux*. 185—Courtesy Bellevue School of Nursing—Byron Co. Inc. from T. F. Healy. 186, 187—National Archives, N. V. Vereenigi Fotobureaux—The Rockefeller Foundation. 188, 189—Wide World Photos—Dr. James Hillier (2), Maurice Miller, Martha Holmes. 190, 191—Alfred Eisenstaedt, Robert Phillips—Julianne Warren, Bill Bridges. 195—Drawing by Jack J. Kunz. Back cover: Nicholas Fasciano.

PRODUCTION STAFF FOR TIME INCORPORATED

Arthur R. Murphy Jr. (Vice President and Director of Production), Robert E. Foy, James P. Menton and Caroline Ferri
Text photocomposed under the direction of Albert J. Dunn and Arthur J. Dunn

X

Printed by R. R. Donnelley & Sons Company, Crawfordsville, Indiana,
and Livermore and Knight Co., a division of Printing Corporation of America, Providence, Rhode Island
Bound by R. R. Donnelley & Sons Company, Crawfordsville, Indiana
Paper by The Mead Corporation, Dayton, Ohio